Contents

Introduction

Many contentious elements exist within most areas of contemporary life and the contractual area of building is no exception. This book attempts to traverse the salient aspects within the area, making connections between them and offering guidance on achieving agreement in a reasonable way. Many aspects are concerned with problems over time and money, but not by any means all. There are, of course, many other areas open to dispute, such as the technical, and no attempt has been made to stray into these.

The contents seek to meet the needs of various disciplines within construction, so that at most points the treatment is not usually addressed explicitly to those on one side only of disputed matters. The client, client's adviser, contractor and sub-contractor alike should be able to read and interpret for his own purposes. The major pattern is to deal with matters at main contract level and, where there are special elements, to take the sub-contract differences alongside. It is always better to understand the problems and strategies of others when in dispute, so that this integrated pattern is given no further justification.

The general level has been set with two types of reader in mind: those who are seeking explanation of basic principles, and those who are looking for more extended treatment of issues with which they are already acquainted. In more precise terms, this dual approach is intended for those who are at such stages of qualifying as tests of professional competence and also those concerned with continuing professional development – or simply pursued by the need to know! It is hoped that a coherent approach has been achieved, so that the levels of treatment do not clash and the result does not fall between the proverbial stools. The types of subject-matter should be reasonably distinguishable by the divisions within as well as between chapters.

The scope covers a compact treatment of the preliminary decisions and actions which determine much of what follows. These obviously attach themselves to the 'avoidance' part of the volume's sub-title. The main bulk deals with the post-contractual aspects. These may be seen as predominately 'resolution', but often the best way to avoid problems is to be clear over how they have been encountered in the past, both in origin and solution. Deliberately, the treatment stops short of arbitration and litigation, which are methods of dealing with disputes when mutual resolution has failed. Nevertheless, much of what is included is of use when considering the presentation of a case at one of these tribunals.

Specifically, discussion in relevant chapters is allied to the JCT 80 contracts and the IFC 84 contract, as two widely used forms, relating to those forms as amended at December 1987 and also taking in the various sub-contracts to the forms. Clauses of the contracts and sub-contracts are therefore considered selectively, from a disputes viewpoint. The discussion is set widely enough to allow principles to be transposed to other contractual bases.

Extended use has been made of case studies in the last part of the book to apply the more generalised discussion of earlier parts to concrete situations, and occasionally to supplement previous discussion. It may be surmised that behind some of the examples described lie real-life cases, from which extrapolations and adaptations have been made for present didactic purposes. Some of the prototypes might have difficulty in recognising themselves – which is probably just as well! The amount of detail has been varied both within and between the studies to avoid impracticable length and also to cover a representative selection of situations and resolutions. As a result, the case studies are not 'worked examples' which may be followed slavishly (always a dangerous policy, as actual conditions may vary so much), but illustrations of what may be done, combined with discussion of the limitations that often attach to specific solutions.

The somewhat innovatory aspect of the case studies is to use an approach to financial settlements based upon the obvious intention of the contracts that this should proceed progressively, rather than occur entirely at the end in the form of a 'big bang'. As a result, there is not the setting up of a target claim, subsequently to be shredded by a series of missiles. In fact, generally the term 'claim' has been avoided, as again not representing the intention of the contracts. If this emphasis helps just a little to dispel the emotive side of many disputes, it can but have succeeded. In recognition of the continuing need for the 'end of contract claim' on occasions, some closing guidelines on such a document are given, so that the preceding chapters may be turned round and applied to it when necessary. To help with the problem of looking at disputes in something of a vacuum, as is inevitable in a book, the studies given are each linked closely to a site layout and programme to indicate more expressly how design delays and disturbances affect progress and performance. In one study, an analysis of the contract bills has been included to give 'scale' to what is happening.

No apology is made for considerable cross-referencing and a restricted degree of repetition of key ideas between chapters. It is realised that no author is sufficiently gripping in style or precise in structure or content as to compel every reader to read such subject-matter hypnotically from beginning to end: many will wish to 'dip'. Given also that readers have differing needs, this is inevitable. But dipping carries the risk of missing some essential point covered elsewhere. Repetition also allows the reader to start with either the more theoretical earlier chapters or the more practical later ones, and then turn to the other set. The order used suggests what is thought to be best,

but dictates of time often lead to some compromise, and so there is some repetition.

While the strict principles have been kept in view, discussion has recognised the difficulties of staying exactly with theory all the time. It is hoped that the text as it has emerged will not cause too much offence to either purist or pragmatist. Reality is, after all, rather like that as well.

In writing, I have been conscious of the value of many experiences over the years – some more chastening than others! They leave a trail of those to whom I am indebted in various ways. I would particularly express my appreciation of comments over some issues from my brother, Alan Turner, JP, FRICS, partner in Building Design Partnership, while reserving to myself the responsibility for how I have dealt with the material in question. As usual, I acknowledge the practical help and support from my wife, Betty, who has now followed me into the dark tunnel of word processing to produce this volume. So far as I can tell, we have not lost any paragraphs before emerging into the fresh air again.

Dennis F. Turner, April 1988

List of abbreviations

The following are the main abbreviations used in the text. The full names of documents are not necessarily the precise titles, but are in common use and what might otherwise have been used in the text. In the case of the JCT documents, several revisions have been introduced. The latest considered are those of December 1987. Where the dating is significant, it is indicated in the text

JCT	Joint Contracts Tribunal.
JCT 80	JCT Standard Form of Building Contract, 1980 edition. This is published in several variants. Unless qualified, a reference may be read as being to any variant.
JCT clause	A clause of the foregoing contract.
IFC 84	JCT Intermediate Form of Building Contract, 1984 edition.
IFC clause	A clause of the foregoing contract.
NSC/2	JCT Employer/Nominated Sub-Contractor Agreement. NSC/2a may be regarded as identical for discussion as given in this book.
NSC/4	JCT Nominated Sub-Contract. NSC/4a may be regarded as identical for discussion as given in this book.
Green Form	Nominated sub-contract relating to the JCT 1963 contract.
Blue Form	Domestic sub-contract relating to the JCT 1963 contract.
SMM 6	Standard Method of Measurement of Building Works, sixth edition. This edition is effectively that current at the date of writing.
SMM 7	Standard Method of Measurement of Building Works, seventh edition. This edition comes into force in July 1988 and will progressively be introduced into new projects based upon it.
ACA	Association of Consultant Architects.
BPF	British Property Federation.

PART 1

Pre-contract activities

CHAPTER 1

The background to contract disputes

A complex process
Clients and the industry
Matters underlying disputes
Outline practical approaches

This book is about building *contract* disputes in particular, rather than about building disputes in general. This is a topic which has exercised the minds of many within and beyond the industry for years, as the Bibliography indicates. It conjures up a number of discrete sub-topics, numbers of which are explored in the detailed sections of this book. Because of the proverbial relation between wood and trees, it is useful to survey some principles which underlie much of the detail. To the initiated, they may savour of nothing new, but it is hoped that any reader will find something of value among them.

A complex process

It is perhaps surprising that more does not go wrong, even today, with the production of buildings when the intrinsically complicated and hazardous nature of the activity is reviewed. This is most obvious in terms of accidents and so forth during construction, while problems of securing quality and ensuring that designs do not fail come close behind. But the operational process is at least as subject to problems, even if they are not so apparent to the outsider. What happens in this process is the spawning ground for the disputes that this book considers.

It has been said that factory production is a line of work going through men, whereas site production is a line of men going through work. This difference arises from the need to install the work on an individual and perhaps difficult site, with all the problems of co-ordination and the added ingredient of the weather. The work is usually also individual in content, even if it repeats the character of other buildings. This is not new, and down the centuries problems of time and money overrun have been found. Several of the old law cases testify to this, as also, for example, do the records of the building of London churches 200 years ago. While today's

refined systems for controlling the process undoubtedly have improved so many aspects, they also show up more starkly things that do go wrong. This reflects the premium on the rapid completion of buildings which are often inherently more complex, and can be much larger than in the past.

What can be done to improve affairs? This theme has occupied numerous top-level committees, as well as those in humbler positions in the industry. It is not the claim of the present work to provide the answers, rather it seeks to make some sticking plaster available for application when an injury occurs. Even so, its basic propositions may be over-simplified as:

(a) Avoid problems whenever it is possible to do so without excessive expenditure of resources.
(b) Accommodate problems in the most efficient way, when (a) is not possible, accepting some disturbance as inevitable.
(c) Resolve any disputes which arise out of the compromise of (b) as smoothly as possible in the circumstances resulting.

This 'counsel of imperfection' is suggested, not as something new, but as something consciously to adopt. It is an approximation to what usually happens, but perhaps by default rather than intent. It is not a call to be careless, but to weigh the options and select the optimum and not strive for the unattainable.

Clients and the industry

Construction clients all want the right building, at the right time and for the right price. They vary in how far they are equipped to achieve these objectives, even if the structure of the industry and prevailing conditions give them the chance.

The entirely 'lay' client, that is one unversed in the procurement process, faces a number of special obstacles. He may not know very clearly what it is that he wants to have produced. Even if he does, he may not know how to present a brief over design or programme. He may well be puzzled by the split between design and construction organisations, how they relate to him and to each other. He may be tempted to opt for the 'cheap' or the 'quick' way to meet his need, without seeing the pitfalls that there may be. In particular, he may be too optimistic about what can be done within the money and time available. When things are rolling forward, he may not realise the effects that his changes of mind will have, even those that embody flashes of near-genius.

All clients face numbers of internal problems. Their budgets are restricted by total limits, by when the money is available and by the return (in any way) that the project must achieve. Time may be pressing to meet markets, to provide social satisfaction or whatever is the target. Technological changes in requirements may affect the solutions that are embodied in a building.

These effects may be in conflict, while they may not be foreseen until work is under way. They may be compounded by the activity of building being on already occupied sites or, worse, in occupied buildings. The individual nature of many buildings has already been touched upon.

The response of the industry to clients as a whole shows first of all in a structure that has evolved over the decades. In the order in which clients may become aware of their existence, there are design consultants, cost consultants, contractors, sub-contractors and suppliers, leaving aside all the more peripheral personnel such as inspectors. It is a tenet of systems theory that organisations tend to become rigid according to the functions that they have been performing and not always to be responsive to change. In addition the structure may make the flow of activities and information more tortuous than a single operation might necessitate.

In the case of construction, the process of providing a building filters through this structure, which largely facilitates it. But because typically there are several organisations involved, the possibility of gaps in communication or co-ordination is present. Indeed it may be said that most disputes, which are not essentially technical or due to changes of mind, occur because of disjunction at interfaces. Some of these are due to misinformation, etc. and some to misunderstanding of what is required. Even when there is some form of integration of activities, as in design and build arrangements, the same gaps are possible, although liability for them is shifted.

In more traditional patterns, the major contractual arrangements are set up on the basis that the client and contractor hardly speak to each other, as the nexus is to be found in the consultants for the project. It may be argued that the objectives of the latter are not entirely identical with those of the two parties to the building contract, that is the client and the contractor. This is not to suggest lack of professional concern, but simply that they are constrained by their own upbringing. Thus an architect may not be primarily concerned with information flow, as against aesthetics and function of the finished project, while a quantity surveyor may not see clearly the importance of cash flow to a contractor, as against ultimate settlement at an uncertain date.

Matters underlying disputes

At risk of some repetition of points just made, some of the more common, if not always more obvious, causes leading to disputes of the types considered most often in this volume may be set out. Many of these are avoidable at some cost, which may or may not be justified. Sometimes a matter may best be left as a risk, while not everything can be foreseen every time. The causes are present, whether they should be pre-empted is a matter of policy, but the decision should be made consciously when the cause and risk are known to exist.

DECISION-MAKING AND RESULTS

A number of early decision areas always exist. It is a fact of most adventures in life that the early decisions are usually the most critical, because they condition those that follow and because they are often irreversible without an unacceptable cost. Fundamental is the quality of the initial concept of the scheme and the design brief into which it is transformed. Hard behind comes the programme time allowed for both design (with accompanying planning permission, etc.) and construction. These are the client's critical requirements, which then must be matched with his resource provisions.

There are also several basic conditions which may be unavoidable and so should be evaluated closely. The site and existing buildings may constrain what can be achieved, both as an end-product and also on the way in terms of phasing and so on. The nature of the scheme may bring in particularly complex constructional or organisational methods, because it is unusually integrated or innovative. External constraints may be present, or archaeological interest may be anticipated.

Implementation of the concept divides into two areas: decisions and achievement. The former is tied in with development of the brief, perhaps happening in part post-contractually, and also with setting up the contract. It lays itself open to the possibility of seeking to pinch pennies while introducing undue risk for the client, for instance by making inadequate provision for elements in the programme needing time or expenditure. An obvious area of doubt is in the legal provisions, where ambiguities or gaps may be left over points of procedure. But conversely, the attempt to be over-smart and cover every option may create fresh loopholes that never existed before. Post-contractually, this type of approach may turn into lack of tolerance that stirs up its own protective reaction. Special care is needed when overlapping contractual arrangements are used, individually impeccable, but together causing discrepancies.

Implementation, by activities to produce the work, follows on what has been sketched in the last paragraph. Inadequate consideration of the management system for the whole operation is a likely cause of weakness. Overcoming this does not necessarily mean introducing something complicated, but rather ensuring that there is a logical, unambiguous allocation of responsibilities, with a clear decision path through the whole programme and watertight procedures for communicating decisions to those who need to know. It is often argued that people produce information to suit their own perceptions of what is needed, and not to give what others need to use. Rationalisation might actually mean less work for the producers! Common problems over information are that it is incomplete, unclear, error-ridden or just plain late in arriving. The rise of some forms of contracting over recent years may be as much due to the attempt to dispose of these failures as to secure any radical difference in the way in which work is organised on the site and paid for by the client.

Even with the appropriate systems, there are still weaknesses that may creep into their use. Changes of mind are not necessarily a sign of

indecision: they may show a willingness to reflect and not be blinkered, but they can spread havoc if they are not controlled. They are another example of optimisation: at a certain level of cost, a good idea ceases to be worth implementing. Further, while the end results may be similar, there are no proper excuses for putting off decisions until too late or for indulging in panic action when a difficult situation does come to light. These instances may look as though they are mainly to be laid at the doors of clients and consultants, but may be the responsibility of contractors also, who can fail to foresee problems or to organise their own activities. This may aggravate a loss situation, or even lead to one which cannot be charged to the client.

TEAM INTERACTIONS

The correct system may have the wrong team members. Consultants, it has been suggested, may be bad organisers, even worse a minority are bad at designing. It is not unknown for them to be unreasonable to a greater or lesser degree. Contractors and sub-contractors too may not be well organised, while they may be of the wrong size (either way) for the work that they undertake. They may lack expertise in particular types of project – sometimes in any type, it appears! It may be their fault that they accept the work, but it may be the precedent fault of others that they were ever selected to tender. They may be commercially inept on particular contracts, something that it may be difficult to foresee will happen. Tenders may be too low for profitability, work may be performed uneconomically, or (with or without these features) firms may be 'claims conscious'. Sometimes, they just do not know how to secure their normal entitlements in the final account.

This survey is cast in a deliberately gloomy vein, to make its point. But when all this is said, many of those operating in the construction field are doing their level best to perform the miraculous today and the impossible not long after. It is also pertinent that authors who live in ivory towers should not drop bricks. There are also a number of factors which arise from quarters other than clients and those with whom they contract. There are the actions or inactions of local authorities and others with powers of approval or who perform work under statutory powers, there are unions and there is that special British institution, the weather. Not all of these sources produce effects over which the client may be liable to meet the extra cost arising, although he may be faced with the resulting delay to his building without means of redress. Eventually clients pay for such hazards as an addition to tenders for jobs in general. It is a matter of policy which risks are borne by the single contract and which are spread.

POSITION OF THE ARCHITECT OR OTHER DESIGN TEAM LEADER

Whoever leads the design effort for a project carries a particular responsibility, not only for the design itself, but for numbers of the issues which have been outlined so far. This is true even if there is some other

person who is acting as project manager and who co-ordinates the total execution.

As a minimum, the architect (as he will usually be called hereafter) has powers:

(a) to inspect the works with a view to approving them and so perhaps to disapproving them;
(b) to issue instructions which change what the project costs both the client and the contractor;
(c) to issue certificates about the contractor's performance, expressing approval over work and other matters, and also to enable the contractor to be paid.

These duties he performs under his contract with the client, so that he is *prima facie* liable to the client for any breach of his contract. But he may also be liable to the contractor in tort for negligence in some circumstances. The courts are tending to enlarge the areas of tortious liability and it seems that architects are no more immune than other mortals.

Outline practical approaches

It is desirable to wind up this chapter on a fairly positive note, as something of a corrective to the tone so far. The central message has been that it is realistic to seek an optimum level of certainty in decision-making and implementation, rather than some perhaps elusive maximum, the cost of which in time or money may not be justified.

This target must be set against the background of what it is practicable to achieve, given the existing structure and working of the construction industry, and the difficulty of evading these constraints at the level of the single project. It must be realised that it is seldom possible to tie down a scheme to give absolute fixity before the contract is placed, so that no change can deflect it from its planned path of serenity and certainty. This means that there must be suitable ways of building in flexibility over the physical works, the financial arrangements and the programme from concept to completion. There are the contractual mechanisms available to satisfy most needs, and these in particular are surveyed in Chapter 2. The more common aims may be outlined here.

DESIGN FREEZING OR DEVELOPMENT

Primary will be the degree of fixity in the scope and design of the works. In an ideal world, design would be done once, in advance, and the works would be built as designed. The reasons why this does not happen need not be rehearsed further. They must be assessed against the degree of cost predictability and control required by the client and achievable for the type of project concerned.

The practicalities of life mean that ways of accommodating changes and of settling the unsettled are needed. Too often it is assumed that the simple availability of a clause about variations gives adequate licence for anything, whereas it is intended to cover only fairly limited changes, introduced into the programme of construction work in an orderly manner and with plenty of warning to avoid disturbance of production. If more drastic alteration or late establishing of intentions is expected, a move to a cost reimbursement contract becomes desirable at the very least. Even without drastic change of intention, such factors as delay in giving information or variations out of proper time need more than a variation clause to allow adequate valuation to be made within the contract.

Four basic state of design situations may be isolated in relation to the time of tendering, and so establishing the financial basis:

(a) *Design complete and frozen at tender*: this has the maximum advantage for price keenness and a straight run at construction, avoiding extra costs then. It also has the longest pre-tender time and, rigidly applied, excludes flexibility over design development.

(b) *Design complete but not frozen at tender*: this has the price advantage, but then loses this during construction, according to how disturbing variations are to progress, quite apart from their own direct costs. There may be both cost and time overruns.

(c) *Design incomplete at tender and declared to be so*: this is indicated by a basis of approximate quantities or prime cost. The pre-tender time is shorter, because less design is done and tendering documents are less precise. Pricing is higher, but an element of later uncertainty is discounted in this, although the contractor is not obliged to accept dilatoriness from the client's side without recompense.

(d) *Design incomplete at tender but not declared to be so*: this is concealed by a basis of firm quantities or (with more difficulty) by one of drawings and specification. The concealment occurs because drawings in any detail are not issued for quantity tendering, while the bills do not usually look any different when the uncertainty exists. This may secure the maximum price advantage, unless detected, and may be used to shorten the pre-tender time. It leads to problems later, usually intensified to the extent that they were unexpected by the contractor.

There are situations in which clients need to rush into construction on site as soon as possible, but the simple question of starting on site does not always mean an earlier completion. Even if it does (and clients may be very pressing on their consultants), the cost of achieving it may outweigh the advantage gained. A rudimentary approach to this problem is shown under 'Client's risk analysis' below.

CONTRACT FINANCIAL BASES

This aspect is developed in Chapter 2 and is fundamental to much of the rest of this book, but is set in context here.

A contract basis usually contains three strands relevant to this issue. One is certainty over the amount payable, so far as this can be achieved, for reasons already indicated. A second is some sort of a formula upon which payment is based. This may range from 'this much for the whole works', through some form of measured quantities and unit prices to payment by costs incurred. In the case of both quantities and a cost basis, the formula awaits the insertion of detailed values into its spaces to give the final amount due. The third contract strand is leeway to negotiate over such elements of excess expenditure as are due to matters which can be attributed to default of the client or his advisers. This is largely the burden of this book. Somewhere between are the effects of uncertainties which are hardly anyone's fault in many cases, such as ground conditions, the condition of existing structures, market changes and technical development.

There are risks of a commercial nature in the market, mostly widely understood and accepted, and others of a less predictable nature, which may or may not be insurable. It is usually the client's advisers who set the pattern of who carries each risk, and this should be properly assessed in any contract with peculiar features. Otherwise, tenders will be loaded to cover excessive risks or clients will face higher settlements to cover the risks which they have assumed. For most regular situations, the standard contracts provide a sharing out of risks which the industry has become accustomed to view as 'fair', but the position should be watched.

When all this has been done, there is need for mutual tolerance between those operating a building contract to avoid the onset of constant niggling over small issues of departing from the 'book'. Given the will, much can be settled by judicious give and take, while still reaching a sensible conclusion. Attitudes of scoring points, or splitting hairs over legalistic interpretation can harden into lack of will to settle at all. Even in the matters considered in this book, where some of the hairs must be split, there are often issues of no moment where common sense can steer affairs through to a safe haven. It is sometimes said that most disputes are settled at the right amount, even if for the wrong reasons. The thought is comforting, although it may be suspected of providing doubtful reassurance for those who do the settling!

CLIENT'S RISK ANALYSIS

Whether to risk delaying design, or what the possibilities are of serious revisions, are not simple matters to assess against the hope of saving time by an early start on site. The model following does not give a 'rule of thumb' for deciding, as there is not a standard disturbance situation. It indicates some major factors which often enter into the picture and which should be weighed in deciding whether a trade-off is likely to be beneficial. When claims situations develop, it is time to consider whether the risk paid off!

A project is assumed with the characteristics below. The terms and ideas

used in what follows are developed in later chapters, so that the model may be left until these have been read, if the extra detail is needed first:

(a) Contract value £1,000,000.
(b) Contract period 50 weeks; whether this is compressed or not is irrelevant.
(c) Work starts 10 weeks before design is completed, the financial basis being unimportant within the broad brush picture.
(d) Liquidated damages are £4,000 per week, and it is assumed that the benefit to the client of 10 weeks' time saving is therefore at least £40,000.

The rate of construction and pattern of expenditure anticipated are shown in Fig. 1.1.

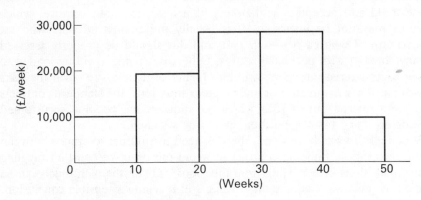

Fig. 1.1   Anticipated expenditure pattern

Present concern is limited to claims due to information not being supplied on time or being inaccurate and needing correction, as the main feature of design not proceeding as intended. Other matters leading to reimbursement are ignored, although what they are and when they occur within the total pattern will affect payment. Often they increase it, perhaps by compounding an effect. Occasionally, taken in combination, they produce less effect than they would have done separately.

It is assumed that a disturbance effect occurs only in *any one* of the five periods, so that the effects tabulated are *alternatives* and not parts of a cumulative series. Effects are distinguished as:

(a) *Prolongation*: simple extenuation of the contract period of a nature qualifying for extra payment.
(b) *Disruption*: occurrence of uneconomical or abortive work, whether or not the programme is extended.

It is also assumed that a disturbance in any one time period affects the next two (if available) in both these ways, although at a reduced

rate, and that the results are then overcome by corrective action, paid for in the figures shown. According to the expenditure rate in a given period and those following, the effects may be rated descriptively as follows:

Period	Immediate effect	Knock-on effect
A	Low	High
B	Medium	High
C	High	High
D	High	Medium
E	Low	Nil

These suggest that there is greater loss and expense during a period when work is proceeding more rapidly and when there is a greater quantity to follow, as might be expected. Subject to these considerations, there is also more risk of knock-on effects when the initial impact occurs early, although the scope for recovery of time is also greater, if the effect can be overcome. Much depends on how an effect can be contained. If a disturbance occurs in a clean-cut way, there is more likelihood of deferring work without much disruption, although prolongation will still take place.

Period	Expenditure	Immediate effect (all 5%)	Knock-on effect (% on next two periods)	Prolongation	Total
A	100,000	5,000	(2%) 10,000	(3 wks) 15,000	30,000
B	200,000	10,000	(2½%) 15,000	(5 wks) 25,000	50,000
C	300,000	15,000	(3%) 12,000	(6 wks) 30,000	57,000
D	300,000	15,000	(3%) 3,000	(4 wks) 20,000	38,000
E	100,000	5,000	—	(2 wks) 10,000	15,000

As the prolongation rate is given as including the loss of liquidated damages as well as reimbursement of the contractor's prolongation costs, each of the totals has to be set against the £40,000 saving due to the initial overlap of design and construction time by 10 weeks. The occurrence of two sets of disturbance, or a slow dribbling disturbance, can have heavier effects, especially in prolongation. As the figures stand, the isolated disturbances in periods B and C each cost more than the value of the project time they save the client.

CHAPTER 2

Contract solutions and risk distribution

More traditional contract bases
Assumptions underlying the more traditional bases
Less traditional contract bases

Several responses are possible in the light of the problematic nature of organising building contracts. It is possible to decide to do better next time, by being on one's toes rather more often and treading on other people's less often. It is possible to ignore the situation and just press on. Neither of these takes a positive account of where the problems might lie. A more realistic response is to accept that the situation is indeterminate in some ways, but that it is possible to respond with such precautions as are available by way of appropriate contract arrangements – as well as doing a bit better! This chapter surveys the common alternatives available in terms of their strengths and weaknesses for present purposes, so that some may be expanded in later chapters. Others are given to afford some basic comparisons. A more comprehensive discussion is given in the author's *Quantity Surveying Practice and Administration*.

The more traditional arrangements described below have evolved over a long period and have become those which clients, or their advisers more often, put forward to contractors as the contract basis. By contrast, the newer methods of design and build and management contracting mentioned have appeared as specific reactions, it must be suspected, from contractors against failure to operate the older methods properly. As often happens, out of such reaction has come methods valuable in themselves, so that clients are embracing and suggesting them quite often to contractors, sometimes despite their advisers in the first instance. Probably these roots give the fundamental reason why the newer approaches need less consideration in a book on disputes: they are adopted in part to avoid the contentious areas caused by failure to use the other methods properly.

Construction covers many technical types of work with great scale variation and where parties seek different risk distributions. They are affected by many factors, including the desired speed, timing of design and information communication, and the extent and nature of sub-contracting. There is room for all the methods of contracting in the complexity of today, provided that a suitable one is chosen in any instance and not abused.

More traditional contract bases

Here 'traditional' simply indicates that these bases have been in use throughout the present century at least, in a substantial way, so that the bulk of work has been performed under one or other of them.

DRAWINGS AND SPECIFICATION

Used to give a financial basis of a simple lump sum, this is the prevailing method for a fairly small, uncomplicated project, such as a single house or a straightforward shed-like building. It gives an 'entire contract', as described later in this chapter, in that the basic commitment is to pay the contract sum for the contract works, neither more nor less. It is intended for projects that have been fully designed before the contract is placed, because it contains minimal provisions for pricing variations. There may be none, but desirably there should be an unquantified schedule of rates (described more fully in Ch. 6) to give details for incidental variations that occur. Such a schedule is usually derived from the contractor's build-up of his tender, that is his own 'builder's quantities' structured and priced however he may choose, rather than in relation to any standard method of measurement. Some editing of the wording of the schedule may be negotiated by the architect or the quantity surveyor before the tender is accepted, to make it more suitable for its purpose, but it is essentially proffered by the contractor. As such it is open to be construed against him on the *contra proferentem* principle discussed in several later chapters, as an independently prepared set of quantities is not (see 'Firm bills of quantities' below), in the event of disagreement over its meaning.

This type of contract works very well for those jobs for which it is intended, by cutting down on unwanted detail. It allows marginal variations to be priced from the schedule, but introduces risks over substantial variations. There are two reasons for this, the first being that the contractor carries the risk in his tender of errors in his quantities, because only the *prices* out of his build-up become part of the contract. Of course, this risk works either way, although major over-estimation of quantity is likely to lose him the job in the first place. The client is also at risk, by the same token. If then a major variation occurs, say by way of omission of the whole of an item, it will be priced at the unit rate in the schedule, but measured at the actual quantity involved, rather than that on which the contract sum was based. It is presumably the case that elsewhere in the contract sum, the contractor will have amounts effectively compensating for such over- or under-provision, but he may find himself in difficulties if the quantity error is substantial.

The second risk arising out of such a schedule is that of deliberate manipulation of the schedule pricing. This is related to the former risk. Because the quantities do not form part of the contract, the contractor may be inclined to adjust his normal level of pricing for particular items, according to whether he expects an increase or decrease due to variations. This is a dubious practice and can easily rebound, if the direction of variations has

been misjudged, as considered further in Chapter 3. It is also an option that may occur to whoever is 'editing' the schedule before acceptance, especially in the light of inside knowledge of pending variations. The contractor is quite entitled to resist editing which seeks to change prices which are genuine, even if high in the opinion of others.

The over-arching risk with this form of contract is that it is used for projects which are too large to be based on such limited apparatus to cover variations. These may be extensive in scope or large in value or, worse, both. Any weaknesses in the schedule content will be magnified on the larger contract. In a highly competitive environment, there are pressures to use this system far beyond normal limits. Much depends on the relative expertise of the parties as to who comes best out of the resulting encounter, but this is hardly a commendation of the practice leading up to it. There is evidence that the JCT minor works contract and the IFC contract (the latter discussed extensively hereafter), are both suffering from this abuse.

Should there be such occurrences as disturbance of progress leading to a claims situation, this type of contract can only be more vulnerable. These occurrences are less likely in smaller contracts, or less likely to be made an issue because they are intrinsically smaller, but the basic contract provisions are the same, while backed up by less financial detail in the schedule.

FIRM BILLS OF QUANTITIES

These remain the most common way of arranging the financial sides of the larger contracts, intended to mean over about £150,000 or rather more for simple works. They are still lump sum or entire contracts. The quantities are part of the contract, but are present to explain what is in the contract sum and not to offer an opportunity to either party to select which parts of the works the contractor will perform.

The regular contents of bills of quantities may be divided into three types. There are 'preliminaries', so called because they come first in the documents, but more properly relating in large part to what are the overheads or what the economist would call the 'fixed' costs of the project. The bulk of the content is in the actual quantities, which give the amount of work to be produced, and so are more the equivalent of 'variable' costs, in that a fairly small alteration in quantity does not produce a corresponding alteration in the preliminaries. They are variable, but only in ways which the contract sets down. Then there are several types of item which may be grouped for present purposes: prime cost sums, provisional sums and daywork. These all represent allowances for work still to be instructed when the contract is entered into, and so somewhat uncertain for the contractor. In fact, some of the allowances may never be needed at all and, except perhaps for daywork, the tenderers have to include the same sums in their tenders. All of these receive further consideration in various chapters.

The pricing of quantities lays itself open to similar practices as may occur with schedules of rates, in drawings and specification contracts and elsewhere.

Where they receive distinct criticism (although it is really a question of degree) is in the facility which they afford to have variations valued. This may seem a strange criticism, and put like this it is, for it is a great strength that the means of controlling changes in the sum payable are so readily at hand. But what those concerned with the design of buildings for the client can be lulled into believing is that variations can be introduced willy-nilly, with the contract formula for their valuation taking account of all the change in cost that is incurred by the contractor. But enough individually innocuous variation instructions can add up to a radical change in the works and their conditions of execution, so that provisions about loss and expense due to variations are also needed. These allow the excess cost to be reimbursed, but lead some designers at least to feel under attack when claims are presented. They may be right.

Even worse, is the fact that 'firm' quantities can be used as a cloak for indecision. Designers can cherish an illusion that everything will come out right in the end. Quantities may be so presented as to look firm, but really be at best an intelligent guess at what the designers will eventually come up with. There is an old saying about a crystal ball. There are even more variations to contend with, while the contractor may have been misled into assumptions over precision about the work when pricing these treacherous wolves in sheep's quantities. The ground is prepared for uncertainty as to what was required and what has been priced, which can hardly help in settling what may be a difficult contract anyway.

The lesson here is that firm quantities should be used when conditions are firm: the client knowing what he wants, and the design team having designed it fully. Uncertain elements can be identified as provisional, but otherwise the contractor can trust what he gets. Human errors in quantities are always possible; these will be corrected. If the use of such quantities disciplines early firm design, and this is possible, there can only be gain. If this is not attainable, it is better to think about the next option.

BILLS OF APPROXIMATE QUANTITIES

It must be admitted that simply labelling bills as approximate does not dispose of the problems – these are just made clear from the beginning. These bills are sometimes attacked because they lead to higher pricing by tenderers, but is this not reasonable? Anyone entering into a less certain commitment is entitled to expect more for doing so, and possibly will be less awkward about settlement as a result. It is true that approximate quantities are an invitation to defer decisions, but when decisions cannot be made they have their strengths. Equally though, the facility to measure what is actually done once it happens, rather than to start with something and amend it later, does not dispose of the extra costs of disturbance or working out of sequence.

If bills are made approximate, only the measured sections should be affected. The preliminaries still need to be definite, otherwise many of the ground rules for the project will be uncertain. Nothing is impossible here,

but it is the area where the greatest effort to be precise is needed.

In the main, discussion of quantities is related to an assumption of firm quantities, as what is said often applies to all quantities. Where necessary the distinctions over approximate quantities are drawn. When the contract is in being, they become effectively a schedule of rates (see below) for final valuation, but one where the basis of pricing is acknowledged to be affected by the weighting and proportioning of the original quantities. It is difficult to assign any confidence level to these quantities, although tenderers must make some assumptions – and put in the higher prices just mentioned! Differences between the parties over the assumptions which should have been made must be expected and resolved against the built-in uncertainties.

This basis is still that of a lump sum, but with the sum actually calculated at the end of the period.

SCHEDULES OF RATES

Schedules of rates are mentioned above, as an adjunct to drawings and specification contracts. The present reference is to contracts without any initial lump sum, but based upon a schedule of rates without quantities, so leading to complete measurement of work as executed. In this case the schedule is prepared by the client's quantity surveyor and is based upon defined rules of measurement, such as those in a standard method of measurement. Effectively, the schedule is used just like bills of approximate quantities once the contract is running. The difference is that when tendering takes place, there are no quantities available, just the unquantified schedule. Tenderers therefore must decide as best they can, the disposition of work in terms of the proportions of work sections or trades. They may not even have a totally clear picture of the nature of the work or its scale, although in such cases some additional formula may be included to allow adjustment for at least the variation of scale. Usually they are pricing by taking a pre-priced schedule and quoting percentages on or off sections within the schedule. This means that on top of uncertainty about the work, they are forced to accept given differentials between items within a section, which may actually cover quite a range of work. This pre-priced approach is the most practical way of obtaining tenders that can be compared with reasonable ease in the absence of common quantities to give immediate comparability, the alternative being to compare every price in an initially unpriced schedule between tenders. It does not help tenderers though, unless they are used to the particular schedule and know its idiosyncrasies.

These schedules lead to higher prices and to more negotiation of additional prices during valuation of work under them, because of the uncertainty that surrounds their use. Usually they are restricted to cases in which the whole contract is beset with uncertainty, such as term contracts for a running programme of small works and maintenance. Here work crops up over a period of two or three years and is ordered and paid for as a series of single

jobs. Commonly, there is a break clause in the basic contract allowing either party to get out at a few months' notice, and this not infrequently happens. This arrangement is thus convenient for what it covers, rather than particularly economical. Because of the small sections of work and the option to break off, it does not often lead to disputes of the types considered in this book, as the problems of operation which arise can usually be accommodated in the provisions for adjusting preliminaries and other allowances for overheads. The basis is not considered further within the scope of this book.

PRIME COST

This arrangement is otherwise known as cost reimbursement. It is mostly frequently used when the nature of work is uncertain, as well as the extent, and when prior estimation of a lump sum price or of unit prices is therefore impracticable. It may also be used when speed precludes other approaches, or when the client has a special relationship with a given contractor. Its essence is that the contractor is paid for most of his direct expenditure on site at the level incurred, such as hours of labour and plant and quantities of materials. Site overhead costs, head-office expenditure and profit are covered either by a lump sum or by a percentage on the directly reimbursed expenditure. The rates for labour and plant and the allowances to be made with materials for elements such as discounts, must be defined and dealt with precisely. Competition between tenderers is limited to these items and no overall tender amounts are obtained, so that often only one contractor is invited to quote at all. It is more relevant to secure a reliable firm which will work efficiently and economically, than apparently competitive rates from uncertain firms.

In operation, these contracts do not lead to disputes in the same way as contracts related to the other bases. This is because they give 'payment for what is spent' in the main, rather than 'payment for what is produced' as do the others, again in the main. If there are disputes over this part of the contractor's remuneration, they are usually over whether he has been wasteful in his use of resources, and whether therefore the client should meet the full amount.

There are usually provisions in the contract for the architect to decline to pay for excessive levels, or even to order labour, etc. to be taken off site. What is excessive can be contentious, as it may well impinge on the contractor's organisation of the work and timely completion, which remain his responsibility. Such a disagreement could be about the substitution of plant for labour, for instance, and lead to division of responsibility over the level of total expenditure at the end of the work. Under other contract arrangements, the architect has even less power to intervene, a point taken up several times in later chapters.

Alternatively, the amount paid on the prime cost basis is regulated by some 'target' cost for the project, agreed in advance against an estimate based on shadow bills of quantities. Deviation from this target results in an adjustment of what the contractor actually receives. This may be set so that

he shares the difference up or down with the client or, not infrequently, so that he concedes the whole difference if this is a saving. The estimate then becomes a maximum. The salient area of dispute here can be whether the works have been varied, while the estimate has not been adjusted sufficiently to take account of this. Although variation instructions are needed in such a contract, they may mistakenly be regarded as of less importance, as the contractor is being paid primarily for what he spends. Proper attention to both legs of the financial system is therefore crucial.

It is, however, the case that quite a substantial part of the price payable is derived from the addition made to the actual prime cost for overheads, etc. When this is by way of a percentage, it clearly varies as a direct function of the other inputs. This is the accepted contract basis, so that there can usually be no argument over its adequacy. When it occurs as a lump sum and there is a gross distortion of the prime cost from what was anticipated, there is room for readjustment even without any element of disturbance of work. The reasoning is similar to that when preliminaries are adjusted (see Chs. 6 and 20).

Assumptions underlying the more traditional bases

While they do not apply uniformly in each of the bases, several common assumptions apply in most instances. Even in the case of prime cost, most of them are relevant.

ENTIRETY PRINCIPLE

The contract is held to be 'entire', that is there is an obligation on each party to perform his part in return for that of the other, while each may expect the other to undertake the whole of his obligation. Thus, the contractor may not break off the works part way through without some penalty – in a contract without any relieving provisions, he will forfeit the right to *any* payment for what he has done. Equally the client may not choose to have the works terminated early without facing an action for breach, again unless there are other provisions. In particular, he may not extract work from the contract and give it to another to perform, at least not while the remainder of the works is under way. To operate a contract under these precise assumptions, it is necessary to have complete definition of the works, in nature, scope and detail.

All the forms of contract referred to later in this book include clauses that modify the rigorous position. All have provisions for effecting variations to the works, that is changes in what is to be built. Some have provisions requiring the contractor to accept that defined sections of work will be executed by sub-contractors, who sometimes are to be chosen by the architect. The variations arrangement expressly, and the sub-contract arrangement implicitly, allow the possibility of introducing incremental changes which may affect considerably in aggregate what the contractor produces. In all

cases it is intended that the changes shall be instructed in such a way as not to disturb regular progress. Otherwise, extra payment arises.

DESIGN AND CONSTRUCTION

It follows from these points that design must be done entirely or substantially before the contract is awarded, both to allow proper tendering and for work to proceed in an organised and, hopefully, profitable manner. Even a prime cost contract based on a form constituted like the JCT fixed-fee document, assumes reasonable definition to make the fixed fee a feasible option. All the arrangements are based upon design by the architect or other consultants acting with him and under his co-ordination. The contractor has no design responsibility expressly given him, and it is a matter of doubt whether any can be passed to him by roundabout means under these contracts.

The construction methods needed to produce the designed works are, however, entirely the contractor's prerogative, unless any stipulations are made in the contract documents. The programme details are his concern also, so long as he meets the end date and any intermediate dates over phasing that may have been given.

The various provisions over these elements delineate the major responsibilities reasonably clearly. Other risks over injury and damage are also allocated, while there are provisions allowing or excluding the possibility of the contractor recouping expense due to market fluctuations in his costs. It is generally true that time is important in the contracts, so that there are provisions over liquidated damages for delay in completing, but that money appears to be more important. Thus, it is common to find that extra time can be granted, but that earlier completion (even to make up lost time and with extra payment) cannot be insisted upon by the client.

There is some imbalance in the way that the parties are cast in the contracts, due to the traditions of the industry. The client has very much a back seat, and even those matters which he may well initiate are communicated to the contractor by the architect. He is silent unless affairs reach the possibility of a determination (see Ch. 16). By contrast, the contractor is in the front line and highly active, as he must be. The balance is held by the architect, with the quantity surveyor in a mopping-up role. Although both are engaged by, or even on, the staff of the client they are required by the building contract to act between the parties and hold the scales over differences between them. The architect even has to hold the scales when he is being weighed in the balances – not the easiest of acrobatic performances! These issues affect a number of points discussed hereafter.

Less traditional contract bases

While they need less consideration later, the position of the newer bases may be set out here. In many respects, they do not diverge from the others, which itself is worth stressing. If they are less prone to disputes, it is because of the

way in which the parties approach them, rather than anything constitutional about the contractual patterns.

DESIGN AND BUILD

This method, otherwise known as 'package contracting' or the 'all-in service', is a variant of the drawings and specification contract already described. Its major feature is the transfer of design responsibility from the client's side to the contractor himself. It is common for the client to provide quite an amount of preliminary design work as part of his brief, perhaps up to sketch design stage. The contractor takes over and develops as much or as little as he gets and is responsible for the whole, subject to the possibility that he may not have been able to check some of the assumptions on which he was instructed to proceed. It is common for the contractor to present a design which is not finalised in all of its details at tender stage, although it should be complete enough for the client to see what he is going to get, before he enters into the contract. The client may still require changes to the design after the tender has been accepted, although how they are implemented is the contractor's concern primarily.

The contract sum is again a lump sum, as perforce it must be when what lies behind it in design comes about in the manner indicated. The contractor gives a contract price which is fixed even though the design is incomplete, although the price will be amended to accommodate the client's later changes. To aid in these calculations, there is usually a contract sum analysis, corresponding to the schedule of rates under the drawings and specification pattern. Its form is variable, but for various reasons (including the potential development of design) it best takes the form of a number of lump sums, breaking down the main sum for the whole contract.

Many of the provisions of such a contract over progress, disturbance and payment are very similar in structure, and sometimes detail, to those in other contracts, needing little independent consideration here. Detailed consideration may be found in the present author's *Design and Build Contract Practice*.

MANAGEMENT CONTRACTING

The essence of a management contract is that design is still performed by the client's consultants, but that an additional operator, the management contractor, is introduced into the basic structure. The details of the arrangement are open to numerous variations, but often this contractor performs no work on site other than to provide a team to manage what happens there. All work is carried out by a series of separate contractors in a direct relationship with the client, but co-ordinated by the management contractor. He also co-ordinates the interface between these numerous contractors and the design team, who manage their own internal affairs as usual, subject to pressures put upon them by the management contractor to deliver information.

How each of the site contractors is paid depends on the details of the

contract with the client, although these will have common elements. The quantity surveyor remains responsible for settlement overall, but there is also a responsibility on the management contractor to ensure that the budget which he agrees with the quantity surveyor is not exceeded without authority. The management contractor usually co-operates with the design team to ensure that the design is developed with a view to ease of physical construction, but he does not assume any design responsibility, nor can he dictate on matters of design to those with responsibility.

The 1987 (December) JCT management contract in fact consists of a group of contracts and other agreements and has yet to be operated and tested. It uses the concept of 'works contractors' to deal with those persons in a contractual relationship with the employer and the management contractor, but controlled by the latter.

The emphasis in such a contract is upon the professional management offered by the new participant, who is acting for the client alone. It is for this reason that it is better for him not to perform any parts of the work. If he did, he might be faced with a conflict of interests between the overall management and cost and what suits his own share of the work. It is urged that this contract approach gives economic, buildable design, with a short programme time, both on site and from initial concept.

If any dispute arises between the client and his management contractor, it can be seen that it will differ from those with a contractor in the traditional role because of the contractor's responsibility for co-ordination, and total progress and budget: all partly shared with others. This introduces difficult areas of dispute, but its rather specialised nature puts it beyond the scope of this book. In the case of the other contractors, such as the JCT works contractors, disputes are more likely to fall into the traditional pattern: they are paid directly by the client, but are operating rather like sub-contractors in other arrangements. They thus may cause delay or disturbance to others, or suffer them, so that claims, etc. of the types discussed in Part 3 of this book are possible and covered in the contracts to allow for settlement and also any contra-charges which may arise.

PROJECT MANAGEMENT

This approach is to be distinguished from that just outlined. It involves the traditional pattern of responsibilities and contracting, but with the introduction of a project manager within the client's team. This person may still be a contractor, but may well have a background in one of the design professions. Again, his role is to co-ordinate the whole matter of design and construction to secure the best integration, but not to organise the interaction of the various persons who may be performing work on site. This, and responsibility for their payment, remains with the contractor as usual.

This pattern does not change any contractual relations, other than to give an extra one – the project manager's own! The project manager may be

regarded as an extension of the client: his own man up front, not needing to be mentioned in the traditional forms of contract. Alternatively, he may be seen as crystallising what the architect has traditionally done in co-ordinating the functions of the rest of the consultants, while also being the primary dealer with the contractor. For present purposes, project management does not therefore introduce any new dimensions. Nor does it dispose of any old ones, although the aim is to avoid some of the interface problems that lead to disputes.

CHAPTER 3

Tendering: the contractor's policy, examination and the contract

The contractor's policy
Examination and acceptance of the tender
Offers, statements and representations
The resulting contract

The first two chapters have reviewed respectively the circumstances of disputes and the types of contract arrangements, more commonly emanating from the client's area, which have evolved to give workable arrangements. This chapter looks at the way in which tenders and their assessment can affect subsequent actions over disputes. This is very much the stage at which the potential contractor is making the running, but when the client's advisers can also sow the seeds for future trouble, or sift them out. Whenever 'contractor' is mentioned, 'sub-contractor' may be substituted, in relation to either the client or contractor as appropriate.

For simplicity, bills of quantities (usually firm) are assumed and competitive tendering, rather than negotiation. As these conditions give the most complicated information by way of detailed pricing, they also provide most opportunities for the interplay of different tactics in structuring the pricing and disentangling any snags before settlement is in prospect. Other patterns are not devoid of these matters, and the corresponding possibilities may be inferred.

The contractor's policy

TENDERING

Tendering is broader than pricing and covers the higher-level decisions about a particular contract. These include preliminary decisions about whether to tender at all.

For all contractors, these are conditioned by the nature of the project. This means attention to the type of work, its scale and location, and such matters as the time given for its construction. It is also important to weigh up the client himself, whether he is stable, known for changing his mind or for being a bad payer, frequently late. Some of these things lend themselves to

counteraction by way of extra reimbursement: late payments do not usually do so (see Ch. 8), but have determination as a last resort, while insolvency can be countered hardly at all. Unless he makes allowance for those matters that do not put him completely off tendering, the contractor can expect a hard time in attempting to make up losses that he did not provide for and that are without remedy.

With these issues cleared, the contractor still has to evaluate the risk elements of the contract itself, such as the market conditions nationally or locally when set against the fluctuations provisions, and whether any undue risks of a contractual nature are to be assumed or may be negotiated. In all these lie his profit margin – or the lack of it! This chapter is not a treatise on tendering as such, but simply illustrates areas where future disputes may germinate.

NORMAL PRICING

Unless there is an extreme deviation, the effects of the decisions so far mentioned are difficult to detect, whether made well or poorly. They are blanketed by the overall tender and do not show in the detailed pricing. Discussion of the latter is now related to net pricing policy, that is exclusive of the risk and profit levels set as a board decision. If ascertainment of loss and expense in particular is related to some analysis of the contract bills (by no means always the case, see Chs 14 and 22), then the structure of pricing can influence the result, or at least how easy it is to arrive at it.

The more straightforward matters are those aspects of measured items which are not usually required to be stated in some special way under the rules of a standard method of measurement, but which affect the price level, sometimes substantially. These include the quantity of an item or group of items of similar work, as scale affects in particular the use that may be obtained from plant. The JCT provisions specifically refer to this aspect as one applying to ordinary variation valuation (see Ch. 6). Allied to this and not expressly mentioned in this way, but implied in the term 'similar character', are the questions of repetition and intricacy, the presence or absence of either of which can affect the cost of 'identical' quantities of work. This is especially true of alteration work, or other 'piecemeal' situations. Phasing or the timing of work within the overall contract period can affect what work will cost. Sometimes, such considerations will influence whether to sub-let the whole or even part of the work given together in the bills.

This is a difficult area in general for pricing, and standard methods are wary about such detail. This is understandable, as projects vary so much in their detailed character. It is also the case that most contractors would readily admit that they cannot obtain site costing information in sufficient detail to make it sensible to try to price all of these factors, even if they were made known, and if estimators then had the time and the aptitude to take them into account. One major national contractor is reputed to maintain that it is practicable to isolate seven cost centres only.

These considerations mean that the approach when tendering in most cases is to assess the general incidence of these unspecified factors and make some allowance in prices on a fairly broad basis. As a result, disputes over the effect of disturbance and so forth start from a basis of uncertainty over what conditions the tender really anticipated. But further, such matters as loss and expense are not to be argued from the tender basis, but on the actual deviation from what should have happened. They must therefore be argued from an average set of conditions, related to items actually more or less costly in the first place and then affected by events during progress! This theme recurs later (see Ch. 14).

ABNORMAL PRICING

Deliberate attempts to distort the inevitable mechanics of pricing can also be made. A common area of difference of opinion is how to deal with preliminaries. The extreme split is between those who price them separately and those who spread their amounts as a percentage or other allowance over the prices for measured items. If preliminaries represent costs which are incurred in a way not related directly to the remaining costs of the project, the former method has the advantage by simple logic. Such costs are examples of the economist's so-called fixed costs, which may remain fixed for some variation in other costs (the variable ones), and then change at a rate or in discrete jumps not bearing a direct relationship to the variable costs.

It may be suspected that those who do not segregate these costs when tendering often do not know with any precision how they are incurred, and so take the easy approach. This may work reasonably well with work of closely similar character, but may lead to disaster with unusual work having an unusual concentration of site overheads, etc. Whether separate pricing occurs or not, the prices given in the contract bills are not to be used in the ascertainment of loss and expense, while those for preliminaries in particular are to be adjusted in relation to variations on quite distinct principles from those used for measured items. However, realistic values can offer useful guidance in some circumstances of investigation (see Chs 14 and 22). It is dubious to suggest that spreading the value of preliminaries over the measured amounts helps the contractor to keep his options open when negotiating extra amounts. Such practices tend to rebound.

More common manipulation occurs over pricing measured work, and two aims may be distinguished. One is to enhance cash flow by front loading the pricing. This means that those sections of work performed earlier, such as excavations, are priced higher than true cost, while others like finishings are priced lower. The result is that the job provides extra working capital early on. This may be fine, so long as the fact is not forgotten by the contractor part way through and too optimistic a view of profitability is not taken. It is even less happy for the client if insolvency of the contractor comes, and there has been an overpayment in the earlier stages. This point recurs hereafter: the significance here is that it may affect not only cash flow, but also the

pricing of variations and settlement in some circumstances.

The other aim of manipulation is to try to anticipate the way in which the project is going to shift in terms of variations. Correct spotting of items due to increase in quantity and higher pricing than usual in consequence, will bear obvious fruit. This is also true of spotting decreases and pricing accordingly. It is correspondingly untrue when the wrong forecast is made and related action taken. Such provisions as those in the JCT forms link variation valuation directly to the prices in the contract bills, so that the consequences follow. As already hinted, the ascertainment of loss and expense does not follow directly, making attempts at disturbance spotting an unproductive activity. But again, price distortion for any reason can have unexpected effects, if it becomes necessary to seek collateral information from the pricing.

Examination and acceptance of the tender

PRICING

Yet another avenue of distortion may come about not by the contractor's planning at all. This is alteration of pricing during examination of the tender. This may be urged by the quantity surveyor to secure consistency between items or to correct imbalances, real or supposed, of the types already discussed. It is sometimes proposed as a way of taking up errors in the arithmetic in the bills, as an alternative to making a percentage adjustment to the total on the summary. This may be convenient for minor amounts, especially if balancing items can be found. But it can sow the seeds of future problems if used for major amounts, and especially if the preliminaries are altered – always a temptation because of the lump sum pricing. It is always the contractor's right to insist that his pricing remains as he has originally given it, even in respect of arithmetical errors on the face of the bills. This may not be wise for practical reasons, or for diplomatic ones either, but it is valuable if a point of significance is at stake. Once an alteration *has* been incorporated, it is as binding a contractual provision as any other figure.

There are more general issues over financial detail, usually resting with the quantity surveyor to clear. (Fuller discussion of these is provided in this author's *Quantity Surveying Practice and Administration*.) Initially, he may well look at how the tender compares with his own cost plan or other estimate – and then at early retirement! Inside the bills as tendered, he will be looking at the elements mentioned above as affecting the contractor's policy, especially those which suggest some manipulation of pricing, because they have a mirror effect for the client.

The contractor should remember that the quantity surveyor, who is to become the impartial valuer between the parties once the contract is in being, is acting for the client during assessment of tenders to ensure a commercial deal for him. This is quite proper at this stage, it being assumed that the contractor will look after his own interests adequately. He must therefore be prepared to do so, and not assume that the quantity surveyor will take his

part, although still pointing out any clear errors. It remains that any errors of pricing or arithmetic which go through into the contract bills cannot be corrected in favour of either party, but are held to have been accepted.

Several particular situations may arise at assessment. There can be effects of the confidence level in the design as developed, both in the documents in general available to tenderers and in the bills in particular. This may show in amendment bills produced for pricing after tenders have been received, or even in alternatives requested in the original tendering. From the contractor's side, there may be qualifications which he puts forward to the tendering basis in the invitation, over such questions as fluctuations, the contract period or phasing. These are not contentious in themselves, but need care in ensuring that the secondary document is not priced in such a way that, if embodied in the contract, it will produce anomalies in the price structure or, worse, lead to the wrong total tender on the amended basis.

This danger is always possible when such elements as plant and temporary facilities are to be used differently in the amended scheme and are not identified separately for pricing purposes. Even more, when bills are approximate there is a tendency to treat them as schedules, as though the very fact of being able to select items and then measure the final quantity imparts some elasticity into what the unit prices then cover. The essential point here is that when such a revision has been agreed and incorporated into the contract, the opportunity for either party to obtain any difference in what is payable has passed. This may then prejudice the course of later negotiations over important changes in the balance of quantities, when prices for them are based upon the earlier structure.

PROGRAMMING

Another aspect of the tender which may need attention alongside the pricing is that of the programme. Standard contracts are somewhat ambivalent over the provision and status of contractors' programmes. The JCT position is to allow for an optional master programme post-contractually and for it then to be kept up to date, but without any significance being assigned to it (see fuller discussion in Ch. 4). Sometimes tendering documents ask for a programme to be supplied with the tender, perhaps again not giving a specific reason for this, or perhaps disclaiming any responsibility from the client's side for it when examined.

Such a programme may be useful in assessing the realism of the contractor's approach, especially in an awkward project, and in checking that he has taken account of any intermediate dates due to phasing, etc. It also warns the architect about when he is likely to have to produce details and schedules for the contractor (see *Leach* v. *Merton* in Ch. 9 on aspects of this). It remains necessary for the architect to hold to the position of non-approval during any discussions over any such programme, otherwise he may find that he has assumed some stance which is beyond his recognised position, so committing his client in the event of a dispute related to the data embodied in the programme.

Whatever may be left unsaid and by implication as not being the case, the provision of a programme (even when not requested) is some *prima facie* evidence of the contractor's intentions. It may be questioned later as to its realism or seriousness, but it can be useful to one party or the other in a dispute. It therefore is well for the architect to look at it carefully and to ask, without commitment, for any clarification during tender assessment, when there should be no special interpretation in prospect, although this cannot be automatically assumed. The post-contract aspects of this issue are gone into in Chapter 4.

Offers, statements and representations

A number of issues hover around the relatively firm area of documentation which constitutes the essence of any contract. Some of these come about in the time of tendering and subsequent discussion.

First there is the question of the offer itself. It is established law that there need to be both offer and acceptance to give a valid contract. Usually, the contractor's offer is based directly and simply upon the documents issued to tenderers, which themselves constitute an offer to treat. Occasionally, he will put forward an offer which qualifies the documentation issued and this too will be embodied in a further document, probably a letter. Whether the contractor qualifies his tender or not, if the client accepts it as put forward, there is a binding contract. On the other hand, if it is not taken into the written contract, it may well be of no effect. Thus in *Davis Contractors Ltd* v. *Fareham Urban District Council* (1956), a letter of the contractor's stating that his offer was subject to adequate labour and material being available was not incorporated. The contractor was unsuccessful in his action over the effects of prolonged delay due to shortages. This must be distinguished from a representation made by one party which induces the other to contract, as discussed below.

If, in either of these instances, the client purports to accept the offer as made, but subject to certain amendments, no contract immediately results. This is true even if the client says in relation to the contractor's qualified offer, 'No, I do not want that, but I accept your tender on the basis of the original terms issued.' The contractor has never made such an offer, so that it does not exist to be accepted. All that the client can do is to put forward a counter-offer, which is then open for the contractor to accept.

Much vaguer situations can come into existence through discussions arising out of queries during tendering, or during more formal pre-tender meetings, perhaps before tenders are actually invited. Some of them directly or indirectly produce effects considered in Chapter 4. It is quite possible for either party to enter into the contract on the understanding that matters not delineated in the documents are nevertheless after a certain fashion. This is especially the case over arrangements about the site or over its character, about the programme and the provision of facilities. The architect may, for

instance, state that an owner of adjoining land has agreed to make an area available to the contractor as a stockyard for the duration of the contract, and that the client is forgoing the rent. As a result, the contractor's tender is lower than it would otherwise have been. Alternatively, the contractor may state that he will complete some section of the works ahead of the rest in the absence of any phasing provisions. This may even be the factor that secures him the contract, against the competition of others. In neither case is anything in writing – what is the contractual position?

In the first place, a building contract need not be in writing at all to be valid, although the question of proving its terms becomes daunting if it is of even average complexity. What is true of a contract as a whole, is true of a part of it. Secondly, there is the distinction between a condition and a warranty. For this purpose at law, a condition is not the equivalent of a clause in the contract form itself, as in common practical usage. It is some representation which induces a party to contract, and which is fundamental to the contract. By distinction, a warranty is a statement that does not go to the root of the contract, although the effects of it not turning out to be true may still be serious. Whereas a breach of condition can lead to damages or to recission of the contract, a breach of warranty leads to damages, but not recission, assuming in each case that money will give adequate recompense. In the examples given, it is unlikely that their breach would be serious enough for them to be regarded as conditions. Even if they were, but were not discovered before work started up (quite likely in these examples), the aggrieved party would possibly settle for damages, rather than have to break off the work.

Underlying this discussion is the question of misrepresentation, that is making an untrue representation that induces the other party to enter into the contract, but which is not then embodied in the contract. Misrepresentation is of fact alone, and not in giving an opinion or statement of the law (the position may be different over giving professional advice). This is a complex area of law, with several divisions of the topic. In many cases today, the defendant in an action is placed in the position of having to demonstrate that he made a statement with 'reasonable ground to believe' it true and that he in fact did so believe, this being the requirement of the Misrepresentation Act 1967. A misrepresentation gives the representee the right to treat the contract as voidable, that is an option to declare it void or to affirm it. It follows that a misrepresentation may become a matter with the standing of a condition.

In the case of *Howard Marine and Dredging Co. Ltd* v. *A. Ogden & Sons (Excavations) Ltd* (1977), the defendants had based their tender for work upon statements by the plaintiffs about the capacity of barges which they were to hire. These turned out to be excessive, although based upon usually reliable data. It was held by a majority that the plaintiffs should have gone back to the basic ships' data, and so that they had not been sufficiently careful. Judgment was given for the defendants, who had already repudiated the contract and counterclaimed for damages.

But it is not only the parties to the contract who may be liable to legal

action over misrepresentation. When a duty of care in giving advice exists, a person who gives advice without due care may be sued in tort for failure to exercise reasonable care. The classic statement of this position arose in *Hedley Byrne & Co. Ltd* v. *Heller & Partners Ltd* (1963). Here, a bank gave a credit reference about a client, which turned out to be negligent when the client went into liquidation soon after. The bank avoided liability only because of a rider that the reference was given 'without responsibility'.The House of Lords was clear that liability would otherwise have lain. There are implications here for consultants who proffer advice, perhaps gratuitously, during pre-contract discussions. Usually, they are acting as agents for their client, but the possibility of other relationships needs to be watched. Even as agents, they may need to look over their shoulders at their clients, who may seek recompense from them after action from the contractor, claiming that he has been misled.

It is also possible for misrepresentation to occur by silence, and this is perhaps an area of greater concern to consultants. It is not that silence constitutes misrepresentation in isolation, but that it may if it occurs in such a way as to distort a positive representation, or when an earlier statement is found to be untrue. There is always the feeling that it is up to the contractor to make up his own mind, and this is true. But he cannot decide what he does not know about.

These are areas on which contract forms are silent, because they are concerned with the operation of the contract as agreed, and not with what led up to it. They are therefore usually areas where the parties must come to some agreement over differences themselves. The architect and the quantity surveyor, if named in the particular contract, can do nothing on their own initiative, because they have no powers given to them, even if they effectively caused the problem in the first place. In the event of failure to agree, the parties have to consider legal action or arbitration.

A thorny situation would occur if a sub-contract tenderer put in a tender which was far too low, the contractor embodied it in his main tender, the main tender was accepted and then the sub-contractor withdrew before he was accepted, as such persons may sometimes do. There would be no breach, as there would be no sub-contract, but the contractor would have relied on the sub-tender and could not obtain another anywhere near so low. Much would turn on how aware the contractor should have been of the inaccuracy (a question perhaps of how specialised was the work), but it has been suggested that an action for tort might lie, in view of the sub-contractor's possible negligence. This has yet to be tested.

The resulting contract

COMPLETENESS

Several comments on the status of elements in a building contract flow from the immediately preceding discussion. While there is always the question of

evidence (perhaps needing both judge and jury, if queried), the recording of an agreement can take several forms:

(a) Entirely oral, that is spoken or parol.
(b) Entirely written, which includes any form of document, such as a drawing.
(c) A mixture of these two forms.

For a building contract of any substance, there is usually a sizeable body of documents. In any contract so evidenced, there is then usually a presumption that the whole intention of the parties is contained and expressed in what has been recorded. If a contract is under seal, it becomes particularly important to ensure that what is evidenced by this formal method is complete. Even in the absence of sealing, the presumption may be critical in later discussion. It will stand against an assertion by one party that he did not intend what he has signed, whether he contends for oversight in reading it or just that he made some other form of mistake in approaching the agreement. Mutual mistake is another question, and normally the parties will seek to rectify this anyway.

The general rule is that a document is both 'exclusive and conclusive' over its own terms, as has been supported in a long series of cases, particularly with reference to leases. These include *Angell* v. *Duke* (1875) where the provision of additional, unmentioned furniture was held to be excluded, and *Henderson* v. *Arthur* (1907) where variant terms about payment were excluded. However, the courts may find that a contract does not express the whole intention of the parties, even though it may appear to do so. Thus in another lease case, *Walker Property Investments (Brighton) Ltd* v. *Walker* (1947), the absence of mention that the tenant might use certain extra storage, did not debar inclusion of this accommodation in the scope. It is rather unclear how the distinctions were defined, without access to the exact documents.

The status of statements in such cases is usually assessed evidentially by when they were made during the course of negotiations, broadly those made later will appear more cogent, because affairs will have become clearer overall. It will also be taken into account whether any part of their immediate subject-matter is in writing and sheds any light on what is not, and whether they were based upon specialised information available to one party only, so that the other had to rely upon it. These statements then have to be weighed against whether the written contract is complete and precise in itself, without ambiguity, obvious error or misunderstanding.

In the absence of clear cases on building contracts here, it is probably safe to say that the primary presumption is likely to hold in the face of silence. If then a situation occurs like one of the examples already given about extra stockyard space or phasing of work, the answer is to be explicit. It is possible that the production of correspondence or minutes not incorporated into the contract would constitute acceptable evidence, but this sort of document is usually vague on the details unless edited and incorporated. In any case, unless the aggrieved party is prepared for proceedings, he cannot find out in the face of opposition whether this is so.

If a contract is patently incomplete, say by the omission of a completion date, the courts will imply a reasonable date if the parties cannot agree. Similarly, they will act to give coherence to a contract containing discordant terms, as may arise when a standard printed document is incorporated alongside other elements specially composed for the individual contract. Here, the normal rule is for the special document to overrule the standard, as this presumably is what the parties intended.

CONSISTENCY

Some standard forms of building contract contain provisions which reverse this last rule of interpretation, in particular the JCT group, so guarding against mutilation of their own close-knit terms by ill-considered additions, but possibly also leading to effects not intended by at least one party when special terms are modified by the standard. Numbers of actions have been brought on these matters, with a variety of detail. *English Industrial Estates Corporation* v. *George Wimpey & Co. Ltd* (1973) and *M. J. Gleeson (Contractors) Ltd* v. *Hillingdon London Borough Council* (1970) may be consulted as examples. The proposed introduction of extra terms of a contractual nature by either party therefore needs careful examination, and possibly legal advice. They tend to appear in the preliminaries of the bills, perhaps as statements of intention to change the standard contract wording, perhaps as seemingly innocuous clauses in their own right. Their effect is the same, however they appear or are expressed, unless the standard wording is directly amended in the actual contract form. It is possible to delete just the standard clause that leads to this situation, and some authorities would recommend this. If so, redoubled care is needed, as then the specially written will prevail in all cases.

It is also a principle of interpretation that in the event of a dispute, a document in a contract will be construed against the party who put it forward, even though the other may have expressed no opposition to it at the time. This *contra proferentem* principle applies to a purpose-written document or to a ready-printed one, if it is proffered by one party. Here, 'proffered' means that the one party has produced a document for use which has originated with him or with his side of the client–contractor syndrome.

The series of contract forms produced by the Joint Contracts Tribunal (the JCT) do not fall into this group, because they have been negotiated by representatives of both clients and contractors, among others. They thus do not count as having been put up unilaterally, even though the individual client and contractor are very unlikely to have been on the JCT, and even though one of them will have initiated the proposal to use the form for the immediate contract. By contrast, those forms produced by the Association of Consultant Architects (ACA) and by central government are unilateral documents, and so are subject to the *contra proferentem* rule.

CARE

It may be seen that attention to detail at the stage of entering into the contract

will be well repaid if there is a difference later over content or interpretation. Both parties should check their records of telephone conversations, meetings and correspondence to ensure that all relevant items have been drawn into the final agreement. Thereafter it is usually too late: documents so embracing as those for a building contract do not admit of being readily circumvented by, 'Well, I meant . . . and you know it.' This may mean amending some of the documents as used for tendering. If so, amendments should be initialled by the parties themselves to avoid doubt or ineffectiveness. Other points may warrant gathering up into a consolidating document, which is then referred into the main list of documents.

Another place for care is whether a contract has come into being at all. This is usually quite obvious: even if the formal contract has not been drawn up and signed, there will usually be a letter of acceptance. This will suffice, if it refers to all the documents already mentioned, although it is to be regretted that greater promptitude in executing the contract is not observed. But it may be quite a distinct matter if the contractor simply receives a letter stating that the client intends to enter into a contract and so would he, the contractor, please proceed with certain work or ordering of materials to save time. This is really an intimation of a separate contract and should include an undertaking by or on behalf of the client to pay separately for what is being ordered if the main contract does not go ahead.

Thus in *British Steel Corporation* v. *Cleveland Bridge & Engineering Co. Ltd* (1981) it was held that a letter of intent from the defendants to enter into a sub-contract with the plaintiffs and asking them to go ahead with work, followed by the plaintiffs performing work, did not constitute a sub-contract with terms. They were entitled to be paid on a *quantum meruit*. By contrast, in *Trollope & Colls Ltd and Holland, Hannen & Cubitt Ltd* v. *Atomic Power Constructions Ltd* (1962) a contract concluded some months after work had started was held to have retrospective effect, covering *inter alia* its payment terms.

PART 2

Contract administration

CHAPTER 4

Physical and time problems

Programme and method statements
Site possession and access

All chapters in Part 2 deal with the principles of matters which may become the subjects of disputes during and following the progress of a building contract. Some of their causes may be seen to have their roots in elements set out in Part 1, while others arise directly from events or non-events during progress. Numbers of these provisions are illustrated in the case studies in Part 4.

The significance of the provisions of individual contract forms becomes important in these discussions. The emphasis is placed upon JCT 80 in its 'with quantities' edition and upon IFC 84, although other editions of the former can usually be substituted without any change of meaning – other than the obvious change from the contract bills to the contract specification.

The client, as he has been termed throughout Part 1, is given his title of 'the employer' from now on, following the terminology of the JCT forms.

With entry into the contract, both parties pass from the area of negotiation, with the possibility of withdrawal at a cost to their separate selves mainly of goodwill. Instead they are bound to actions of various sorts, constrained within the contract time-scale. These actions start with the activity of the contractor to get work under way, even if off site, of the employer to make the site available and of the architect on his behalf to provide initial information. The importance of prompt action all through cannot be over-emphasised, with so many causes of dispute flowing from its breach.

Many of the more 'routine' problems encountered during contract progress fall into the group looked at in this chapter. They happen with depressing frequency across the range of building work to affect the smooth flow of work which the contractor is entitled to expect from the employer under many contract arrangements. Often, but not always, they are symptomatic of insufficient planning before construction begins or of undue changes of mind by the employer's team during construction. Sometimes they represent a deliberately assumed risk of partial planning to allow an early start to be made, followed by some unevenness in progress, for which the employer knows he will then have to pay. They may be contrasted with the less

frequent hazards set out in Chapter 16 and the more specialised difficulties in other chapters in Part 3.

Because many of these problems stem from the employer or his agents, standard contracts deal with them in such ways as to relieve the contractor of the more obvious ill effects. However, there are others which remain his responsibility almost entirely, so far as cost and time go. These include the wider state of the economy and the effects of government actions whenever fluctuations, provisions, and closely circumscribed extension of time clauses do not help. He is cushioned against the weather only to a limited extent, and against such matters as traffic conditions not at all. While he may gain extra time to offset strike losses, he receives no further payment and nothing else to compensate for unexpected union actions. The effects of variations in the regional workload of the industry are entirely his, for better or for worse. Sometimes, these items may overlap in effect with those over which he is afforded some protection, as is considered in Chapter 9.

As well as problems there are several contract issues which are related to problem areas, to be taken in passing.

Programme and method statements

CONTRACT STIPULATIONS

It is a matter of pre-contract activity to examine and evaluate any statements put forward by the contractor in support of his tender, but they are considered here in view of their later effects. These statements may have been specifically required of the contractor, perhaps even being an elaboration of outline requirements given by the employer in the enquiry documents. They should have been checked so far as practicable for reasonableness, while the contractor should have been questioned about how far he really expected to stand by what they contained. It is important that no one on the employer's behalf should have actually accepted them as binding upon the employer, or have given any explicit approval of them. At most, there should be an expression that they have been 'noted' for information only.

If it is necessary to include some requirements over the contract programme in the tender information, this should be limited to the essentials, so that the contractor has the maximum scope to organise his operations himself for greatest efficiency. Usually only the start and finish dates will be important to the employer, and even these may be expressed as so long after the date of acceptance of the tender. Provided acceptance is not delayed unduly, a little flexibility here is not objectionable, while the contractor can protect himself against too much by stipulating how long his tender remains open for acceptance when he submits it. Standard contracts as a group ignore the possibility of a staggered commencement of the works, but usually have some provision (perhaps in a supplement) for staggered completion. Any such options should be clearly incorporated into the tender, paying

special regard to the possible pitfalls over liquidated damages for delayed completion (see Ch. 11).

Inside the end dates for the contract, there may be dates that are critical for the employer's wider operations. These intermediate dates may be fixed dates by which certain work is to be completed. While these may not lead to the handing-over of the work concerned to the employer, they may, for instance, be required to allow direct contractors to enter upon site work. Other dates may not be absolute stipulations in themselves, but may act as constraints within which alone the contractor may perform defined parts of the works. As a general rule, the more such dates are given, the more causes of difficulty may arise, either from failure to give all relevant information about what are essentially complex matters or from affairs miscarrying in practice. There is also a peculiar problem in entering enforceable contract provisions against the contractor here, when the standard provisions relate only to final overrun of the programme and special provisions can easily conflict (see *English Estates* v. *Wimpey* in Ch. 3 and the discussion under 'Payment' below).

Working methods are even more difficult, or even dangerous, to delineate. JCT forms refer to several particular obligations and restrictions which the architect may require to be varied, but give no guidance over how to introduce them initially (see under 'Status of documents post-contractually' below). Some of these are more in the category of programming points than working methods proper, although this is an area where some overlap exists. It is best not to require the contractor to perform work by particular methods, but simply to restrict positively those which he may employ when, for instance, noise or pollution is unacceptable. A requirement that he must carry out demolition or alteration work in defined ways technically is a likely recipe for shared or transferred responsibility when something goes wrong.

STATUS OF DOCUMENTS POST-CONTRACTUALLY

When the employer has put forward specific requirements for tendering and these are incorporated into the contract, the position is clear. There is also no doubt if the contractor has made any stipulations over such matters as the contract period, and these in turn are incorporated.

The least clear position under contracts in general exists over the contractor's own master programme setting out how he proposes to perform the works. If this document is not proffered before the contract is awarded, it remains the contractor's private document for his own use, with no contractual status. JCT clause 5.3.1.2 is specific and requires the contractor to 'provide the Architect (unless he shall have been previously so provided) with 2 copies of his master programme' and also to provide amendments to take account of extensions of time granted by the architect. This clause is singularly unhelpful by virtue of what it leaves unsaid.

In the first place, the level of detail in the programme is not given: a master programme certainly indicates no more than major dates, which

will give the architect just a broad forecast of the contractor's progress. Secondly, the 'unless' provision means that no contractual significance can be assigned to a document that may not have been produced (in any sense of the word) before entering into the contract. Further, the document has no definite post-contract role, which is what is at present under review. There are several principal options and gaps over a programme under the JCT contract, the IFC contract being similar in effect, but without mentioning a programme at all:

(a) *As information for the architect's use when supplying information in time for the contractor's work to proceed*: clauses 25 and 26 (which see) refer to the contractor requesting information closer to the event in most cases than 'So soon as possible after the execution of this Contract'. Further, the programme is hardly detailed enough for guidance in this way.

(b) *As information for the architect's use when deciding upon claims and extensions of time*: this is not said anywhere, and only an assumed connection can be deduced over the latter from the reference to incorporating the effect of extensions when granted.

(c) *As a binding initial statement of what the contractor is going to do*: this is nowhere stated and the contractor has no greater (or less) obligation than to 'carry out and complete the Works' in accordance with the contract under clause 2.1.

(d) *As a regularly revised statement of what the contractor intends to do*: apart from the reference to revisions due to extensions of time there is no requirement for the contractor to amend the programme at all, quite apart from work to it. It may therefore be amended for extensions and at the same time be quite out of step with reality and misleading.

USE OF DOCUMENTS POST-CONTRACTUALLY

The only indisputable purpose of method statements and programmes in the absence of special provisions is to help the contractor in performing his own contractual obligation, noted under (c) above. This is to proceed to completion by or ahead of the contract date, and in all other respects as contract. How the contractor does this is entirely his own concern, so long as he is not bound by any subsidiary stipulations of the types already discussed. It follows therefore that he may vary the detail given in his programme in any way that does not prevent him achieving the objective. A possible point of doubt is over his further obligation that he shall 'regularly and diligently proceed' under JCT clause 23.1 or IFC clause 2.1. This appears to require him to maintain *regular* progress even when he has time to take a break and still meet the completion date, although *GLC v. Cleveland Bridge* hereunder throws a query over this when there is an excessively long contract period. The case is in the context of fluctuations, but appears to relate.

It is nevertheless the case that the contractor's programme and other data

prepared for his domestic use may provide *prima facie*, and perhaps even sole information from which to assess what should have happened when some form of disturbance occurs and leads to a dispute. For this reason, there is something to be said for the architect or another adviser seeing what the contractor has available pre-contractually, even if not formally requested and however rudimentary it may be. In fact, the less polished it is, the more may it be taken as an unbiased statement of intent. The longer it has been around, the more may the more devious contractor have 'adjusted' it!

If the contractor has been working to a programme fairly closely during the earlier stages of the works, there is again a strong presumption that it represents a fair projection of what was intended for the rest of the time. In all cases, as close an examination as possible should be made to establish whether the programme should be used as part of the basis for a settlement, or whether a fresh construction is effectively needed for this purpose.

Such an assessment should take account of several basic factors:

(a) The logic of the programme in respect of sequence and interrelation of sections of work.
(b) The durations assigned to each section in relation to the overall programme time.
(c) The reasonableness in amount and character of the resources allocated to each section, and of those resources allocated to be available for wider purposes throughout the project.
(d) Whether factors other than those adduced as causing the disturbance under discussion have affected the programme, adversely or otherwise.
(e) To what extent the contractor has chosen to revise the programme, and whether this has led to greater efficiency.

The last point returns to the contractor's right to amend any programme at his sole discretion, within any constraints placed upon him. It may arise out of consideration by him of the preceding points in part, or simply represent wider second thoughts.

The architect or the quantity surveyor, as most likely to be involved in discussions, should therefore regard a programme as useful, but not infallible. He is entitled to disregard it where it is faulty for his purposes, and substitute some other basis for his calculations. This becomes a delicate matter when the contractor indicates that his programme is faulty, but that he had plans to revise it in its later stages to compensate for this. He then further indicates that these plans have been frustrated by the causes of disturbance that he now alleges. It is no part of a concession of extra time or money to make good the contractor's deficiencies for him. On the other hand, there is no presumption that any contractor is always going to execute his work with perfection, if left to himself. The starting-point for adjustment should therefore be a reasonable, if occasionally fallible, plan of action by the contractor, but not one which is heavily flawed or deliberately distorted.

When the contract has been awarded, there is clearly no power to require the contractor to produce any programme or method statement beyond the contract requirements. Similarly, what can be required cannot be asked for during general progress in any special form (such as a network), unless the contract documents are explicit. If a dispute situation occurs, the contractor is obliged to give necessary information to those assessing the extent of compensation. While they cannot *insist* on any particular presentation, it will obviously be in the contractor's interests to do what he can to ease their understanding of his case, and so comply with reasonable requests.

SPECIAL PROGRAMME FEATURES

Control

Several elements can affect the operation of the programme. One is the incidence of nominated or named sub-contractors under the appropriate contract form. Here it is necessary for both the architect and the contractor to be involved to different degrees in agreeing the sub-contract programme with the sub-contractor. Special considerations may obtrude if a particular sub-contractor is cheaper on price, but cannot meet the programme which the contractor requires. Even more special considerations crop up if re-nomination becomes necessary. These aspects are looked at in Chapter 7. Here it is simply noted that a 'trade-off' calculation may be relevant in the employer's interests, between what is arranged and becomes payable to the contractor or to the sub-contractor, according to the solution.

Another pressing situation is that in which considerable factory production of units specially designed for the individual contract is needed. Disturbance of the programme here can be more drastic, while more difficult to evaluate because of its off-site effects. It may cause dislocation to factory production for more than the immediate contract, because of the difficulties of absorbing a build-up of units not yet wanted at site. The alternatives become whether to deliver items to the site and use up what may be very tight storage, whether to store at works and use up the normal buffer space quite rapidly, or whether to seek storage elsewhere off site. These are quite distinct from the problems caused by disturbance of the programme entirely on site. They may be easier or harder to evaluate, according to whether they are self-contained effects or not (see case studies in Chs 19 and 21).

More subtly, the effect of a disturbance will be changed according to the extent to which the contractor sub-lets work and varies his flexibility. What is serious for him, with a whole programme to arrange, may have little effect on a sub-contractor who just comes and goes. Equally, the reverse may be the case, because it is the complete commitment of the sub-contractor for that project.

Payment

Given a generous contract period and no intermediate constraints, the contractor may choose to perform a heavy weighting of his work early

or late in the period, rather than spread it evenly. If he performs early, the employer pays early but receives no benefit until practical completion. If he performs late, the employer pays late but probably pays more if the contract is on a fluctuating basis. It was held in *Greater London Council* v. *Cleveland Bridge & Engineering Co. Ltd* (1986) that the choice remained the contractor's. Here the contractor could have manufactured gates for the Thames Barrier some three years before installation and have saved increased costs for the employer, but then have borne financing costs until he was paid on installation. He was within his rights to postpone manufacture, despite statements of intent about manufacture in his programme. It was stated that, as a general rule, a contractor was not obliged to operate the programme to his maximum detriment to obtain the maximum benefit for an employer. Here specifically, this was despite a provision that the contractor was 'to execute the works with due diligence and expedition', the equivalent of the 'regularly and diligently proceed with [the Works]' contained in the JCT and IFC contracts.

Those latter provisions continue with 'shall complete the same on or before' the completion date, so that the contractor appears to have the right to finish early and be paid accordingly, perhaps by proceeding very diligently. It is difficult to modify contracts to avoid these effects, as most stipulations can be circumvented by stratagems of timing work. Only numerous intermediate dates may be successful and this policy has been criticised earlier on other grounds. The best answer is a realistic contract period.

Site possession and access

CONTRACT PROVISIONS AND THEIR LIMITATIONS

JCT contracts are no exception to the general range of building contracts in the ways in which they treat matters relating to the site of the works. In fact, they say very little about the site itself, by implication 'the site of the Works'. They usually refer to 'the Works' as the locus where it all happens, once the contractor has been given possession of the site. This blurred distinction is commonly of no consequence, but may be unfortunate in some circumstances.

References to the site are made specifically in respect of the employer giving possession to the contractor and of any obligations and restrictions (discussed hereunder) which the employer may impose over use. These are given respectively in JCT clauses 23.1 and 13.1.2 and in IFC clauses 2.1 and 3.6.2, and their intentions are clear. It would appear that a single, undivided site is envisaged by the contracts, although there is no difficulty in having a site in parts physically separated, provided that this is adequately described in the preliminaries of the contract bills or specification.

There is no provision for the contractor to be given possession by instalments, and this would need amendment of the relevant contract in

both clause and appendix and also inclusion of details in the preliminaries. JCT 80 (amended 87) and IFC 84 have provision in clauses 23.1.2 and 2.2 respectively for the employer to defer giving possession for up to six weeks beyond the contract date for possession, provided an insertion in the appendix gives a specific period. Delay beyond any defined period under those contracts, or any delay at all under other contracts (including the unamended JCT 80) constitutes breach of contract. This is a post-contract deferment, but reasonably the contractor might claim for loss and expense due to inadequate notice. This allows the possibility of action for damages and also, in a serious case, of the contractor treating the contract as repudiated (see Ch. 10). The contractor must use his discretion here, as he needs to consider goodwill and, even when matters are seriously disturbed, whether he wishes to proceed with the contract. This of course he is still entitled to do, and negotiation of a sum (especially needed in inflationary times) is likely to sour continuing relationships less than an initial resort to legal action.

Beyond these points, the contracts refer to the works for all major purposes. These include the distinction between materials 'delivered to or adjacent to the Works' and materials 'before delivery' to these places, affecting issues of payment and responsibility treated elsewhere (see Ch. 8).

The term 'adjacent to the Works' is usually interpreted as something like 'not too far away', rather than actually contiguous, which is not at all helpful. It appears to be the intention that 'Works' here is equivalent to 'site'. If so, anywhere adjacent is not intended to be the site. If then, the employer makes an area belonging to him and detached from the site available for storage, workshops, etc., it becomes necessary to define it either as part of the site or as not. This is then not strictly the site of the works, but this distinction is only an inference. The site is best regarded as what the employer makes available for the contractor to perform the works. If the contractor himself obtains the use of an adjacent area of land, this should not be designated as part of the site, since questions like ownership of materials will not be determined by location on this area.

The contracts are also silent about conditions around the site, such as private roads, accesses through areas belonging to the employer and not part of the site, and temporary easements and risks of trespass to land or air space (but see questions of ingress and egress in later chapters affecting extension of time and loss and expense). These are quite variable matters, needing careful consideration and legal drafting in many cases.

While normally the site will be obviously larger than the works in extent, or coextensive with it, there is a particular need for definition of working areas in the case of alteration work contained entirely within an existing building or (confusion!) spreading without possession across an existing functioning site of the employer. Here, the question of phased possession rears itself, perhaps in a multitude of small instances, and is best dealt with by provisions about 'by mutual arrangement between the employer and the contractor, from time to time'. Each of these goes beyond the plain

contemplation of the contract, but needs care none the less. The routine pattern of sole possession by the contractor will not apply, and this should be spelt out.

It is quite common for the employer to impose particular requirements on the contractor, some positive and some negative. These may well overlap with points discussed under the preceding heading and with the wider contract programme discussed before that. It is therefore important to ensure that any such provisions are not at odds with contract clauses or with other standard clauses in preliminaries. If they are in conflict with contract clauses, these latter will prevail by reason of such clauses as JCT clause 2.2.1 and IFC clause 1.3. If they conflict with other documents, there is no certain way of establishing priority and the documents will be read as a whole to obtain the presumed meaning. If other ready-printed documents are included in the bundle, then the specially prepared clauses are to be given precedence over these.

There is no restriction on what the employer may introduce, should he have special circumstances on or around the site. He may be concerned about noise, dirt, smell, traffic and a host of other possibilities, but must be reasonably specific. It is not enough to say that the contractor must observe any regulations which may be imposed upon him during progress. He is entitled to tender on the basis of definite conditions, either stated or gathered from an investigation of the site while he is tendering. This does not necessarily mean an absolutely clean run when within an occupied and operating area, but it should be consistent with the right of possession that he has in the absence of information to the contrary.

Standard contracts are by definition not suitable vehicles for material about the introduction or bounds of such stipulations. JCT clause 13.1.2 and IFC clause 3.6.2 both allow *variations* of obligations and restrictions of categories as listed, a position with its own problems over just what may be varied, as discussed in Chapter 6. The clauses are restricted to four categories:

(a) Access to the site or use of any specific parts of the site.
(b) Limitations of working space.
(c) Limitations of working hours.
(d) The execution or completion of the work in any specific order.

The express inclusion of these categories may be seen effectively as restricting the matters on which the architect may instruct variations, beyond physical changes in the works, while not restricting the sorts of matters over which obligations and restrictions may be introduced in the initial contract. This is because the architect's power to issue instructions at all is limited to those matters expressly given in the conditions, variations as defined being one such matter.

This suggests that particular care is needed in selecting and describing these categories of stipulations in the first place, if any out of this list not covered by the contract bills (or any at all under other contracts) are strictly not eligible for variation. This is hardly a practical or fair position in many circumstances, but appears to be legally correct under all but JCT 80 (amended 87), as discussed in Chapter 6. What appears easier to accept is that the architect is not able to introduce extra obligations and restrictions of types not already provided in the contract, during the post-contract stage. If so, the lesson is to include whatever is thought to be required in as precise a form as possible, and then vary it later or even omit it altogether, as requirements crystallise. This does mean negotiation over amounts which are among the more imponderable, and so should not be the chosen path unless really worth while.

SITE CONDITIONS: NORMALLY ENCOUNTERED PROBLEMS

It is relevant to emphasise that the contractor faces a variety of difficulties to be overcome on many sites, even without the employer imposing any special ones. Many disturbance situations involve the compounding of these problems or the subversion of well-laid plans.

Apart from the disposition of the workforce to secure best results, there are considerations of site layout which can affect the costs of storing and handling materials, the grouping of temporary accommodation and the effectiveness of plant. These can mean problems in securing efficiency in combining the use of these facilities, or selecting the optimum sizes of items. Disturbance of the 'best fit' cases can therefore involve extra costs permeating many operations. What effect there is depends very much upon the site configuration and the restrictions which are introduced by the employer, quite apart from the intrinsic nature of what is being constructed.

Again, these elements are intensified when the works are fragmented by consisting of alterations, or are located in several places within a large occupied site. It may be very difficult to obtain high utilisation of facilities, even without disturbance of what has been planned. What is the best sequence for, say, plant may be at variance with the dictates of site offices or supervision.

These points are obvious enough to any contractor, but are mentioned briefly as what may escape the notice of those usually concerned more with the finished product than with the means of producing it. Sometimes their incidence should deter those responsible from introducing even quite desirable variations, in view of the resultant costs linked to the stage at which they are introduced.

DIRECT CONTRACTORS AND OTHERS

Standard contracts are usually linked to the concept of the contractor being given full and uninterrupted possession of the site for the duration of the contract works. But they also introduce the possibility of the employer engaging

others to perform work outside the contract, but going on concurrently with it on the site, or even of the employer himself performing such work. Such cases occur in JCT clause 29 and IFC clause 3.11, although curiously the former omits any reference to work being carried out actually on site.

These two clauses both take account of two situations in which such direct contractors, independent of the building contractor, may intrude into what is otherwise his undoubted right of sole possession of the site during his contract period. One situation is that in which the contractor has notice when tendering that such contractors will be present, the other that in which he is advised during the contract period.

In the former case, it is required by JCT clause 29.1 that the contractor is to be given in the contract bills or specification 'such information as is necessary to enable the Contractor to carry out and complete the Works in accordance with the Conditions'. IFC clause 3.11 refers more briefly to 'Where the Contract Documents provide for work not forming part of this Contract', thus allowing a more simple identification of the work within the context of a more simple contract.

The JCT requirement has two sides. There must be enough information given in the documents to allow the contractor to perform his own work in accordance with his own contract. This presumably is intended to mean enough information for the contractor when tendering to price the effects of any direct contractor being present and working, rather than for him actually to perform his own work without any hindrance at all; there must be enough information in due course for the contractor to proceed with site work.

While neither category of information need be entirely contained within the other, it is likely that the latter will be the more detailed, by covering such features as precise setting out data. These the contractor does not need when tendering, and their absence could hardly be held to invalidate the provisions of the clause. (He will expect, at least with quantities contracts, to receive much positional and similar information during progress in respect of his own work, as the contracts permit.) To avoid contention and doubt, it is useful to agree during tender examination or negotiation that enough information has been made available for pricing within the contract documents, and that further information is properly recorded for issue later as part of the supplementary detail to be given to the contractor when the contract is formalised.

The other side, inferred in the IFC clause and made express in JCT clause 29.3, is that the contractor has no responsibility towards these persons as sub-contractors. This affects the extent of his liability over indemnities and insurances and removes from him any responsibility for their work as performed.

In the present context, significantly, it means that he is not responsible for organising their operations, this being the concern of the employer or the architect. The contractor should look to the architect for technical and programme information, while acting to co-ordinate his precise activities by day-to-day consultation with direct contractors to the extent set out in the contract bills, etc. This will probably be given in a manner broadly similar

to that applying over sub-contractors, but the contractor is not responsible by any implication for more than is expressly laid upon him.

In particular, the contractor has no responsibility to perform attendance or afford temporary facilities unless these have been itemised adequately for pricing. He should only deal with these elements under a variation instruction, and should pay especial attention to any transfer of responsibilities which may be bound up in an apparently simple mandating of extra work.

The second way in which direct contractors may be introduced, by post-contractual action of the employer, is covered in JCT clause 29.2 and, again, IFC clause 3.11. Here, the contractor has a right to withhold his consent on reasonable grounds, which might be valid if the proposed extra work would interfere drastically with the works as such. It is to be hoped that any direct work proposed during progress would in fact be relatively incidental or free-standing, and not extend to something of as great consequence as the structural frame, which should have been foreseen! If something quite critical did arise, without which the finished works would be severely diminished in value to the employer, it is likely that it would be held to be unreasonable for the contractor to withhold consent, even though his own work would be greatly affected. Beyond this question of consent, the clauses say nothing, and the extra work falls into the same category as that under the previous clauses in all other respects.

Several factors come into play to safeguard the contractor against the effects of extra direct work introduced during progress, or indeed against any unexpected effects of any work already described in the contract. There will be variation instructions to cover any attendance, co-ordination, changed finished work and the like. Then the provisions for extension of time and loss and expense are available when appropriate. There is even the big stick of determination over delay by such contractors. Each of these is discussed in later chapters.

No aspect of these provisions gives the employer the right, through the architect or otherwise, to take work out of the contract and give it concurrently to direct contractors. If it is desired to remove work from the contractor, it must be omitted by variation instruction, with the routine effects on valuation, and be left out until after the contractor has achieved practical completion. Only then is the employer free to give it to another without being in breach of contract.

GROUND CONDITIONS

What is contained within the sub-strata of the site is of peculiar interest in many cases, because the contractor not only works within them, but does such things as digging out, holding up, filling back, taking away and disposing of water! This interest is intensified by the uncertainty as to the precise nature of the sub-strata until it is actually exposed. While contract clauses are usually quite reserved about ground conditions, the Standard Method of Measurement of Building Works is anything but, a pattern also to be found in other such methods.

The traditional practice has been to place as much risk over the costs of excavation and associated works on the contractor, when tendering, as is reasonable. This has sometimes meant all risks, with transgressions of reasonableness not unknown. Because conditions can vary quite radically within short distances horizontally or vertically on some sites, rules have emerged to provide as many data as are available and to cope with the diversity.

A key principle is to provide bore-hole or trial-pit information about ground conditions to tenderers, perhaps with pits left open during tendering. A full report encompassing close technical analysis of the soil and of water conditions is regarded as essential for any major project, and no contractor should sensibly proceed without one. Even with this provided, there remains the question of its contractual status. If it is erroneous at the points and times at which it was obtained, then the contractor is entitled to any redress for being misled. If it is unrepresentative of the conditions throughout the site, the position is more complex; under the sixth edition of the above method (SMM 6), there has been some shift from the earlier position that the contractor is responsible for making up his mind upon the data given, or in any other way, and that his pricing is then binding upon him in these respects.

SMM 6 leaves it to the contractor to assess from the detail given, the practical nature of what he will excavate and subsequently handle, so that he cannot assert that a properly described gravel stratum is more difficult to deal with than he had anticipated. It is well known that the rules of measurement ignore the position in plan of excavation on the site and are preoccupied with depths below starting levels, which are not necessarily original ground levels and which are not always required to be stated. As a result, there may not be a precise correlation between the quantities and the ground survey (see Fig. 4.1), so that this remains a 'contractor's risk' area.

Where the method changed earlier practice, was by introducing in clause D.3.1.a 'the pre-contract [ground] water level'. This is to be re-established

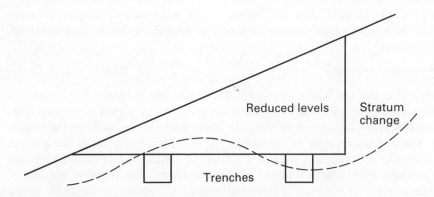

Fig. 4.1   Excavation conditions and measurement

during progress, so that a remeasurement of the quantity of excavation below the level occurs under clause D.13.13. The pricing of the water item itself must take account of the effect of the water on the material being excavated, and on its handling characteristics thereafter.

If information about sub-soil conditions is not available, SMM 6 clause D.3.2 requires an assumption about ground and water to be made in the contract bills, upon which pricing and quantities are then held to be based. While SMM 6 is not explicit on the point, these assumptions will then be corrected by remeasurement, not only of the water item, but of the excavation, support and other items, so as to reflect any revised balance of soil conditions. It is also implicit in this arrangement that the prices may be amended for different constituents, as they are not when actual data have been provided and the contractor makes his own assessment.

It is long-standing policy that particularly hard and soft ground conditions merit separation in the contract bills. The contractor won his contention that rock should have been measured (and so priced) separately in *C. Bryant & Son Ltd* v. *Birmingham Hospital Saturday Fund* (1938), as the then current SMM required. The existence of trial holes showing rock, but not made plainly available to tenderers, was not sufficient for him to assess his obligations properly. Thus rock is given separately for excavation but not support, usually as a provisional item subject to remeasurement. The main problem is one of definition, and SMM 6 holds to a definition in clause D.13.1 which, by its use of 'can be removed only by', is alone in the method in making the method of execution the criterion for measurement. Soft excavation means unstable ground, such as running silt and running sand. Here the position is reversed and the excavation is not distinguished, but the support is under clause D.22. No definition is given, so that one should be supplied.

When SMM 6 does not apply, these rules may be changed by the applicable method and the effect should be noted closely (for instance, SMM 7 should be compared carefully). When the contract is based upon a specification, schedule of work or other unquantified document, some statement about ground conditions may be needed when the project involves extensive ground works or the conditions are expected to be difficult. This should take account of any ground exploration, or make assumptions, so that tenders are not unnecessarily inflated to cover major uncertainties. Any schedule of rates provided by the contractor will need similar qualification in complex cases.

It will be clear that anyone not familiar with the concepts involved under this heading should seek advice before drafting any provisions on the topic.

Some sites are in areas where the discovery of antiquities during excavation work is highly likely. It is not practicable to add anything in the contract bills or specification to ease the way through. The contractor is entitled to extra time and payment in severe enough cases, while in advance the employer can only take account of his own risk and then hold his breath. The type of situation arising is illustrated in Chapter 19.

CHAPTER 5

Information, instructions and approvals

Functions of the employer
Authority of the architect
Mistakes in contract and other documents
Approval of the works

This chapter surveys the matters contained in its title. Before this, it also needs to set out the positions and operations of those originating such matters: the employer and the architect.

Functions of the employer

While the functions of the contractor are in general too obvious to need separate mention by way of introduction, those of the employer are otherwise. This is because he actually has very few functions in contractual terms, as the architect acts in relation to the contractor for most purposes. In fact the employer mainly pays when advised to do so and takes certain actions in emergencies. His other activity takes place behind the scenes in conveying his wishes about the building to the architect.

This division is not unimportant, as is seen from the functions allocated to the architect and introduced in this chapter. It courts confusion for the employer to take an active role when the architect acts in a manner like that of a separate project manager and carries the primary design responsibility as well. The employer should therefore avoid giving direct instructions to the contractor about any matter and always see that these are issued by the architect. This helps to avoid discrepancies and conflicts, and the possibility of gaps in communication. The contractor for his part is advised to decline politely to receive such instructions, as is his contractual right, by referring the employer to the architect as the proper channel. Faced with a persistent employer, he should discuss the position with the architect, who will not wish to see such strains occurring – especially if they affect design matters!

The employer himself may wonder what his power is to query what he receives from the contractor in terms of quality, and what he pays for it, when his hands are so tied. His direct contractual avenue is to resort to arbitration or court action against the contractor himself. His other avenue is to proceed against the architect over matters in which he considers that

the architect has failed in what he has allowed the contractor to produce physically and in time. Here the employer is acting under his own contract with the architect, rather than through the building contract, just as he would over a design fault or other lapse of the architect which does not overlap with the contractor's responsibilities. He may even choose to act against both at once on matters arising out of the contractor's activity, so that he may obtain satisfaction from them both in some proportion or other.

A list of the major obligations and rights of the employer under or in relation to JCT 80 and IFC 84 is given in Table 5.1.

Authority of the architect

PROCURING THE WORKS

A key feature of the standard forms taken in this volume is the naming of the architect or an equivalent person to exercise special functions *within* the building contract, in addition to the design functions which he performs

Table 5.1 Major obligations and rights of employer

	JCT	IFC
Obligations		
Agreeing supplementary domestic sub-contractors	19.3	—
Insuring works, etc, as contract option	22B, 22C	6.3B
		6.3C
Meeting amounts interim and final certificates	30.1.1.1, 30.8	4.2
Paying nominated sub-contractors direct when contractor defaults	35.13.5	—
Rights		
Receipt of completed works from contractor:	17	2.9
in entirety	2.1	1.1
to specified standard	2.1, 14.1	1.1, 1.2
on time	23.1	2.1
Defects and defaults remedied:		
by contractor	17.2, 17.3	2.10
by others, contractor charged	4.1,2	3.5.1
Indemnities over patent rights	9.1	—
Indemnities over injury	20	6.1
Liquidated damages for late completion	24.2	7.1–7.3
Determination of contractor's employment	27.1, 27.2 28A.1	7.1–7.3 7.8
Completing works after last and recovery of costs	27.4, 28A.3	7.4, 7.9
Collateral agreements with nominated sub-contractors over design, delay, loss and expense, determination	NSC/2, NSC/2a	

Note: The lists of clauses cover major elements only, and should not be read as exhaustive. JCT references are to the contract as amended 1987, where there is any distinction.

under his agreement with the client. These special functions exist partly to allow him to carry his design concept through to realisation, when built by another with whom he has no contract. They also allow him to stand between the parties and decide various matters, as is convenient when he is already in that mediating position. There is no intrinsic connection between all of these functions. In all, they do give him considerable power and responsibility, but they are strictly defined and so limited. He has been described in these respects as 'the creature of the contract'.

Directly related to his design function, the architect (as he may be termed alone for simplicity) has powers to ensure that his design is what is built. These cover inspection to see that the building is correct in layout and disposition overall, while the quality is right and sufficient in detail. Subservient to these is his power to have tests performed on materials and work. But in the way that building design and tendering proceed, it is usually necessary for supplementary information about the design to be fed to the contractor during progress to 'explain' the requirements. This involves working to a time schedule and also implies that no change will be introduced by what is provided as explanation. However, since changes are almost inevitable, the architect may also introduce these into his design in a regulated way, and so change the amount payable to the contractor as a result. In each of these areas, there are corresponding provisions to protect the contractor from laxity or abuse of power on the part of the architect.

TAKING DECISIONS

The further role of the architect is very much that of keeping the parties in as harmonious a relation as possible. He is the focus for communication in both directions, and the contract machinery provides for him to issue and receive most notices and to be the one who issues instructions and certificates on a range of matters. All these items are listed in Table 5.2.

These include a number of issues over which the architect is to act as decider of matters of potential dispute. Some are day-to-day elements such as whether work is up to standard, but others are questions of whether the contractor is entitled to an extension of time or to extra payment for disturbance of progress. Here, there is room for some tension, as the architect may be acting as judge and defendant in the same matter, to the extent that what is under consideration may be the result of his own dilatoriness or error. This point recurs in later chapters explicitly, and underlies some discussion in the present. It may be suggested too that the architect is in an awkward position, because he is ultimately responsible for the cost of the project to the employer. So too is the quantity surveyor, in that he has prepared the cost control information, but he does not then make decisions that add to the cost in the way that the architect does. At worst, he is to be blamed for a bad forecast, whereas the architect has actually incurred the expenditure for the employer. The contractor may be forgiven for the occasional feeling of unease when contentious matters arise.

Table 5.2 Architect's instructions and certificates

	JCT	IFC
Instructions		
Discrepancies or divergences	2.3	1.4
Statutory obligations	6.1.3	5.4.3
Setting out works	7	3.9
Opening up, testing, removal, excluding persons	8.3–8.5	3.12–3.14
Variations and provisional sum expenditure	13.2, 13.3	3.6 3.8
Defects during liability period	17.3	2.10
Postponement of work	23.2	3.15
Account documents to quantity surveyor	30.6.1.1	4.5
Protective work during hostilities	32.2	—
War damage	33.1.2	—
Antiquities	34.2	—
Nominated or named sub-contractors	35.5.2, 35.8, 35.10.2, 35.11.2, 35.18.1.1, 35.24.4.1	3.3.1– 3.3.3
Nominated suppliers	36.2	—
Certificates		
Practical completion of works	17.1	2.9
Completion of making good defects thereafter	17.4	2.10
Estimated value at partial possession	18.1.1	—
Completion of making good defects thereafter	18.1.3	—
Payment of insurance monies after damage	22A.4.4	6.3A.4.4
Failure to complete works	24.1	2.6
Expenses, etc. after determination by employer	27.4.4	—
Interim certificates generally	30.1.1.1	4.2
Interim certificate to pay off nominated sub-contractors	30.7, 35.17	—
Final certificate	30.8	4.6
Failure to prove payment of nominated sub-contractors	35.13.5.2	—
Failure of nominated sub-contractors to complete	35.15.1	—
Practical completion of nominated sub-contract works	35.16	—

Note: JCT references are to the contract as amended 1987, where there is any distinction.

LIMITS TO POWERS

There are though, distinct limits to the architect's powers under the contract, because he has only those powers that the contract gives him. For instance, he can issue instructions only on those matters stated, and the contractor can challenge anything apparently out of line, as discussed under 'Issuing instructions' below. More widely, the contractor has the right to seek arbitration over the architect's decisions, etc. although under JCT 80 most arbitration has to wait until completion of work on site (the same delay does not apply under IFC 84). The employer too is protected by this appeal

to arbitration, while both parties have the possibility of court action also. The costs, procedures and scope as between the two channels differ, so that which is the more desirable depends upon the individual situation. These are too extensive to be considered in this work. Most of the arrangements for agreeing the final account rest in the hands of the quantity surveyor, and there is doubt as to whether the architect can interfere with these, provided the quantity surveyor has proper authority for all that he includes.

What the architect is not able to do is to intervene in the contractor's construction organisation to direct how he shall perform the works, in such terms as how he disposes his equipment about the site, the sequence of work and how much labour and plant he uses. The contractor's overriding obligation is to 'carry out and complete the Works' (as in both JCT 80 and IFC 84), that is to produce the finished article within the time given. For another to interfere with this activity would be to undermine the basic contractual responsibility. This is a clear area where the contractor may protect himself by asking the architect to substantiate his own authority under the contract. This immunity of the contractor from meddling, as it might become, extends to the detailed means of producing an individual piece of work within the whole.

In each case, the implied restriction on the architect is subject to any specific provision to the contrary in the contract documents. Thus, there may be requirements over phasing or restrictions of when the contractor can obtain access to sections of the site. In detail, there may be precise specification clauses about how he is to mix concrete, the weather conditions in which he may lay it or how he is to protect it, giving a more restricted situation in some respects than under a purely design-mix specification.

There is a distinction among these examples. There is no authority for the architect to instruct over the level of productive resources, such as labour, that the contractor may deploy, including whether the hours per week should be increased (or for that matter decreased). This is irrespective of whether extra payment is held out to the contractor for such changes. Only in prime cost contracts do such powers intrude to some extent.

By contrast, the architect has some authority to instruct over amending phasing, access and cognate matters, at least when the contract contains some initial statements about them. He also has authority to instruct postponement. (See again for each of these under 'Issuing instructions' below and also in Ch. 9). He may clearly amend the specification, even to the extent of changing the basic philosophy of how work and materials are covered to produce roughly the same finished product. But exercise of these powers carries with it a balancing right for the contractor to seek an upward adjustment of the contract sum, or concomitantly for a downward one to be obtained from him in appropriate cases.

ISSUING INSTRUCTIONS

Situations often arise during progress on site when the architect must instruct over what has to be done, subject to the limits on his power discussed

immediately above. Under the standard forms, the scope of his instructions is restricted to areas specifically authorised, as listed in Table 5.2, so that the contractor has a right to challenge whether an instruction comes within this list under JCT clause 4.2 or IFC clause 3.5.2. If it does not, he need not comply. He should follow the procedure carefully and be clear on his position first. Equally, the contractor need not comply at once with an instruction on *any* subject which the architect 'purports to issue . . . other than in writing', as JCT clause 4.3.2 has it.

That clause allows, but does not require, the contractor to confirm oral instructions back to the architect within seven days of issue and then to act on them 'within 7 days from receipt' by the architect, unless the latter has dissented. This is a slightly precarious arrangement in a closely timed instance, as the contractor does not know exactly when the architect receives the confirmation. If the contractor places an urgent order quickly, its cancellation due to the architect's slow reaction may lead to an extra payment. Strictly, the architect cannot dissent outside the limit. If there is any doubt, he should therefore issue a further instruction cancelling the former. This gives the contractor authority for payment.

Most contractors operate the 'confirm back' system in the interests of progress. It also allows them to give their version of a dubious instruction, particularly over some matter other than a variation. It is however, strictly in order for the contractor to ignore an oral instruction, even if its later proper issue causes extra cost. Subject to questions of goodwill, this may even be worth considering with an architect who is persistently remiss. The burden of proof is his and, in the nature of the case, he is hardly likely to have good records.

Alternatively, the contractor may choose to press on with unconfirmed instructions and rely on the provision for the architect to confirm at any time before the issue of the final certificate. This can be risky when faced with an architect with a bad memory or records, especially in the face of a high final account. This risk runs either way, according to who can make out the stronger or more unscrupulous case. The provision is always useful to deal with the items which are overlooked by everyone until, for instance, the quantity surveyor digs them out during his tedious final working through.

INSTRUCTING SUB-CONTRACTORS

It is axiomatic to the operation of a normal building contract, as with other areas of commercial life, that the contractor's sub-contractors are his responsibility. This statement must be qualified, because standard contracts provide for various types of sub-contractors:

(a) *Domestic sub-contractor*: the freedom of the contractor under common law to choose a sub-contractor to perform some part of the works *prima facie* to be performed by him directly is constrained by a requirement for him to obtain the architect's consent to any sub-letting. Conversely, the contract documents may require him to sub-let a specified part of the

works to one person out of a number listed by name in the documents. Under either arrangement, the contractor is dealt with and paid as though he performs the work concerned, and in turn deals with the sub-contractor entirely as though no limitation has been placed upon him during selection.

(b) *Nominated sub-contractor*: the contract documents may reserve some part of the works to be performed by a sub-contractor whom the architect nominates to the contractor after entry into the contract. Subject to safeguards, the contractor must otherwise accept the nominee as his own sub-contractor. At the tender stage, the contractor will have included a prime cost sum given to him to cover the amount of the sub-contractor's account, rather than an amount affecting his own competitiveness. Thereafter, the sub-contractor is paid through the contractor an amount related to his own terms and set against the original sum. Although he is a sub-contractor, he receives special treatment over a number of matters relating to his programme and other matters defined in the contract.

(c) *Named sub-contractor*: the contract documents may state that a named person is to perform some part of the works as priced by the contractor. At the tender stage, the contractor bases his tender for the part concerned upon the price of the sub-contractor supplied to him as part of the tender documentation. Thereafter, the contractor is dealt with and paid for the work as though he himself performs it. The sub-contractor receives some special treatment over given matters, but these are less extensive than when there is nomination.

The three types of sub-contractors are taken in detail in Chapter 7 and over specialised aspects in other chapters. The important facts for present purposes are that they *are* sub-contractors and that this status is modified only to the extent provided in the contract concerned. The architect must therefore conduct his dealings post-contractually with each class of sub-contractor entirely through the contractor over all matters affecting the execution of the works, including such aspects as quality, programme and variation instructions.

This philosophy maintains the position of the contractor as controller of the construction itself and avoids the classic confusion situation arising when lines of communication are incomplete or crossed. There is no single method of creating havoc quite as effectively as passing information or instructions randomly among the participants in the building process – except perhaps deliberately ignoring the proper channels! The contractor is perfectly entitled to ignore any communications directed at *his* sub-contractors of all varieties, but not sent through him. He should ensure that a proper pattern is established from the first day and, so far as possible, that it is not broken. The standard contract provisions, and those of sub-contracts, make no allowance for direct communication between architect and sub-contractor.

Sub-contractors themselves should ensure that their own positions are clear and protected, by receiving instructions through, and only through the

contractor. Otherwise they risk performing work which is not co-ordinated with the rest, so that alterations are needed, for which they will not be paid. Even worse, they may not be paid for the work itself as 'instructed'. Whether the contractor receives proper instructions and confirmation is for him to sort out; sub-contractors are entitled to be paid by the contractor for what *he* requires them to do.

The standard sub-contract forms oblige the contractor to pass any relevant instructions of the architect to sub-contractors. They distinguish 'directions' of the contractor, which are requirements which he originates. These may be such matters as general site operations, for example where to position temporary works, and so not the concern of the architect. Alternatively, they may be supplementary aspects of what the architect has instructed, relating to precisely how sub-contractors carry out their activities. Sub-contractors are advised to confirm back to the contractor immediately whether, in their view, any of these matters carry financial implications over and above what is evident from any architect's instruction leading to them.

These extra costs may trace back to the terms of the sub-contract or to delay in passing on the architect's instruction, so that work has progressed meanwhile to a stage beyond where it was when the architect acted. There is no slack time allowed by the contracts for the contractor to act, and he must ensure that sub-contractors are notified immediately of any urgent matter. This is an area in which three-way disputes can easily arise, unless very careful routeing and timing of requirements are observed and corresponding confirmations are issued and records kept. The tendency is for sub-contractors, especially if they are smaller organisations operating across numbers of contracts, to be the ones less well equipped and so unprotected at the time of settling accounts. As they are on the end of the line for payment, the lesson should be obvious.

If there are elements of work which sub-contractors have undertaken to perform, they should watch that the contractor does not perform them instead and then render a contra-account. This can be particularly contentious if there is work which the architect instructs to be removed (under, for instance, JCT clause 8.4) and so, by implication, replaced. If the work is integral with work performed by others, sub-contractors have little option about the principle of removal, whereas they should expect to deal with it physically themselves where practicable to reduce the effect on their remaining work. When there is work by several persons in question, the simple instruction to remove does not, of course, settle whether any one person's work is what is actually defective. Again action and records at the time are needed, so that reimbursement for the reinstatement can be sought where appropriate.

The distinctions between the several types of sub-contractors do not affect the procedures and underlying positions outlined above. Even in the case of nominated sub-contractors, just the same channelling of information remains correct, despite the modified position over some programme and other matters. However, there is one area of difference which must be considered under 'Design by sub-contractors' below for the various sub-contract types.

DESIGN BY SUB-CONTRACTORS

Two situations may be distinguished over the initiation and transmission of 'design', as distinct from responsibility for its adequacy (a subject discussed in the present author's *Design and Build Contract Practice*). One occurs under the main contract umbrella and the other beyond it.

The former is the situation in which a domestic sub-contractor is required to develop some details of design, as also may be the contractor. At the extreme, the size of screws for a fixing is strictly 'design'. More reasonable examples are:

(a) Layouts of final sub-circuits for an electrical installation.
(b) Choice of materials or components to fulfil a performance specification.
(c) Design of connections for structural steelwork.

Of these, the first usually happens on site as work progresses and the second may be little different. On the other hand it, and regularly the last, may be subject to approval of the proposals by the architect or other consultant. While it is generally held that no design liability can be placed on the contractor under a JCT or IFC arrangement, so far as communications go, the design must pass through the contractor if it originates with a sub-contractor, and approval must return the same way. This allows the contractor to make any comment which affects his responsibilities. It is submitted that approval in this case transfers responsibility for the design adequacy to the architect. The contractor should be satisfied with nothing less under these contracts.

The last is the situation in which the architect requires a sub-contractor to perform design by parcelling out to him work which either he, as architect, or some other consultant might be expected to do. This is permissible under the forms concerned only when the sub-contractor is nominated or named. While the sub-contractor is paid for the design as part of his sub-contract price, he performs the design quite separately under the terms of the appropriate employer/sub-contractor agreement. There is therefore no reference to the design work in either main or sub-contract, and no liability attaches to the contractor for the design or any consequence of its lateness or error.

In this situation, the contractor is not responsible for the transmission of information between sub-contractor and architect, and it should pass directly between them. Indeed, it may pass before the contractor or a nominated sub-contractor is appointed. In the case of a named sub-contractor, it always does so. If the contractor becomes involved in passing information, he acquires an added responsibility over the time-scale, and may acquire one by implication over some aspect of the design. For the purposes of the contract, such information becomes part of the design detail which, when it is settled, the contractor is entitled to receive as part of the architect's design – even when he then passes it to the sub-contractor who originated it, and whether or not he himself needs to utilise any of it anywhere else in the works. As much as any other information, it ranks within the provisions about errors in information, extension of time, loss and expense and so forth. Any redress

which the employer may seek for errors or the consequences of late supply of information from the sub-contractor, which holds up any part of the works, will lie against the sub-contractor under any employer/sub-contractor agreement.

Mistakes in contract and other documents

With the general positions of the various persons delineated, it is relevant to look at the categories of mistakes which crop up in the documents which are used in a building contract. It is primarily the contract documents which are in view here, but others issued during progress and related to the contract set are included, particularly instructions as these often modify the contents of the contract documents.

It is indicated at the close of Chapter 3 that the contract is expressed in the documents alone, unless peculiar circumstances exist to need examination of any representatives. There now arises the question of mis-statement within the documents. This is distinct from misunderstanding of what they actually say, where the result of misapprehension will lie with the party under it, unless the question of ambiguity leads to invocation of the *contra proferentem* rule (see again Ch. 3). In the case of mis-statement, this same rule comes into play, in that the party composing a document is *prima facie* responsible for its contents. There are three statements about mistake that may be distinguished within contracts based upon JCT 80 or IFC 84:

(a) The contract conditions will prevail over all other documents, by virtue of JCT clause 2.2.1 or IFC clause 1.3. A plea of accidental clash will not usually stand to reverse this, although a case like *English Industrial Estates* v. *George Wimpey* (see Ch. 3) was otherwise decided on special facts and should be noted. As any clash is likely to be verbal, rather than arithmetical, it will be corrected as it emanates from the employer's side. If necessary, adjustment in the final account will follow.
(b) Mistakes in or between the text or graphics of documents are to be corrected and financial adjustment will follow on the same reasoning. The situations leading to this position are considered below.
(c) Mistakes in pricing or in arithmetic on the face of the documents are not to be corrected and so are borne by the contractor, in either direction. This follows explicitly from JCT clause 14.2 and implicitly from the agreement to pay the contract sum in IFC article 2.

The leading clauses relating to (b) are JCT 2.3 and IFC 1.4. While they are broadly similar, the latter shows an advance in drafting, due no doubt to the opportunity to review what the former clause does and does not say (although the 1987 version expands it).

Two editions of JCT 80 need considering with IFC 84 here: that 'with quantities' and that 'without quantities', the latter being *with* the specification as one of the contract documents. These give the following documents to go

with the conditions and the drawings, which always form part of the contract. In the case of IFC 84, the options are mutually exclusive.

(a) The contract bills as mandatory for JCT 80 with quantities, and optional for IFC 84.
(b) The schedules of work as optional for IFC 84.
(c) The specification as mandatory for JCT 80 without quantities, and optional for IFC 84.
(d) 'Numbered documents' as optional for JCT 80 (amended 1987) in any version, to allow for nominated sub-contract documents as required.

For work definition in each case, there are therefore the contract drawings and one other document, or several parts of the same document, and perhaps the numbered documents. There may be what JCT 80 terms 'discrepancy in or divergence between' documents, or 'inconsistency in or between' them, which is the umbrella equivalent term in IFC 84 (see under 'Mistakes affecting performance' below). All of these amount to mistake, either within a document or in terms of what has been given in two or more documents, perhaps by two or more persons, such as the drafting consultants. There may also be a mistake in the sense of a single error, say of a figure, which is not at odds with anything else in the documents, and which may therefore be more difficult to discover.

These various locations of mistakes have several effects, notably at the tender stage and during progress, that is pre- and post-contract. They may lead to adjustments of the contract sum, and perhaps also to rectification of information or even of work performed.

MISTAKES AFFECTING THE TENDER AND THE CONTRACT SUM

While aspects of tendering have been outlined in Chapter 3, the effects of mistakes in the documents supplied to the contractor may not appear until the contract is under way. As the contractor's tender sum, with any adjustment during examination, becomes the contract sum, any undiscovered mistakes of this type will be carried forward. Contract drawings are not mentioned separately here, but they are related to the documents which are mentioned, by containing the other element of any divergence or by containing a discrepancy which will have been interpreted in some way in the documents mentioned. The numbered documents for nominated sub-contractors should not have any effect, as prime cost sums cover their value at this stage to the extent that there is a directly financial effect.

 Contract bills

When there are contract bills, JCT clause 14.1 and IFC clause 1.2, in its third paragraph, both state that 'the quality and quantity of the work included in the Contract Sum' are those in the contract bills. This means that the bills prevail for financial purposes under the contract, as well as for giving the specification. JCT clause 2.2.2.1 and IFC clause 1.5 give the Standard Method

of Measurement of Building Works as applying to these bills, unless something contrary is stated in 'any specified item or items'. There must therefore be an explicit and particular indication of any change to the method of measurement underlying the bill items. This method requires various matters of description to be covered, as well as essentially computational points.

The means of indicating a change are left open. Possible ways include:

(a) Special explanatory endorsement of an item or group.
(b) Clear description of an item or group which shows without emphasis that it includes or excludes some liability which is normally treated in the opposite way.
(c) Definitions in the preambles governing the group.
(d) Measurement in a unit different from that prescribed and in some way highlighted.

These are listed in what is usually seen as descending order of clarity to the estimator, whatever may be said about his responsibility to read every word, no matter where and how it may be presented to him. Departures from the norm like these should be made extra plain.

There are in principle two ways in which the contract bills may be in error: by not agreeing with the contract drawings over quantity or description, and by having some mistake originating inside themselves. Non-compliance with the standard method, without saying so, would come into this latter category. The two forms of error may effectively have the same result in many cases: an incorrect amount is included in the contract sum or the contractor is misled about what to produce, or even both.

Each contract provides that any of these errors is to be dealt with by correction, as though a variation instruction (see later in this chapter) has been issued.

Schedules of work

If there are schedules of work under IFC 84, the same principles apply, except that there is no recognised method of measurement to support any quantities given. For this reason, the provision of quantities is of dubious value. There need not be any quantities; a schedule can simply be a specification arranged in such a way as to allow it to be priced paragraph by paragraph. This contrasts with the contractor taking off and pricing quantities which relate more loosely to a traditional specification, so that he may draw upon several specification items for the content of a single measured item. With schedules of work, the contractor may need to take off some form of quantities to price each item, but his effort is contained within the item in each case.

If supplied with quantities in such schedules for tendering and ultimately for contract purposes, the contractor therefore has to read what he is given with particular care, in case anything unusual has been done. To the extent that definition is uncertain, he would be well advised to endorse his tender as being based upon the understanding that the usual standard method of

measurement has been followed so far as relevant and unless some other principle has been made explicit for any item of work. Clause 1.2 (third paragraph) gives these schedules the same status as contract bills, while clause 1.4 allows them to be corrected in the same way, except for silence over anything to do with the method of measurement.

Specification

The use of a specification without quantities is the last option, applying under JCT 80 without quantities and under IFC 84. There is no standard method of specification writing giving rules to be followed and deemed to underlie an actual specification, although there are published documents which are widely used, such as the National Building Specification, and the newly published Common Arrangement system has given standardisation a further impetus. Both writer and estimator are therefore on their own to exercise reasonable judgment to a large extent. JCT clause 14.1 states that what is in the contract sum is what is 'shown upon the Contract Drawings or described in the Specification', without establishing either as prevailing. Presumably work may appear in both places or only one. IFC clause 1.2, in its first paragraph, gives the content of the contract sum as being what is in the contract documents 'taken together', but with the contract drawings prevailing if there is inconsistency. This is more helpful than silence.

When there is silence, the contractor is left with doubt. If something is in one document only, he must include for it, unless there is some strong reason against it being required. Thus he should include for an unspecified cupboard shown upon the drawings, subject to querying what its construction is to be, if he lacks information on the drawings. Equally, he should include for two roof ventilators if they are clearly specified, even though their exact positions are unsure. But if he finds a specification for 'the basement tanking' when there is no basement, he may reasonably not include the tanking in his tender. If a cupboard is not shown and presumably cannot be inferred, again the contractor cannot be expected to include it in his tender. If he finds that he has some complete inconsistency, such as differing numbers of floors on plans and sections, he can do nothing without having the position cleared up by the architect. The possible illustrations are unlimited.

This is a difficult area, because there are some fairly old legal cases which support the view that the contractor must allow when tendering for whatever is reasonably necessary to complete the works in an entire contract. This is what a building contract usually is and in particular is in the forms being considered, with some modifications not affecting the point at issue. In, for instance, *Williams* v. *Fitzmaurice* (1858), it was held that the contractor had to supply without further charge floorboarding which had not been given in the specification and, it appears, not shown on the drawings for a house. Apparently, the view was taken that the floorboarding was a necessary part of the house.

The doubt that lies over these decisions for present-day purposes is that the technology of construction today is more complex and varied, so that the

contractor will not necessarily know as standard practice what has been omitted and needs to be supplied, while contract documents have also developed to show more detail as regular practice. Industry-wide standard documents, such as methods of measurement, drawings codes and specifications, under a common arrangement system, set standards of communication which the courts are increasingly likely to accept as normative. Even so, at the level of smallest detail, the contractor must ensure that he covers what reasonably is left to be inferred.

If, however, matters do not go so far as legal proceedings (and they are not very likely to warrant it for the smaller contract), it is likely that an inconsistency will be resolved in favour of the contractor who did not proffer the faulty documents. The contract provision under JCT clause 2.3 and IFC clause 1.4 is again for the architect to issue an instruction resulting in a variation. In general, it is necessary for a specification-based contract to be tied up more thoroughly than a quantities-based contract, because it cannot contain major uncertainty, as the other may do, explicitly or concealed. Only by the use of a provisional sum can undecided work be covered, as provisional quantities are not available. This removes competitiveness from this portion and so should be restricted to work of minor value.

Although it is not strictly within the area of error, the principle of the architect being able to issue such supplementary information under the JCT without quantities form is highly suspect. When the IFC form is used without quantities the same doubt occurs. This is because the contractor, when tendering in the absence of quantities which are to form part of the contract, is preparing his own quantities without redress if they are incorrect due to his own error. He therefore needs virtually all the construction information as tendering information, to eliminate uncertainty over what is required, which may lead him to make injudicious guesses during the hurry of tendering. He is unable to tell which rooms are to have painted walls and which wallpapered without a schedule or annotated drawings. He may, on the other hand, be indifferent when tendering to the precise position of a door in a given wall, so long as he knows all of its characteristics.

There should therefore be far less need for the contractor to receive information when drawings and specification are in use. If this happens frequently, there are probably variations or errors underlying the situation.

MISTAKES AFFECTING PERFORMANCE OF WORK

Many of the mistakes considered above may also affect work on site, because they lead to erroneous understanding of what is required. What is said is therefore applicable here as well.

Relationship of documents

The documents forming part of the contract with the several sets of conditions have been set out, but are repeated in less detail with the other

post-contractual documents, which are mentioned in JCT clause 2.3 and IFC clause 1.4 as possibly not agreeing:

(a) Contract drawings.
(b) Contract bills, specification or schedules of work (but not a contract sum analysis or schedule of rates, however, which does not or should not convey information to the contractor).
(c) 'Numbered documents', such as nominated sub-contract documents.
(d) Instructions issued during progress, other than those introducing variations (the latter are bound to be 'out of step' with the contract documents, because they change something).
(e) Descriptive schedules or other like documents 'necessary for use'.
(f) Further drawings or details 'to explain or amplify the Contract Drawings or to enable the Contractor to carry out and complete the Works'.
(g) Levels and setting-out information.

All of these are intended to fit together and not change what is to be produced, or any obligations and restrictions governing activity. Bearing in mind that the contractor has tendered and obtained the contract on a defined and adequate basis (it is to be assumed) without the latter three sets of items in particular (which are not given as introducing variations), their inclusion as contractually recognised may occasionally bring something of a chill to the spine. This is especially so when the contract is based on a specification which, with the drawings, purports to tell the contractor everything in the absence of quantities.

When there are contract bills, the reasonable intention of these extra items is to give the contractor information of a positional nature or detailing small parts of the works. Most, but not all, of this information was needed by the quantity surveyor for the preparation of what have now become the contract bills. That he does not always receive it or that it is not always subsequently based on what he included in his bills, is a well-known cause of many of the discrepancies and divergences being discussed. It is information which the contractor did not need when tendering, because the quantities contained the relevant quintessence of it.

Whether the basis is contract bills or specification, it is important that any supplementary information is just that: supplementary. The danger stage comes when it introduces changes which should be covered by variation instructions. It is often tempting to combine small variations into supplementary details, but this must be strenuously avoided by the architect or resisted by the contractor to escape confusion. When uncertainty over what is in the contract and what is variation is combined with what is mistake, the potential for chaos assumes unfortunately common proportions. There is no answer, other than a pedantic adherence to a rigid procedure.

Relationship of mistakes

Even assuming a straight run through the issues just raised, there may be

errors in the documents emerging. Two categories of mistake are mentioned in the JCT clause:

(a) Discrepancies within individual documents.
(b) Divergences between two or more documents.

The IFC clause rolls these together as 'inconsistency in or between' documents. The effect is the same, and much of the earlier discussion also relates to these points. A further area of potential divergence exists over statutory requirements, as JCT clause 6.1.2 and IFC clause 5.2 recognise. This area lies outside the sphere of purely inter-documental differences, but extends to include possible clashes between variation instructions and these requirements. In all cases, the contractor is required to give notice to the architect, so that the problem may be resolved.

There is no automatic 'this document prevails' option, as mistakes do not come like that, so far as what is actually required to be performed is concerned. This position must be distinguished from that of the conditions prevailing in contractual interpretation, and that of the contract bills (if any) prevailing over what has been included financially within the contract. These two principles can reasonably establish certainty in their own areas, so that adjustment can be made from a declared base.

The architect is to give instructions to resolve the tension. These are not defined as variation instructions, nor as instructions which are deemed to constitute variations, except over statutory matters. This is because they may not introduce a variation but, by the choice of the one alternative, may simply confirm what is already included in the contract sum, be it in bills or otherwise. If therefore, a variation is being introduced, it must be covered by an instruction in suitable form. If the effect is to show an error in the contract bills, or if it can be construed that way, it is possible to rely on JCT clause 14.2 or IFC clause 1.4 for the adjustment to be treated as a variation, deemed in the former case and actual in the latter.

In the case of statutory requirements, the conflict is between some section of the contract documents or a variation and an outside set of stipulations. If the requirements prevail, in the sense of a waiver not being available, a variation or further variation is almost inevitable. The instruction issued by the architect in response to the contractor's notice is therefore to be treated as though it were a variation instruction.

Responsibility to discover mistakes

Both JCT clauses use the term 'If the Contractor shall find', while the IFC clause on statutory matters uses the term 'If the Contractor finds', as an accommodation to movement in the language. The IFC clause on general inconsistencies has no such expression, but simply starts where the others continue, by saying 'The architect shall issue instructions in regard to' the various matters listed. It is suggested that the silence is as helpful as the statements. It also leaves affairs open to cover the situation in which the architect finds inconsistencies unaided.

The problem with the three clauses, and it is there by implication in the fourth, is in the 'If'. This is sometimes held to mean 'If there are any mistakes' or, more reasonably, 'If the contractor finds them'. A contractor has a clearly established duty to warn of any errors of design and so on which he notices, and this would extend to any clashes or deficiencies in the documentation. In undertaking construction work, he holds himself out to be an experienced and competent builder, as distinct from an expert in matters of design which lie within the special sphere of an architect or engineer. The courts are tending to take stricter views of the liabilities of skilled persons in general, and designers and constructors are no exception. But this does not mean that the latter are to be as expert as the person whose work they receive as constituting what they are to construct. It is one thing for the contractor to notice that reinforcement has been omitted from a concrete beam, it is another for him to realise that the detailed reinforcement does not allow an adequate factor of safety by its quantity or positioning (see the cases at the end of this section).

This is an example of a mistake upon the face of a document apparent to the specially knowledgeable, but not to all. More difficult is a divergence between two documents, even if it does not require special expertise to discern it. If a nominated sub-contractor indicates in sufficient time a need for pipes through a concrete upper floor, this may mean rearrangement of reinforcement designed by the structural consultant, who should be advised and co-ordinated by the architect. If the point is missed by the latter, it may then be that the contractor also does not notice when setting about construction and working from the structural drawings. In principle, it is fine to say to him, 'You should have combed every drawing, as you knew that such holes were required in places', but it does not always come about that way in the sequencing of information supply to him. Another example might be in co-ordinating specialist window details with the structural frame. If the same person, say the architect, produces the divergent information, it is often all the more difficult to suggest that the contractor is at fault. The inclusion of the numbered documents category in JCT 80 (amended 87) heightens this problem.

A clash with statutory requirements is a rather distinct issue. These divide most commonly between matters of planning and building control. The former should be cleared before work proceeds and are generally at too high a level of concept for the contractor to be likely to fall foul of them. On the other hand, building regulations are his own backyard. They pose a distinct issue, because they stand outside the project as separately constituted, but bearing on it. Usually, therefore, a clash with them should be more apparent to the contractor than other discrepancies which could either be missed or which might be mistaken for special requirements of the designer. With this said, the clauses in both contracts do not place an explicitly greater responsibility upon the contractor to find and report.

In the end, the contractor is responsible for sorting out what he is building, but the original responsibility for getting it right lies with the designers. There

is a whole area of uncertainty lurking in the shadows. Given the 'if' of the clauses and the realities of operations on and about sites, there is room for a deal of tolerance in treating these inconsistencies. The designers cannot pass to those who construct the responsibility for discovering the results of skimped work, while those who construct cannot avoid all responsibility and not perform routine and sensible checking. When they do find something, they must report it. If they do not, and this can be established, they are liable for the consequences of passing it by.

Two recent cases illustrate these principles and the way in which intricate technical questions have a bearing, while varying from case to case. In *Equitable Debenture Assets Corporation Ltd* v. *William Moss Group Ltd and Others* (1984), leaking curtain walling designed by a nominated sub-contractor was in question. In addition to the sub-contractor's liability, it was held that the architect was negligent over acceptance of the sub-contractor's design and in other ways. The contractor should not have been expected to check the design in advance, when the architect had spent some time on this, but he should have reported the faults in the curtain walling which became apparent during erection, so that he was liable in this respect. A term was implied in the contract by the court to this effect, as none was express in the JCT 1963 form. Design apart, the contractor was also liable for the sub-contractor's bad workmanship on site and for breach of the building regulations.

In *Victoria University of Manchester* v. *Hugh Wilson & Lewis Womersley (a firm) and Pochin (Contractors) Ltd* (1984), the problem was with external ceramic wall tiling applied to irregular concrete surfaces, a method untried by several of those involved. The architect had failed to warn the employer of the risks and the design was defective. The sub-contractor had failed to fix the tiles adequately. Again, there was an implied term that the contractor would warn of any design defects believed to exist (something less than a complete duty to search for and find defects), but he was not liable for breach of this duty. This appeared to be based largely in his lack of previous experience of such tiling and therefore practical inability to warn. He was, however, liable for failure to supervise his sub-contractor adequately, despite the contributory negligence of architect and clerk of works. Several other distinctions of liability were drawn, making the case interesting reading.

The 'duty to warn' question appears to be heading towards another instance of what is reasonable, as the courts develop a more structured attitude to a problem which is growing with the intricacy of buildings. When work is once constructed incorrectly, because the contractor did not notice, there is the direct cost of correction and, associated with it, the contingent matters of extension of time and loss and expense which the contract provisions allow as appropriate. Even if the matter is raised early enough for redesign to prevent abortive construction, it may not be early enough to avoid delay and extra expense. The question then becomes not only should the contractor have noticed, but how soon should he have noticed?

There is no clear provision for the contractor to be paid for excess supervisory costs of sorting out the mistakes and shortcomings of others, and

often it is difficult to segregate this from routine checking and co-operation. In a major instance, it could well fall to be reimbursed, as part of the managerial expenses incurred, following the reasoning in *Tate & Lyle* v. *Greater London Council* set out in Chapter 15.

Approval of the works

THE OVERALL SCHEME OF APPROVAL

The standard contracts make limited reference to the question of approval of the works by the architect, and none to approval by the employer. The main scheme calls for little comment for present purposes and may be summarised to highlight responsibilities and show where problems might occur:

(a) The contractor undertakes to 'carry out and complete the Works in accordance with the Contract Documents', as the IFC version more succinctly puts it. The primary responsibility is upon him to perform, rather than upon the architect to ensure that he does and has.

(b) During progress, the architect has a right of access to the site and other places where work is being performed. The purpose of this is not stated, but may be inferred as to allow inspection and checking to take place.

(c) Also during progress, the employer may appoint a clerk of works as inspector under the directions of the architect. The clerk of works also has a right of access, but no power to issue instructions, which thus precludes him from instructing the removal of defective work (see below on this matter). Anything which he 'directs' must be confirmed by the architect.

(d) The architect is not obliged by the contract provisions to give approval to any work during progress. This is particularly true over quality, but would be difficult to sustain over grossly incorrect setting out of work, so that the works were wrong in position or scale.

(e) The architect may instruct the removal of defective work or materials during progress (see below on this matter).

(f) When the architect forms the opinion that practical completion has occurred, he is to certify this, and the employer may take possession of the works. There are subsidiary provisions over phased completion in various ways, but these may be ignored here. The architect is not required to have checked the detailed quality or completeness of the works at this stage.

(g) During the defects liability period following practical completion and usually of 6 months' duration, defects may be found by the employer or the architect, it may be assumed, and notified to the contractor within 14 days of that period ending. The contractor is obliged to make good any such defects at his own expense.

(h) Following making good of defects and up to the issue of the final certificate, the contractor is still liable for the cost of making good defects, but is not obliged to put them right himself. It is good law that he should be given the option of so doing, before others are engaged to do it, as applies during progress and the defects period.

(i) During the whole period before the issue of the final certificate, no certificate is conclusive over compliance of work with the contract requirements. This includes certificates of payment which include the work in question.

(j) The final certificate ends the operation of the contract, leaving the parties with their residual rights and liabilities during the limitation period which applies, and subject to the Latent Defects Act 1986.

(k) The final certificate provides that it is conclusive over those elements of the works which were expressed in the contract documents as to be 'to the reasonable satisfaction of the Architect', so that there is no further redress against the contractor, except for fraudulent concealment. It otherwise does not express that the architect is satisfied that the contractor has complied with the contract, although the architect does not issue the certificate until he is happy that the works are not showing any patent defect at the time of issue.

The effect of these several steps is that the architect has kept the works under observation during progress and for some time after, so avoiding the complication of having to take action against the contractor over every defect which is found. Also the contractor remains liable for the works in respect of latent defects during the usual statutory period applying to contracts.

DEFECTS DURING PROGRESS

The contracts are more explicit over this aspect than any other of those listed above. Both the JCT and IFC forms contain the same basic provisions, but the IFC form goes further with extra provisions.

Common provisions

The basic, common provisions are in JCT clause 8 and IFC clauses 3.12 and 3.14. Their scheme is for the architect to be able to instruct the opening up of any work or testing of any materials, whether or not there are clauses in the contract documents mentioning specific tests, etc. There may be such clauses in respect of such matters as regular testing of concrete cubes or runs of pipework. It is then usually possible for the cost of tests to be included in the contract sum, as they form a predictable proportion of total costs. Whatever may have been said or not said, the contractor is obliged as usual to comply with instructions given. If the results of tests show that the items were not in accordance with the contract quality, he must bear the cost of tests (if not in the contract sum) and replacement. If the items are in order, the contractor is reimbursed his costs. In addition in a major case, he may

find that he has a right to extension of time or loss and expense payment, because of the disturbance factor.

It would be possible for the architect to run riot in using his powers, but it is not likely that he will, in view of the penalties incurred if he is wrong. There is no time limit after work, if so it be, is performed within which he must act. This makes sense, as defects may be suspected at any time after work is carried out. As the architect is under no liability to clear inspections as work proceeds, this aspect needs reasonable application to avoid upheavals long after work is installed and perhaps encased by other substantial and expensive work. Many critical features of work are covered progressively by the distinct inspection of the local authority, who have separate powers to condemn from those of the architect.

The contractor is advised in any case of difference which cannot be resolved to take sufficient evidence for future use, as he is obliged to comply with the architect's instruction. Under the IFC contract there is alternatively the possibility of immediate arbitration, but under the JCT contract it is deferred until after completion. The evidence may be samples, photographs, independent reports or whatever is suitable. If the contractor refuses to remove anything after further notice, the employer has powers under JCT clause 4.1.2 or IFC clause 3.5.1 to engage others to do the work of removal and counter-charge the contractor. It is reasonable in such an impasse to allow the contractor time to take his evidence first.

In an extreme case of dispute, if the works are 'materially affected' by a refusal to remove, the employer has a right of determination against the contractor (see Ch. 16). This should be reserved for such situations as major foundation problems which, if left, would prejudice the whole structure and cause extensive costs and lost building use. Even damages might not adequately cover this in terms of the employer's disturbance aspects, especially during occupation.

Special IFC provisions

Clause 3.13 of the form contains additional provisions which are, as yet, largely untested in practice. They are included to deal with the situation in which some work of a category is found to be defective and there is the question whether other work in that category is defective. It is of course possible under the clauses already discussed to have successive sections of work opened up and tested, with the attendant risks over costs. The present clause aims to allow an exploratory procedure, which may stop short of destructive testing, but it also places the cost with the contractor in the first instance. The steps in the procedure are:

(a) Work or material is discovered to be defective, presumably under the basic procedure in the preceding clause. This is also put right under that clause.

(b) The contractor is to inform the architect of what action he 'will

immediately take at no cost to the Employer' to check that no further similar defects exist.

(c) The architect may instruct the contractor to open up work or test materials at no cost to establish that there are no similar defects, if one of three contingencies exists:

   (i) the contractor provides no statement within seven days;
   (ii) the architect is not satisfied with the proposals;
   (iii) safety or statutory factors give great urgency to matters.

(d) The contractor is to comply with the instruction 'forthwith'.

(e) Without prejudice to compliance, the contractor may object to compliance and, if the architect does not withdraw his instruction, arbitration automatically ensues over the 'nature and extent' of what is being required.

(f) If and so far as the arbitrator decides in favour of the contractor, the latter is to be paid his compliance costs.

The procedure therefore puts the contractor under an obligation automatically to act under (b) every time there is a discovery under (a), in case the architect acts under (c). It then allows the architect the option over whether to accept what, if anything, is proposed but, either way, the contractor has to act without charge, unless he can persuade the architect to change his mind completely. There are the additional hazards of the contractor not acting quickly enough (and the matter may require prolonged investigation) or of urgency existing. His only relief over the time pressure lies in putting forward a provisional proposal for action, to be followed by another when he knows more about the problem. Beyond this he must hope for the prospect of a favourable arbitration, if all else fails. The use of the procedure lapses at practical completion, whereas it could be useful during the diagnosis of defects thereafter.

The contractor is therefore being placed at risk, when one defect is discovered, of having to pay for what could become an endless series of investigations, with only arbitration to help him, and this coming in willy-nilly if he but complains and the architect remains silent. It is also possible for uncertainty to arise as to which clause, basic or continuation, is being invoked, as matters are not always as clearly segregated in time and place as discussion on paper may suggest. This leads to doubt over who is to act in what way, and over who is paying for the actions taken. There appears to be no power for the architect to agree to 'split the difference' with the contractor or otherwise apportion responsibility. Only the arbitrator may do this.

It is to be hoped that, in practice, the architect and contractor will usually discuss procedures when a first defect has been found, before either of them rushes into a process which could be far more arduous than expected. The clause is a useful attempt at pointing a way through a common maze, but it does create its own dead ends.

CHAPTER 6

Variations and provisional sums

Authority and instructions under JCT 80 and IFC 84
Definitions under JCT 80 and IFC 84
Principles of valuation of variations and provisional
sum expenditure under JCT 80 and IFC 84
Rules for valuation of variations and provisional sum
expenditure under JCT 80 with quantities
Special provisions for valuation under JCT 80
with quantities
Comparison of valuation provisions under contracts
other than JCT 80 with quantities

This subject is extremely important for present purposes, because building works of even moderate scale are habitually beset by continual instructions resulting from changes of mind by the employer or his consultants, quite apart from those forced upon the parties by outside agencies, ground conditions and a selection of other hazards to progress. The result is often quite drastic amendment of what was to have been produced under the original contract documents, with equally drastic amendment of the contract sum, due to the cost of the actual variations and of their consequences in terms of disturbance and delay.

This chapter first examines the contract provisions over variations and then considers how they are to be implemented financially in their own right. This leads on to their relationship with the provisions over loss and expense for disturbance of regular progress.

Essentially similar provisions are contained in the JCT 80 and IFC 84 contracts to deal with variations, those in the latter being rather more simply expressed. Reference is made initially to JCT clause 13 in the with-quantities edition. Separate discussion is given of the differences arising when the other editions of JCT 80 are used, while discussion on IFC 84 is given where most suitable.

Authority and instructions under JCT 80 and IFC 84

VARIATIONS

It is necessary under JCT clause 13.2 and the first paragraph of IFC

clause 3.6 to give the architect power to instruct variations, so that the entire contract principle (see Ch. 2) may be modified. The power is not given to the employer, to any consultant other than the architect, to the quantity surveyor or to the clerk of works.

It is possible, but not often desirable, for the architect to delegate some part of his powers to another here, as indeed it is necessary for him to designate which members of his own staff have any power to instruct variations or communicate with the contractor in other ways. Usually the effect of other consultants acting other than through the architect is confusion, while the effect of the employer acting direct may be anarchy. The quantity surveyor cannot act or even accept any variation not properly instructed by the architect, but must seek confirmation, even when it leads to an omission.

There is some case for the clerk of works dealing with small items, such as minor details or the positioning of subsidiary parts of services, subject to confirmation by the architect. This, among other things, is what JCT clause 12 regulates quite closely, in fact its time limit of '2 working days' for the architect to confirm will often be impracticable. There remains the danger that small variations will have large consequences in the wider works, so that rapid checks are needed.

The contractor is within his rights not to comply with any so-called instruction issued by anyone but the architect, subject to the points just made. Instructions generally are discussed in Chapter 5, and the comments about the contractor confirming oral 'instructions' back to the architect before complying are particularly relevant here.

In addition to the contract provisions for confirming instructions in general, there is also JCT clause 13.2 allowing the architect to sanction any variation in particular which the contractor may introduce 'otherwise than pursuant to an instruction' proper. No procedure or timing is attached to this, so that the contractor cannot rely on any actions of his own to make the option binding. It is useful to cover such cases as requests of the employer with which the contractor has complied, or even variations which the contractor has introduced himself. It is entirely at the architect's discretion whether to follow it, so that the contractor cannot expect to abuse the provision.

In the nature of variations, instructions in writing include graphic data, which should be accompanied by some form of signed authority. Even a sketch or amendment endorsed on the one copy of a drawing being used on the site is acceptable as an instruction, provided that it is authenticated by a signature. The main disadvantage here is that no one else may have a precise copy.

While all of the foregoing applies under the JCT form, IFC clause 3.5 does not legislate for any system of confirming oral instructions or those issued by an unauthorised person, except by having the sanctioning provision mentioned above. Under the IFC form, the contractor should therefore when appropriate use a system which does not 'confirm back', but which requires the architect to put his purported instruction in writing, say by returning

the contractor's form signed. Otherwise the contractor is best advised not to conform.

Both contract forms require the architect to issue instructions about 'the expenditure of provisional sums'. (The JCT form includes a reference to sums in sub-contracts, which need no special discussion here.) Such sums are commonly used to cover 'work or costs which cannot be entirely foreseen, defined or detailed at the time the tendering documents are issued'. This definition is extracted from clause A.8.1.a of SMM 6 and is almost the only published one around. SMM 7 expands the definition, creating two sub-types of provisional sums. When either Standard Method is used, as it is with quantities under either contract form, it permits provisional sums to be included in the tender and contract sum. In all other cases, the power to include sums depends on custom, as does an understanding of what they are.

When once such sums exist, the architect does not have a discretion over whether to deal with them, as with variations: they must become the subject of instructions, even if only to say 'leave them out'. The contractor in turn should apply for instructions within the time band laid down in the clauses about extension of time and loss and expense, provided the sums are described clearly enough for him to know when they are needed. If they are described in a misleading way or are for 'undefined work' under SMM 7, this very fact may lead to a sustainable claim over time or loss and expense, if the contractor has reasonably made wrong assumptions about how the work portrayed affects other work.

Subject to these comments, there is nothing special to remark about provisional sums. They are effectively a premeditated variation waiting to be activated and valued like any other.

Definitions under JCT 80 and IFC 84

Provisional sums have been defined above, so that only variations need be dealt with here.

The JCT and IFC contracts contain the same definitions of variations. These fall into two parts: physical variations and variations to site conditions. Both parts are subject to the proviso that 'no variation . . . shall vitiate this Contract' (JCT wording). This venerable expression is stating that variations may be indulged in without upsetting the integrity of the contract.

Beyond some point, variations shade into 'variation of the contract', that is the substitution of something other than the works originally in the contemplation of the parties. Where the boundary is crossed is a matter of fact, depending upon the individual situation in the contract. A drastic 'all-in-one' change, such as the inclusion of a fourth block of flats in

a contract for three blocks, or turning a contract for a factory into one for sheltered housing, would certainly constitute 'variation' in the grand sense. A change of this magnitude and character is something which the contractor is entitled to decline, because the subject-matter of the contract has been changed. A mass of smaller 'variations' could produce such a situation as an end-result, but it is far less likely that the contractor could object in time, as the process would be incremental. Some major reassessment of the basis of payment might be due in retrospect, but this lies beyond the present scope. All of this points with much more likelihood to physical variations taken next, than to the other sort taken thereafter.

VARIATIONS OF PHYSICAL WORK

Physical variations are given in JCT clause 13.1.1 and IFC clause 3.6.1. They cover variation to the 'design, quality or quantity' of what is in the contract, and these terms are amplified by way of illustration, but not limitation, in respect of amounts or standards of work, including the removal of what is already there (other than for defects). These categories cover all the usual changes that are so familiar, without need to split hairs over the elements. Importantly, no limit is placed on when the architect may issue such instructions, so that the possibilities of disturbed sequence, etc. are present in embryo.

The distinction between the valuation of variations and the ascertainment of loss and expense is important with both types of variation. It is usually easier to maintain with physical variations, although care is needed to follow the principles set out in this chapter and in those dealing with loss and expense.

VARIATIONS OF OBLIGATIONS AND RESTRICTIONS

Variations affecting site conditions are dealt with differently, in JCT clause 13.1.2 and IFC clause 3.6.2, as the lists given are not illustrative, but specific and limited. An example occurs in the case study in Chapter 21. There are four categories, giving the precise wording:

(a) Access to the site or use of any specific parts of the site.
(b) Limitations of working space.
(c) Limitations of working hours.
(d) Execution or completion of the work in any specific order.

There is therefore no authority for the architect to vary any 'obligations and restrictions', as these elements are termed, other than what is given here. He may introduce 'the addition, alteration or omission' of any of these only, and so cannot amend other matters of the contractor's working methods, such as health and safety. This does not prevent the inclusion of other obligations and restrictions in the contract, only their variation. SMM 6 clause B8 and SMM 7 clause A35, for instance, give the present list in substance, and also several other categories of less radical obligations and restrictions.

But further, under the unamended JCT 80 and under IFC 84, the

list is restricted to 'obligations and restrictions imposed by the Employer *in the Contract Bills*' (emphasis added). This suggests that the employer, via the architect, must give a specific category of restriction, etc. in the contract bills before the architect can amend it. This is in face of the fact that 'the addition . . . or' becomes difficult to interpret in any way, unless it be rewritten as 'the addition of . . . or'. This there is no authority to do, and it must be held, on the wording as given, that if the employer wishes to control obligations and restrictions in some way, then he must ensure that he has something about the particular category which he anticipates in the contract bills. Even if what is included is not thought to be correct, it will at least allow him to change what is there, rather than to be able to do nothing.

In practice matters are often adjusted in the absence of such inclusions, but strictly the architect cannot issue instructions without the contractor validly querying them under JCT clause 4.2 or IFC clause 3.5.2. The only way round the impasse is then for the employer and contractor to come to a supplemental agreement on whatever terms can be negotiated to induce the contractor to concede a change. JCT 80 (amended 87) revises the wording so as to remove these limitations and allow the 'addition of' obligations and restrictions even when not in a category already in the contract bills. IFC 84 still does not do this.

The four categories given may overlap to some extent. For instance, a restriction on access may mean that certain work inevitably has to be performed in a given order, or that working space has to be restricted. If this sort of consequential effect occurs, the contractor is bound to accept it, while it then forms part of the revaluation which follows. It may thus not be beyond the bounds of possibility for an ingenious architect to vary a category not given in the contract documents by such a roundabout means, but perhaps at excess expense as excess disturbance is caused.

This type of variation to the contractor's general working arrangements on the site is especially likely either to overlap with matters leading to loss and expense payments, or to cause such a payment because the very variation throws progress out of normal. The initial remarks made under 'Principles of valuation of variations' below about choice of reimbursement methods become critical in such a situation.

Principles of valuation of variations and provisional sum expenditure under JCT 80 and IFC 84

SCOPE OF VALUATION

Before dealing with the more detailed aspects here, the distinction between these clauses and those covering loss and expense should be noted.

The present clauses authorise the adjustment of the contract sum to cover the immediate valuation of variations themselves. This immediate valuation allows for differences in the quantity of finished physical work, and also for any special feature in the conditions under which the parcel of work is executed.

These may include such elements as performance out of normal sequence, but still in the context of regular progress, a term discussed in Chapter 13. But they do not include any consequential effects in the wider programme, which may mean that unvaried work is subject to disturbance of its regular progress, the criterion for meeting loss and expense.

If this distinction were simply one of using different clauses as the authorisation for adjusting the contract sum, little would be at stake. The significance is that loss and expense is to be dealt with on a basis similar to that for common law damages, so that the contractor's actual loss is ascertained and he is put back into the position in which he would have been had the disturbance not occurred. There are therefore elements of cost for which the rules are closely circumscribed (see Ch. 15), while profit on the extra work caused is not allowable, although it may be that loss of profit on other work outside the contract does fall to be reimbursed. There are also strict rules about giving notices over disturbance occurring. The valuation of variations on the other hand is to be made on a basis similar to that used for the items in the contract sum, inclusive of the same elements and calculated at a similar level by using the *pro rata* or 'fair valuation' approaches described in this section.

Despite the distinctions of definition, it is not always absolutely clear in practice into which category some items of reimbursement fall. There is some room for manœuvre between the parties in settlement, affecting how much may be payable. This arises because the basis is actual loss in the one case, and in the other a level related to that of the original contract, fully inclusive of head office overheads and profit (see Ch. 15). How desirable it may be to use the contract level will depend upon how fiercely competitive it was and, of course, upon which party is viewing the desirability. Sometimes settlement based upon the contract level can be achieved more rapidly and so helps cash flow. It also then has the virtue of representing a 'bird in the hand', while a loss and expense claim can be subject to more dispute, owing both to its constituent calculations and to its often more emotive origin. If the quantity surveyor is dealing with variations and the architect with loss and expense, care is needed to avoid duplication.

BASIS OF VALUATION

The term 'valuation' is not altogether happy in the context of variations, and the less explicit term 'pricing' would have some advantages. What is being calculated is not necessarily the value of a variation to either party. The employer may value it in economic terms far higher than the additional or reduced price payable suggests. Presumably he would not want it at all if he did not perceive, or think that he perceived, some balance of value in his favour. It is a fact of life, though, that he often does not know the economic effect of his decisions, or his architect's, until too late. Sometimes he never knows, among the mass or lack of detail which he receives.

From the other angle, it must be wondered whether the contractor sees a variation as a thing of value. He often expresses it rather differently! Maybe

its main 'value' is as a lever for demonstrating that chaos has arrived, so that he now deserves extra financial consideration. But equally, he does not receive his 'cost' in most instances. What he is paid is some construct based largely upon the prices in the contract bills, or whatever document underlies his contract sum, and this may differ noticeably from his costs as they arise. This is one of the points about tendering policy and pricing described in Chapter 3.

The rules given in the standard clauses leave no room for any basis of calculation other than by relation to the contract bills etc., for what are usually the bulk of variations. In the case of omissions little else would be suitable anyway. As noted above, the results are inclusive of overheads and profit, automatically in most instances.

IFC clause 3.7 is less detailed than its JCT counterpart, but will usually lead to a similar result. Its lack of some details in fact allows it to cover in one contract the options which JCT clause 13 gives in its separate editions, but this then requires the other contract documents to be more explicit over rules. Failure here may lead to doubt and dispute at critical junctures, perhaps leading to documents being construed *contra proferentem*. This will commonly mean against the employer. Discussion of the rules is related mainly to the JCT with quantities pattern, with differences covered later.

WHO VALUES AND WHEN

Both clauses allocate the duty of valuation in accordance with the rules to the quantity surveyor, who at this point is acting independently of the architect for authority. This is a distinction from loss and expense, where he can act only if the architect requires him to do so. The clauses both provide for the employer and the contractor together to override the use of the rules by the quantity surveyor, but do not approach this position in the same way:

(a) JCT clause 13 stipulates that the quantity surveyor shall act in accordance with the rules, *unless* the employer and the contractor agree otherwise, meaning that the quantity surveyor will then use different rules – presumably, but not necessarily, as agreed by the parties.

(b) IFC clause 3.7 starts at the point of the employer and the contractor agreeing amounts of variations *before* the instructions are implemented, without necessarily involving the quantity surveyor at all. The complete alternative is then for the quantity surveyor to value in accordance with the rules only.

The usual course of events is for the quantity surveyor to value variations progressively as work proceeds or when drawing up the final account, and this is possible under both clauses in the absence of any timetable for the quantity surveyor's work. This can be seen as a weakness of the system, as neither party knows where he is and procrastination of settlement is encouraged on both sides. On the other hand, it is not always easy to settle variations at the time, as they may be interrelated with other uncertain work or be affected

by questions of sequence verging towards disturbance of progress. There is the difference that, under the IFC clause, the quantity surveyor strictly needs to check that the parties have not agreed something in advance, before he becomes involved as of routine in what may be abortive work. Usually, this becomes a matter of 'know your employer and his habits', but an initial clearance of procedures can only help.

No guide is given in the JCT clause as to when the parties may wish to agree that the quantity surveyor should depart from the laid-down rules for valuation, which cover most unusual options in principle and give the quantity surveyor plenty of scope. Indeed, in places the rules amount to little more than 'sort out something reasonable'. While nothing is said in the other clause, the parties can always agree to something like this if they wish, simply because they *are* the parties, even though strictly a supplemental agreement is needed.

Despite their differences, the clauses are capable of being used similarly over advance valuation. Thus with either, it is possible for the parties to decide that the desirability of a variation for the employer is conditional upon what the price will be (the 'value' question outlined above) and so seek to agree it in advance. But it does not permit the contractor to refuse a variation just because a prior suggested price is not high enough. On the other hand, it does not force him to agree a price with the employer in advance, as there can be no binding 'agreement to agree' in law. If there is no prior agreement, with or without the attempt being made, the variation can still be instructed and the contractor must then proceed with it and be paid on the basis of the quantity surveyor's valuation. This is always subject to arbitration, if the contractor and the quantity surveyor cannot agree on its amount, as are most matters.

As with many dealings, it is usually better to come to an agreement when once the hand has been put to that particular plough, otherwise relations may be soured. The alternative is not to embark on that approach at all. It is fair to suggest that major variations of obligations and restrictions are those most likely to lead to a need of prior agreement, of at least a basis of valuation. They are also the one area of instructions to which the contractor is allowed to lodge 'a reasonable objection' under JCT clause 4.1.1 or IFC clause 3.5.1. While such an objection should not be based directly upon lack of price agreement, but upon subversion of the contractor's programme or method of working, prior agreement of an acceptable price or basis is likely to reduce the possibility of an objection arising at all.

Rules for valuation of variations and provisional sum expenditure under JCT 80 with quantities

VALUATION OF ADDITIONS BY MEASUREMENT

This heading is broad enough to cover both variations and provisional sum expenditure. Only the former is referred to for brevity.

In the various contract rules, the JCT clause alone uses the expression 'valued by measurement', which is hardly precise, as measurement does not in itself value. A similar process may be read into IFC clause 3.7.3 (discussed hereunder), when quantities form part of the contract with clause 1.5 also applying.

JCT clause 13.5.1 gives three rules, which are to be applied in turn to a piece of work in a variation to see whether they fit, until the suitable one is reached:

(a) Work may be of 'similar character', may be 'executed under similar conditions' and may not 'significantly change the quantity' in the contract bills, presumably of the work to which it is similar. If all three criteria are met, the contract rates are to 'determine the Valuation'.

(b) Work may be of 'similar character', but the conditions or quantity, or both, may not accord with (a). Here, 'a fair allowance' is to be made for differences.

(c) Work may not be of 'similar character', which by definition changes the other two criteria. Here, there is to be valuation 'at fair rates and prices'.

Several comments are needed on the three criteria themselves:

(a) 'Similar character' is sometimes taken to mean 'identical in every respect', such as material, application, size and any other feature which the Standard Method of Measurement requires to be stated in an item description. If this is accepted, then under the first rule 'determine' really means 'use the bill rates exactly as they are', so that no *pro rata* pricing arises. It may be seen not to arise under the second rule either on this argument, while it clearly has no place in the third. It is more in accord with normal usage for 'similar' to mean 'like', while not excluding the identical (although pedantically perhaps it does). On this basis a reasonable scope for the term is 'work of the same material, perhaps differing in size and with some difference in application'. This will be recognised by the initiated as allowing *pro rata* pricing, as well as direct bill prices.

(b) 'Similar conditions' may be taken to mean broadly those aspects of a piece of work which the Standard Method of Measurement does not expressly require to be stated. Thus, when deciding similarity or dissimilarity, location on a ceiling rather than a wall often falls to be considered under (a), while location on a first-floor ceiling rather than a tenth-floor ceiling may fall here. Again *pro rata* pricing can deal with the results. It is best to adopt a 'give and take' approach to much work in these respects, and to reserve adjustment to large cases, as almost any piece of work can be shown to be different from another in some minor way.

(c) 'Significant change [in] . . . quantity' may occur quite independently of change in conditions, although one may shade into the other. Its more obvious effects are matters like different gang sizes, plant types or sizes

and scale or phasing of delivery of materials. These effects are susceptible of *pro rata* pricing again, with some more give and take mixed in. (But see also under 'Changed conditions for unvaried work' hereafter.)

In practice, the precise distinctions between these criteria and the rules in which they are embodied are not too important. While they may be viewed as classic examples of quantity surveyors' desire to dance on the point of a needle, they do have the virtue of covering most options by a sort of blanket bombardment of overlapping shell fire.

When work goes outside the first criterion, the basis of valuation is to be 'fair'. This is to be interpreted as fair to both parties, so that the contractor receives a level of payment which covers the labour, etc. which he reasonably uses or should use in the operations concerned. Very often, the work will be common enough in character, but just has not been included in the contract. The prices are then generally known and accepted within the industry within a fairly narrow band as reflecting inputs for work performed under 'average' conditions, etc. and can be adjusted for any actual differences of conditions and quantity.

This approach means that the contractor does not receive his whole cost, when he has been inefficient, but also that he may receive distinctly more if he has been particularly efficient. If the approach is used quite impartially, it should not even be necessary for the quantity surveyor to enquire what the level of efficiency has been. This ideal becomes more difficult to achieve when the conditions become far from normal, so that routine data are not available. Then some review of actual costs, modified by considerations of conceivable efficiency, may be needed.

A departure should also be considered if the contractor chooses to use some technique or piece of plant which is innovatory and the use of which is not reflected in standard data. This is a difficult area, as the contractor may contend that he, and not the employer, stands to gain from his own initiative. The test may be 'what would he have done if pricing similar work in competition?', and the answer may be 'he would have priced somewhere between the old and the new, if he thought that his level of competitiveness would carry it'. If so, a 'fair price' for a variation may be pitched at a similar level.

Added to these direct inputs must be overheads and profit. Both should be at the level included in the contract sum. There is no argument of substance for adjusting the profit level in particular to something higher or lower, because current tenders in general are coming in at a different level of competitiveness, or even that one from the same contractor has done this. Fair prices should be fair in relation to the contract bargain as struck, so keeping in step with *pro rata* pricing.

Another argument, which may be regarded as a special case of profit margin, but bigger because it edges into negative profit margin, is that over using erroneous prices in pricing variations, either directly or as the basis of *pro rata* prices. It is not always easy to say with confidence that a price is in

error in either direction, but even when it is, the price should still be used. The clause being considered states plainly 'the rates and prices for the work so set out' (that is in the contract bills) 'shall determine the Valuation' of 'additional or substituted work'. In fact, the present clause is the only one in the contract which specifically requires the use of the contract prices at all, so that their primary purpose must be seen to be as a schedule of rates for valuing variations. The provisions about interim valuations do not require the use of the contract bills, except indirectly in that the calculation of formula fluctuations so requires.

It is sometimes argued that a contractor is not obliged to perform more work at an erroneous rate than the quantity which he priced in his tender. Put thus crudely, it ignores the direction of the error or what should happen if the quantity goes down. This is a four-edged sword which the employer might want to wield in some circumstances. It is also affected by the possibility of 'variation spotting' (discussed in Ch. 3) and of a gamble not succeeding. In the case of *Dudley Corporation* v. *Parsons & Morrin Ltd* (1959), the contractor had priced rock excavation at some 10 per cent of an economic rate, the bill item being provisional. The actual quantity was about three times the provisional. The Court of Appeal held that the rate must stand, after considering the various proportions of rock and other excavation. It was said 'one must assume that [the contractor] chose to take the risk of greatly underpricing an item which might not arise'.

VALUATION OF ADDITIONS BY DAYWORK

This heading again relies upon the peculiar use of 'valuation' within the contract, this time in JCT clause 13.5.4. What is really being done here is to use the contractor's cost as the basis of payment, in circumstances where measurement or subsequent pricing is impracticable, and often where relatively expensive working occurs. The rules given require the incorporation into the contract of a schedule of percentage rates related to one or more standard definitions of daywork. Daywork is chargeable at current market rates, that is adjusted for fluctuations in market costs, with the addition of the percentage appropriate to the category of cost.

To operate this method of valuation, little more is needed beyond a record of the inputs incurred by the contractor, to which the costs and percentages may be applied. The contract requires the contractor to deliver 'vouchers . . . for verification' within the week following work being performed, and it is mainly this matter of vouchers which needs comment in the present context.

The stipulated procedure assumes that the architect himself can deal adequately with what may be a flow of sheets. Alternatively, it allows them to be routed to the architect's 'authorised representative', usually meaning the clerk of works as the person on the spot. This is the norm, as only someone present can properly keep a close eye on events. There is no statement that the appropriate signature authorises that valuation shall be by daywork or

that the rates upon the sheet are correct; it merely verifies the time and other quantities given. Daywork is used only when 'work . . . cannot properly be valued by measurement' and the decision over this rests with the quantity surveyor. Even before the work is performed the architect should not authorise that it is to be performed on daywork, and it must be questioned whether he can, even if he tries. It would be possible for the employer to do so under the arrangement already discussed, but an agreement by the architect would appear to be invalidated by the rules here as a whole.

It is a mixed blessing, but really desirable, to have a valid agreement in advance by the quantity surveyor for daywork to be allowed for defined work. It means that uncertainty is removed and should ensure that records will be kept. On the other hand it removes the incentive to perform work as economically as possible, in case daywork is not finally allowed.

It is common practice for daywork records of work to be kept 'for record purposes' when prior authorisation has not been given, and this can be useful, so long as it does proliferate and get out of hand. Sometimes the practice is followed of signing all daywork sheets as 'for record purposes only', even when daywork has been agreed in principle. This does no harm, or good, because the sheets are always just records.

When once sheets are signed, the quantity surveyor has only two options over hours, etc. stated: to accept them for use in daywork payment or to decline them and proceed with measured valuation instead. He cannot decide to reduce amounts because he thinks they are too high. With this said, he may still find that the evaluation of work performed in unusual circumstances (even of loss and expense) is helped by light shed from such records, although the dividing line between the two approaches is thin.

A different situation may arise when daywork overlaps with measured work. The two may be very difficult to segregate in the complexities of site working, but some split must be made, rather than that the whole area of work should be dealt with by daywork.

VALUATION OF OMISSIONS

It will be obvious that when work is omitted from the contract, the means for its evaluation lie to hand in bill items, etc. Nothing more need be added over this direct evaluation prescribed in JCT clause 13.5.2, although the comments below on JCT clause 13.5.5 may be noted regarding remaining work.

SUBSIDIARY PROVISIONS OVER VALUATION

JCT clause 13.5.3 gives three stipulations, two of which are innocent enough. These two are for measurement of variations to follow the same principles as in the contract bills (anything else is a recipe for disorganisation at the least), and for any percentage or lump sum adjustments of the contract sum to be reflected in valuation. The latter are usually the result of action during examination of the tender.

The third relates to the possibility of adjusting the amounts of items in the preliminaries of the contract bills. This does not occur as a direct percentage of the additions and omissions, but on assessment of what effect variations have on the sorts of items given in the preliminaries. The principles of adjustment are considered in Chapter 15. For fairly marginal amounts of variations, very often little or no adjustment will occur. Expenditure of provisional sums may not lead to any adjustment, as their amount should have been taken into account in assessing the contract preliminaries. If the amount expended is significantly different, some adjustment may lie. The exception is for sums for 'undefined work' under SMM 7, where the amounts are *not* to be taken into account, so that an adjustment is more likely to be due. Because of this category of adjustment, it is important that values be included in the contract bills for appropriate items, rather than just a total for the whole bill of preliminaries or, worse, that the value is spread over the measured rates at large.

The clause wording is that 'allowance, where appropriate, shall be made', rather than that 'the rates and prices . . . shall determine the Valuation', as for measured valuation. This can have two significances. It may be recognising that preliminaries are priced almost invariably as lump sums, and so these sums will be adjusted by some 'allowance'. Alternatively, it may be permitting the evaluation of the true extent of adjustment, even when the full pricing has not been shown in the contract. On balance, it appears reasonable to accept both of these possibilities together, rather than as alternatives. Acceptance of the former only would remove or limit adjustment in the case of partial or no separation of pricing. If an adjustment of some calculated value of preliminaries is then made, it needs to be remembered that some level of adjustment is automatically being made as part of the net effect of measured variations. This question is also illustrated in Chapter 15.

Special provisions for valuation under JCT 80 with quantities

There are several provisions, hardly precise enough to be rules, set out in the latter part of JCT clause 13. These both extend and limit the main rules in special circumstances when straightforward valuation of the variations, etc. is not adequate to deal with all the financial aspects.

CHANGED CONDITIONS FOR UNVARIED WORK

Sometimes the exact localised effects of a variation can be dealt with by measurement, for instance, without covering all the consequences. Other work may not have been subject to the instruction, but is nevertheless affected in its cost of execution to some significant degree. JCT clause 13.5.5 allows a revaluation of such work 'as if it had been the subject of an instruction . . . requiring a variation', with the rules as already explained covering revaluation. Use of the clause is subject to the qualification that the variation 'substantially changes the conditions' for the unvaried work.

An example of this class of effect would be the omission of work requiring

the same scaffolding or other facility as other unvaried work, although whether it would justify a financial reappraisal would depend on how the scaffolding had been priced in the contract bills. If priced in the several items, varied and not, it would need an adjustment to reinstate the part cost of scaffolding otherwise being omitted. The addition of work sharing a scaffold would not create this problem, as it would be priced without scaffolding, unless it were an item already in the contract bills, when adjustment might be needed to avoid an over-inclusion for the scaffolding. It might, however, lead to less continuity in performing the work which originally had the scaffold to itself, so increasing its cost.

This example is one of many which are really matters of access and other facility in performing work. It could be matched by others in which the dominant feature was sequencing, repetition or continuity, either in programme or physical disposition of work. Even without these aspects, there are ways in which an addition or omission of the whole of one type of work at one end or the other of a programme, while leaving the rest of it intact, can mean a shift in costs. Rather similarly, a part high or low of some work originally spread evenly at the various levels in a building can become spread unevenly due to additions or omissions, so changing the amount of hoisting costs as averaged in the original pricing.

Two comments are called for here. One is that the clause refers specifically to 'conditions', which expression in JCT clause 13.5.1 is differentiated from 'character' and 'quantity'. As the work in question is itself unvaried, no question of character arises. But addition to or omission from work already in the contract bills may change substantially the overall quantity. While that clause authorises pricing of the varied work (provided it is an addition) to cover this effect, it does not allow repricing of unvaried work to this end. The present clause does not do so either, so that strictly there is a gap in the provisions, as noted earlier. One solution which may be tried is to price the whole effect in the additional work, if it is additional, which is clumsy in arithmetical detail. The other is to interpret 'conditions' as equivalent to 'quantity', which comes close to some of what have been given as examples in the preceding paragraphs, and so reprice all the work much more rationally. Neither solution is really supported by the clauses, but something has to be done, and the second is suggested as filling the gap in contractual logic.

The second comment is that this clause, like the rest of JCT clause 13, is to be used to price work which is executed under changed conditions which can be foreseen before it is performed, so that the programme is adjusted to allow for as economical working as is practicable. No question of disturbance arises here, as discussed below.

FAIR VALUATION OF VARIATIONS

While many variations can be dealt with by measured valuation or daywork, supplemented by some ingenuity, others resist these means completely. In these cases, an undefined concept of 'fair valuation' is introduced by JCT

clause 13.5.6. This is obviously intended to be some calculation not primarily dependent on measured quantities of the traditional variety, but assessed at a level that is reasonably consistent with that of the contract sum, in terms of allowance for overheads and profit.

Two divisions are given: where the 'Valuation does not relate to the execution of . . . or the omission of work', and where some part of a valuation otherwise performed in accordance with the main rules cannot be dealt with in that way. The former division is particularly applicable to the valuation of variations in obligations and restrictions, where some amounts arise from broad analysis of a range of prices or from considerations needing lump sum adjustments. It is also related to adjustment of preliminaries, in fact the two classes overlap very often, as may parts of them with the second division.

This second division may relate to cases in which variations change elements of cost like a central concrete batching plant or a tower crane, without changing drastically what is happening to each unit of work at the point of depositing or fixing. To arrive at revised measured prices for such work, it is often necessary in any case to calculate the cost of the central element and then spread it across the unit prices. It makes sense not to perform the latter operation, which at the best may have to be delayed until the total quantities are available. This provision also covers any case of special supervision or staff costs, due to intensive working, reordering or other repeated work and so on.

Again, this is an area which tends to lie close to that of disturbance of progress, so that an overlap must be avoided.

DISTINCTION FROM LOSS AND EXPENSE

It has been pointed out several times that the variation provisions are not to take account of loss and expense, and JCT clause 13.5.6 makes this explicit. It is suggested that the dividing line between the two camps is not always clear in practice, although the theoretical distinction is there.

The primary difference is that loss and expense under JCT clause 26 flows from disturbance of regular progress of the works. While variations in themselves may lead to work being rescheduled into patterns and sequences which were not envisaged in the original programme (be it that used for the tender or drawn up for construction), they may still be instructed in such a rhythm as to allow the rescheduling to be done well ahead of work on or off site, so that maximum productivity is achieved. This may of course mean dearer, or cheaper working, than would have occurred – which is the point of having clause 13 at all!

The difference financially has been touched earlier in this chapter and is explored more fully in Chapter 14. Where there is room for genuine doubt over which theoretical category fits, the practical decision may be tempered by the likely financial outcome and the ease of achieving it.

TIMETABLE FOR VALUING VARIATIONS, ETC.

No timetable is given for agreement of variations, nor is there any explicit statement that they will be agreed in quantity or price. This is implicit in JCT clause 13.6, which simply allows the contractor to be present to take notes when the quantity surveyor is measuring. It also shows in the scheme for preparing and presenting the final account, followed as it is by the issue of the final certificate and the option of arbitration.

In the interests of progress, the quantity surveyor and the contractor may well arrange some form of progressive agreement of measurements and prices, as well as of the less difficult daywork sheets. Even when they do reach some extent of agreement, it is as well for it to be understood that, on prices in particular, there must be room for review of agreements if unexpected factors emerge. There may have been the agreement of prices related to one scale of working, when further variations undermine the basis used. Alternatively, it may turn out that a minor price agreed without too much consideration of its level suddenly becomes the fulcrum on which major negotiations hinge.

It is a well-established principle of law that prices used for interim payments on account do not bind the parties in final settlement, as to amount or even as to whether an item should be included at all (see Ch. 8). These facts should reassure those agreeing interim valuations that they have a right to review, while not encouraging them to be rash in what they include. Even when variations are not accurately agreed, they should be included in payments on account when performed, as JCT clause 13.7 requires, as well as JCT clause 30 dealing with preparation of the payments. This is important for the contractor's cash flow, although his redress if not satisfied is rather limited (again see Ch. 8).

Comparison of valuation provisions under contracts other than JCT 80

SUMMARY OF KEY FEATURES OF THE PROVISIONS FOR VALUATION UNDER JCT 80

In view of the length of JCT clause 13 and the foregoing comment upon it, the more important features are listed in outline, to help comparison:

(a) Where possible, measured valuation is to be used for additions, with prices derived from those in the contract bills, either directly or by the *pro rata* method, to take account of differences in the varied work.
(b) If these prices are not suitable, other prices of a similar level of competitiveness are to be applied to the measured quantities.
(c) If measurement and pricing are not suitable at all, daywork is to be used for additional work.
(d) Measured valuation is to be used directly from the contract bills for all omissions.
(e) Elements of original pricing, such as preliminaries and percentage adjustments, are to be taken into account where suitable.
(f) The effect of variations on conditions in which unvaried work is performed is to be allowed.

(g) Special fair valuation may be used for elements of cost not susceptible to any of the foregoing methods, in whole or in part.

(h) Loss and expense due to disturbance of regular progress is not to be allowed as part of the valuation of variations.

None of the complications or inadequacies already described are mentioned above, while 'variations' should be read as including 'provisional sum expenditure'.

PROVISIONS UNDER IFC 84

While this contract is identical in its effects to JCT 80, there are a few points to note. For ease of reference all parts of the two clauses dealing with valuation are listed:

JCT 80	*IFC 84*
13.4.1	3.7.1
13.5.1.1	3.7.3
13.5.1.2	3.7.3
13.5.1.3	3.7.4
13.5.2	3.7.2
13.5.3	3.7.6
13.5.4	3.7.5
13.5.5	3.7.8
13.5.6	3.7.4
13.5 (proviso)	3.7.7
—	3.7.9

Most of these indicate straightforward rearrangement of order, needing no further mention.

The priced document

IFC clause 3.7.3 refers simply to 'the priced document' and to 'the relevant values therein', rather than to 'the Contract Bills' and to 'the rates and prices . . . so set out', as does JCT clause 13.5.1 in its several parts. What the priced document is depends on the financial basis of the contract, indicated in the IFC recitals, to which IFC clause 3.7.1 refers back. The recitals give alternatives between which to choose:

(a) A fully priced specification, schedules of works or contract bills. Any one of these implies a complete breakdown of the contract sum.

(b) A specification supported by a contract sum analysis or a schedule of rates. Either of these implies a limited amount of data from which to price variations, etc.

Of these, contract bills and a schedule of rates both give measured items for reaching a quantified valuation. The former is discussed in the main section on valuation preceding the present, while the latter follows when JCT 80 without quantities is discussed. The latter must contain its own rules for measurement, as the usual method of measurement cannot be assumed. IFC clause 3.7.3 should be sufficiently fulsome over pricing aspects, even though more compressed.

A priced specification and priced schedules of work are by no means clearly different, as both envisage a division of the works into a series of items each permitting self-contained pricing. For a specification to be laid out in any way that helps valuation of variations, or for that matter the original estimating on the basis indicated, it must be broken into items related to parcels of work, rather than to trade divisions which may spread all over the project. The only reasonable distinction is that schedules of work can be used alongside a trade-based specification to give a rearrangement of material for pricing purposes without great detail in the works.

When this has been said, the distinction between schedules of work and a contract sum analysis is also not absolute, other than that the employer supplies the former and the contractor the latter. It may be inferred that the schedules are intended to be divided in some detail, while the analysis may not be. (The term 'contract sum analysis' has come into regular currency through the JCT with contractor's design form, where it can mean many things; see the present author's *Design and Build Contract Practice* in some detail.) It is always desirable that the architect or the quantity surveyor should provide the main divisions of the analysis and a clear guide to the level of detail for the contractor before he tenders. Otherwise, less than enough detail is more likely than the opposite, as well as the possibility of unsuitable divisions. There will then be a need for recasting and editing, as can happen with a schedule of rates (see later discussion).

Which of these options to use is matter to be decided in the light of the individual project. The intention is that IFC 84 is used for 'works of simple content', as is endorsed on its cover, but this is not entirely the way it is working out in practice. Further, even simple works can be subjected to undue torture by way of variations, so that the likely extent of these should also influence the decision. It makes no sense to use none of them, that is just to have a specification and no pricing, indeed the contract then becomes unworkable by uncertainty and possibly an analysis would have to be imported later. It may be even more damaging to try to use more than one of them, as all manner of clashes and doubts over precedence can arise. One is needed, but only one.

The possibility of the contract sum analysis or the schedule of rates not providing all the data needed for valuation of variations is recognised in IFC clause 3.7.9, which allows a fair valuation in those circumstances, as becomes inevitable. This option may be needed in the case of omissions, as well as additions as in other contracts. It will then be reasonable to look into detail in the contractor's estimating papers, although these do not form

part of the contract and are not binding. Subject to this and to any errors or special adjustments made within it during tendering, the detail may be useful in conjunction with other information and judgment.

The 1987 revision of NSC/4 allows the revaluation of sub-contract work affected in this way by main contract variations. The earlier version is deficient at this point, as considered in detail in the present author's *Building Sub-Contract Forms*.

Subsidiary provisions

Nothing is said in this contract about the treatment when valuing variations of lump sum or percentage adjustments given in the priced document. This should nevertheless follow the principles of the JCT clause, which is spelling out normal practice. The smaller the contract sum, the less likely is it that any lump sum will be taken into account.

While the provisions for daywork terms are given in IFC clause 3.7.5, there is no procedure for verifying records or forwarding them to the architect, within a given time or at all. This should be dealt with in the specification, the contract bills or whichever document applies.

PROVISIONS UNDER JCT 80 WITHOUT QUANTITIES

Under this contract, the only possibility offered as standard for valuation prior to the 1987 revisions was that of a schedule of rates. That revision also introduces schedules of work as in IFC 84 just discussed, and the comments may be read to apply here. The original JCT clause 5.3.1.3 requires the schedule of rates to be provided by the contractor post-contractually, if it has not been provided already. The advantage always lies with it being provided before the contract is entered into, thus saving an area of possible disagreement later. It would be possible, say, for the quantity surveyor to prepare the schedule unpriced, so avoiding any problems of wording and layout. Usually it is considered sufficient, for the small projects envisaged for this form of contract, for the contractor to use his own work, subject to any editing of wording.

This is so, because the routine procedure is for the contractor to take the build-up which he prepares for his tender and use it as the basis of the schedule of rates. In conjunction with the quantity surveyor, if any, he will delete all the quantities and extensions, so that just item descriptions and unit prices remain. With any editing for presentation purposes, the result is the contract schedule, with the advantage that it is clearly related to the price level of the tender, and so of the contract sum. Not only are the quantities and extensions removed, but they are denied any significance over accuracy, so that the contract is based upon a lump sum without quantities, but with a schedule for variation purposes only (which is strictly how contract bills are used also). This position must be adhered to rigidly during all post-contract work.

With the schedule so provided, the present version of JCT clause 13 runs

extremely close to its with-quantities cousin. Rather like the one in the IFC form, it ignores lump sum and percentage adjustments, but the same comments apply. It does not give the provision about fair valuation if the schedule does not cover the variation, because it is more detailed in other respects. If the schedule has been prepared as outlined above, at least omissions should be fully covered.

The main problem areas with this contract are in deciding how to apply the clauses about errors, or rather to decide when errors may exist, so affecting the starting-point for adjustment of variations. Errors in quantity included in the contract sum lie with the contractor, as given above. JCT clause 14.1 states that both 'quality and quantity of the work included in the Contract Sum shall be deemed to be that which is shown upon the Contract Drawings or described in the Specification'. The use of 'deemed' shows that the contractor's own quantities are not relevant. The 'shown . . . or described' provision means that work need only be shown in one place or the other for it to count as in the contract sum, so that the contractor has read the documents together.

JCT clause 2.2.2 clouds this position somewhat by dealing with 'error in description or quantity or omission of items' in the contract drawings 'and/or' the specification. It requires any of these to be corrected as though variation has been instructed. Thus, whereas JCT clause 14.1 allows an item to occur in either document, the present clause seems to be considering the possibility that omission from one only will constitute an error. It is suggested that the correct interpretation must be that clause 14.1 overrules this clause, which then refers to errors in description in one document alone which cannot be seen to be in error when the other is read. Omissions must be seen in the same light: there must be a item which should by normal practice be in one document only and which cannot be seen to be missing, or the item must be missing from both, where it would normally appear. Error in quantity is less easy to reconcile: it can best be interpreted as a drawing error such as the wrong height of a wall, or a specification error such as giving the wrong number of brackets for a shelf. The discussion of discrepancies and divergences in this type of contract in Chapter 5 is also relevant here.

The drawings and the specification are to be read together, without either taking precedence. JCT clause 2.3 requires the contractor to refer any discrepancy or divergence to the architect for resolution. Dependent upon how the architect resolves matters, will be whether a variation instruction is needed, so leading to a difference in payment. This same clause places 'further drawings or details . . . to explain or amplify' within its orbit, which is reassuring, as the contractor should have had all these to be able to tender! This provision applies of course to removal of doubt as to what has to be done, as well as to what is to be paid, a matter discussed for the with-quantities form in Chapter 5.

JCT clause 14.3 affirms that any quantities supplied to the contractor 'at any time . . . shall not form part of this Contract', which can only reasonably be interpreted as supplied beforehand and presumably for tendering. Any

practice of supplying such quantities cannot be too strongly condemned: if no one is prepared to stand by them, they should not be used.

PROVISIONS UNDER JCT 80 WITH APPROXIMATE QUANTITIES

Several features in this form build up the background picture of the one distinctive feature here, the uncertainty about the original quantities and the necessity for complete remeasurement and valuation for the final account. The uncertainty under any contract based on this approach occurs at three levels:

(a) The extent to which the design is incomplete, so that the scope and detailed nature of the scheme is in doubt. Only rarely will the design be complete, with time alone forcing the use of approximate quantities.
(b) How accurately the quantities represent the scheme as designed, be the design advanced or otherwise.
(c) How uncertain the contractor's pricing is, in view of his uncertainty over what it is he is tendering for.

These levels have a cumulative effect. The first affects the contractor's view of his preliminaries and of how far to reflect such features as repetition and buildability in his unit prices, as well as determining the best that the quantity surveyor might achieve by way of accuracy. The second is the result of the first and also depends on how long a time is available to prepare the quantities. One feature of approximate quantities is that they can be of any degree of approximation, allowing very rapid preparation when the need arises, but less coincidence with reality as a result. The third level is that not only are the quantities uncertain, but the prices attached to them are based on an uncertain assessment.

Approximate quantities are very useful to the employer in some circumstances, but they do throw more responsibility than usual on the contractor. Some of this he will tend to absorb by including a greater margin in his pricing for the greater risk he takes, but the rest is what he may expect to come to him in settlement, not just in correct, final quantities, but in review of the pricing. The less accurate the original basis, the more sweeping this review may need to be. The employer should be prepared by his advisers for the financial result, even if he is less than aware of how it will be incurred.

Against this backcloth, the JCT form aims to achieve middle ground. This is indicated by the note at the head of the articles of agreement, but not forming part of them or of the rest of the contract, that the form is intended for works which have been 'substantially designed but not completely detailed'. The note also mentions the approximation and the need for remeasurement. In principle, there is nothing within the contract which specifically limits its use to so high a level of prior design, while it is fairly difficult to produce a form which facilitates a far less well-developed scheme. The major problem is dealing with price adjustment, which is more a question of how the bills of quantities are composed, than of what the contract says. It can only allow leeway, as this one does.

Within the articles, the reference is made to 'Drawings and Bills of Approximate Quantities showing and describing, and intended to set out a reasonably accurate forecast of the quantity of, the work to be done'. It is a clear, grammatical deduction from the order of this rather compact form of words, that both sets of documents are to show and describe the work and both are intended to forecast the quantity of work. Whether this is precisely what the drafters intended may be wondered, as it is at odds with normal practice.

The functions of drawings and quantities are somewhat distinct in that usually the former 'shows' the major dispositions of work, while the latter 'describes' the detail, if not its positioning. In this sense, they may be seen as performing the two functions jointly but essentially apportioned between them, and the wording given may be accepted as tolerably correct. The inadequate alternative would be to deny the drawings any part in what follows and to allocate all the functions to the bills, which do not properly 'show' work. Such a construction would also run across what is the obvious interpretation of the rest of the wording in this paragraph of the articles.

The concept of apportioned functions recombining to give the total picture cannot be applied to the one function of 'setting out' the quantities. It is accepted practice, when bills form part of the contract (as they do here), that they are to be taken as alone embodying the quantities without need for recourse to the drawings. The exception lies with such elements as scaffolding and other temporary items, which are either not measured at all or are given in more rudimentary quantitative form than is otherwise the practice. These are likely to vary from one contractor to the next, according to detailed site method, and so are commonly assessed by inspection of the configurations shown on the drawings. The resulting sums must then be allocated against the quantities, including preliminaries items. For the quantities as 'set out' expressly, the present wording is unfortunate if the two types of document diverge considerably in the picture of scale which they paint.

JCT clause 13.1 states the usual basis that the contract bills give both the quality and quantity of the work in the contract, which should be held to override the uncertain wording just discussed. It must be held then, in general, that only the bills can supply quantities, while the drawings continue to indicate character, complexity and other features of the work as usual. It can be seen, however, that the possibility of dispute is latent here, if the drawings and bills diverge widely, particularly over pricing plant and similar items.

JCT clause 14 deals with 'Measurement and valuation of work, including variations and provisional sums'. The mention of variations might be unexpected in an all-remeasurement contract, if it did not cover variations of obligations and restrictions, as distinct from physical, designed work. Even so, it is intended to cover both varieties of variation. The contract has three sets of information which need mention here:

(a) Contract drawings recorded in the articles and which may not be
    complete, but which are to be assumed to be correct so far as they go.

They are not automatically laid aside when the contract is formalised, so that it is necessary to vary them if they are altered in some way. In a contract in which they are simply rough drawings, they should be omitted by a single variation instruction, stating that all working drawings will be issued thereafter under separate instructions. If they really are capable of development from where they are, it may be possible to issue instructions varying them. Often the reality will lie between these options. Usually, it is safer to assume the former situation and to omit all of the original drawings at the beginning, even if a few are reinstated later.

(b) Drawings and details to explain and amplify under clause 5.4. These have a definite place in a firm quantities contract, where only a few drawings become contract drawings out of those which, were intended, to be available for preparation of the contract bills. In such a contract, they are issued without an instruction, because they vary nothing. In the present contract, their purpose is the same, but the execution may be faulty in that what is in the contract for them to explain and amplify is none too clear, as between drawings and bills. If they are issued without an instruction, the quantity surveyor has no authority to use them, if once the contract drawings which they purport to amplify are removed. Even with those drawings still current, the supplementary drawings are confusing in status, so that the facility to issue them as such is best not used. A variation is always to be preferred.

(c) Variation instructions, including drawings, under clause 14. If the advice under (a) and (b) is followed, these become the embodiment of everything to which the contractor works, so avoiding doubt.

As far as valuation goes, the provisions follow the other JCT variants closely, allowing for the absence of omission measurement. In place of the reference to a significant change in quantity leading to a change in rate there is 'Where the quantity of the work was not reasonably accurately forecast'. It is to be expected that this provision will have greater importance in this form of contract. It really covers at least three situations: that in which an individual item or set of items is affected; that in which the whole content of the project varies; and that in which a swing in the distribution of trades affects their balance and interaction in the progress of the whole. As ever, there is a need to keep a sense of proportion as to what constitutes a serious departure from a reasonably accurate forecast.

What is serious when the contractor is looking at a sub-let trade may look quite different when looking at the job as a whole, so that he may be conceding a change in prices in the sub-contract, which is absorbed in the main contract by the wider compensating adjustments. On the other hand, an adjustment of preliminaries is more likely to occur in a remeasurement contract. There is no special mention of change in quantity in clause 26 here as leading to loss and expense, as the effect of the variations clause is to take up the various differences, while leaving disturbance of programme as a distinct issue.

CHAPTER 7

Sub-contractors: appointment and control

Basic distinctions in sub-contracting
Domestic sub-contracts
Nominated sub-contracts
Named sub-contracts

This chapter deals with the contract control of the various types of sub-contractors listed immediately below, especially obtaining them initially and replacing them in special circumstances later. Other aspects of sub-contracts are given in Chapter 5 and in chapters hereafter, with the same aspects of main contract work.

Basic distinctions in sub-contracting

STANDARD ARRANGEMENTS

There are four readily distinguishable treatments of sub-contracting allocated between the JCT and IFC contracts. These are:

(a) Domestic sub-contracts at the contractor's own initiative, that is cases in which he chooses entirely for his own reasons to pass out some portion of the works to another. This is a process also termed sub-letting within the contracts, while within the industry the results are also known as private sub-contracts. This treatment occurs in both contracts.
(b) Domestic sub-contracts which the contractor is required to enter into, with the permitted choice of sub-contractors given to him when tendering. The alternative terms again apply. This treatment occurs only in the JCT contract.
(c) Nominated sub-contracts which the contractor is required to enter into, with a sum of money stated in each case for inclusion in his tender and the actual choice of sub-contractor notified to him by the architect, usually after the contract is in existence. This treatment also occurs only in the JCT contract.
(d) Named sub-contracts which the contractor is required to enter into, with a single sub-contractor named in each case to whom he is to go for a sub-tender on which to base his own tender. This treatment occurs only in the IFC contract, although there is a minor reference which has similarities in JCT clause 35.1.

A comparison of the main contract provisions over nominated and named sub-contractors is given in Table 7.1.

There are two salient ways of departing from standard practice. One is to set up a sub-contract which is not one of the four standard arrangements listed above: perhaps by creating a hybrid, perhaps by producing a new strain. This is not very likely, but may occur on the initiative of the employer or his advisers. The sub-contractor should look carefully for the underlying motive, as it usually increases his responsibilities, probably over design and other liabilities towards the employer by way of some collateral warranty. The arrangement may well be faulty legally and also introduce procedural flaws.

The second departure is to use an amended or non-standard sub-contract for a standard arrangement. This can be done properly in any JCT situation only for a domestic sub-contractor, as the other forms are obligatory under the related

Table 7.1 Comparison of main contract clauses dealing with nomination and naming of sub-contractors

	JCT	IFC
Local authority, etc. not sub-contractor	6.3	3.3.8
Definition	35.1	3.3.2
Contractor tendering	35.2	3.3.2
Documents relating to sub-contract	35.3	—
Contractor's objection to sub-contractor	35.4	3.3.2
Choice of nomination procedures	35.5	—
Limit on persons nominated	35.6	—
Pre-nomination action	35.7	—
Contractor/sub-contractor failure to agree	35.8	3.3.1
Withdrawal of sub-contract offer	35.9	3.3.1
Issue of nomination instruction	35.10	—
Use of agreement NSC/2a	35.11	—
Sub-contract NSC/4a	35.12	—
Interim and direct payment of sub-contractor	35.13.1	—
Extension of sub-contract period	35.14	—
Failure to complete sub-contract works	35.15	—
Practical completion of sub-contract works	35.16	—
Final payment of sub-contractor and defects	35.17–35.19	—
Position of employer and contractor	35.20–35.21	3.3.7
Restrictions in contracts	35.22	—
Proposed nomination not proceeding	35.23	—
Circumstances where renomination/naming	35.24	3.3.3–3.3.6
Determination of sub-contract/employment	35.25	3.3.3

Note: The clauses are listed by primary reference to the JCT nomination subject-matter, so that the IFC references give only partial correspondence, in view of the differences between the two sub-contracting methods.

main contracts. Even small amendments are likely to need corresponding main contract amendments. The contractor may well put forward his own domestic sub-contract conditions, which again the sub-contractor should check closely before acceptance. Most of the chapter headings in Parts 2 and 3 of this book suggest areas worth looking at, particularly those of programme, valuation and payment (such as 'pay when paid' and set-off). The individual sub-contractor often cannot secure standard conditions for an individual sub-contract, and has to rely more widely on the broader pressures from his trade association or similar body. He has to weigh the terms offered against the need to obtain the work within his own bargaining strength, but should never sign without understanding. Strictly, nothing can be done from the employer's side and usually nothing will be in practice.

Both these departures are undesirable. They may be seen as mutually variants one of the other and the comments made apply to some extent to both. As they are so variable, they are not considered elsewhere, but their significance should be assessed when they are encountered. One case indicates the degree of care which the sub-contractor should employ in reading the terms offered.

In *Martin Grant & Co. Ltd* v. *Sir Lindsay Parkinson & Co. Ltd* (1984), the sub-contractor had carried out work under a non-standard domestic sub-contract to a JCT form which contained a provision 'at such time or times and in such manner as the Contractor shall direct . . . the Sub-Contractor shall proceed with the said works expeditiously and punctually to the requirements of the Contractor so as not to hinder hamper or delay the work'. It was held that the contractor was not obliged, as the sub-contractor put it, to 'make sufficient work available to the [sub-contractors] to enable them to maintain reasonable progress and to execute their work in an efficient and economic manner'. The terms were sufficiently clear and express to preclude an implied term, such as the sub-contractor sought. When in doubt, a sub-contractor should seek advice before commitment.

CONTROL OF SUB-CONTRACTING

Within the broad legal position affecting sub-contracts, a contractor may sub-contract or sub-let any part of his work, unless he is restricted by the terms of his own contract. This latter is what the JCT and IFC contracts do, to varying extents according to the type of sub-contract involved. Some of the major reasons for controlling aspects of sub-letting are:

(a) *Quality of what is produced*: while the specification may be identical, different firms may perform differently against it, although still within its limits. Even if they fall short, indifferent performers are not always easy to pin down by reference to the written word. If possible, it is better to eliminate them in advance.

(b) *Programme compliance*: this is another aspect of performance, usually more sensitive in the way in which it affects performance of elements not

within the sub-contract, but offering somewhat more scope about what may be tied down in writing.

(c) *Design*: with specialised work, it is frequently the sub-contractor who designs it, so that the design cannot be performed on a consultancy basis for execution by another.

(d) *Price*: this may be the other side of all three coins so far listed, so that some form of direct involvement from the employer's side becomes desirable.

None of these considerations, or even all of them in combination, make contractual control indispensable, but it is often held to help. They may also be the seed-bed for later disputes, which is the reason for stating them here.

While the methods of sub-contracting vary to quite an extent in their detail, they all result in *sub-contracts* as such. The sub-contract documents accompanying each are more similar than distinctions at main contract level might suggest.

Domestic sub-contracts

The root principle of any domestic sub-contract is that the contractor selects and appoints the sub-contractor to perform work for which he, the contractor, has tendered as part of the main contract, so that several key factors emerge:

(a) The detailed terms of the sub-contract are a matter entirely between the parties, unless the main contract imposes any obligation on the contractor to include any particular terms. This is not done in the contracts here considered, except by stipulations that fluctuations be in keeping with those in the main contract and that there are provisions about property in materials passing from sub-contractor to employer when the contractor is paid. There are standard forms available to produce a harmonious result over all issues, but their use is optional.

(b) The method of tendering is left to the contractor, as is the financial basis (subject to the fluctuations point) and the nature of all contract documents, including drawings and specifications.

(c) The sub-contract price is between the parties alone. The price payable by the employer to the contractor for the work concerned is not affected by any difference between the two prices, in either direction. Settlement of the final prices payable is similarly separate.

(d) Control of the sub-contractor over performing his work in time, site organisation and quality, rests with the contractor, who is responsible to the employer for any fault affecting him.

(e) Unless there is a design responsibility placed on the contractor (as there is not under the JCT and IFC contracts), none can be placed on the sub-contractor via the sub-contract. By the time that the latter is

appointed by the contractor, it is too late for the employer to arrange anything by another route, as may occur with the other sub-contract arrangements.

(f) Mutual responsibilities and liabilities over commercial and other matters such as injury and damage, rest between the parties. Responsibility for some insurances are, however, governed by the main contract provisions.

(g) There are no stipulations about appointing another sub-contractor, if the first is lost for any reason. The contractor must settle the consequences himself and either complete outstanding work himself or obtain consent to another sub-letting.

These features flow from the general principle that privity of contract is solely between the parties to a contract, even when some terms (as here) are dictated by another. They are equally applicable when the contractor has decided to sub-let or when the employer has required it. In most respects, they also apply under the other forms of sub-contracting taken below.

CONTRACTOR'S INITIATIVE

When the contractor wishes to sub-let, he is required by JCT clause 19.2 or IFC clause 3.2 to obtain the architect's consent, which is not to be unreasonably withheld. Reasonable grounds would be that the proposed sub-contractor regularly performs inadequately over quality, but also over programme if he is to perform a critical section of work. Immediate signs of serious instability would also qualify, as would a strong reason for the employer to insist that he had chosen the particular contractor for special skill in the type of work concerned, so debarring any sub-letting. The giving of consent in no way relieves the contractor of his responsibilities over the work concerned, nor does it prevent him taking it back on himself.

It is implicit in this arrangement that the architect would have to demonstrate his reasonableness to the contractor, although if the architect did not demonstrate anything, the position would be the same. Ultimately, 'unreasonably' in the clauses has reference to what the courts or an arbitrator would hold. In the event of deadlock, recourse to one of these tribunals would be necessary. Reference to arbitration during progress is possible on any issue under the IFC form, but only on a few issues under the JCT form, of which the present is not one. Court action is not so constrained, but is not notorious for its speed, so that a quicker solution is unlikely.

If then there is disagreement, but the contractor does not wish to or cannot push his rights at once, he must accept the architect's decision under protest and seek another sub-contractor. This may run him into delay finding a replacement or extra expense because of a higher price. These points should be recorded to the architect, so that suitable redress here and on any other consequential issues may be sought later.

Even if the architect gives consent to a particular sub-letting, he may do so too late to meet the contractor's programme. Here the provisions over

extension of time and loss and expense do not apply, as these relate only to delay by the architect in providing 'instructions, drawings, details or levels' (see Chapter 11). Early action is recommended on these grounds, with a statement included as to why any particularly early consent is needed. If the architect still delays, it would appear to become a case of unreasonably withholding consent, as no reason has been given or at least substantiated. The contractor cannot proceed without consent and must revert to the remedies mentioned in the preceding paragraph.

Such early action may also be needed to secure a suitable sub-contractor who would otherwise withdraw his tender in favour of taking other work. Provided that the architect has been properly informed, the simple fact that the contractor has lost a more favourably priced sub-contract is a cause of extra expense to him. In any of these instances, the contractor must base his claim upon the general principle of a breach of duty by the employer's architect and not upon a specific clause. Recompense here can be included in the final account (as distinct from being sought in proceedings) only with the employer's express agreement, uncomfortable though this may be for the architect. Conversely however, the contractor cannot delay finding a sub-contractor, just because he is still looking for one to match the price of one lost.

When major cases of sub-letting are involved and when the contractor knows whom he is choosing, it is highly desirable to clear these during pre-contract discussions. This gives certainty to the contractor and avoids later disputes. It does not debar him from second thoughts, leading to a fresh consent, so long as he has not committed himself to a sub-contractor.

EMPLOYER'S OR ARCHITECT'S INITIATIVE

The other way of prefabricating a sub-letting is that contained in JCT clause 19.3, but not available under the IFC contract, where the use of a named sub-contract is more restrictive. This provides for 'certain work measured or otherwise described . . . and priced by the Contractor' to be sub-let to one of a given list of three or more persons given in the documents. The person chosen by the contractor 'at [his] sole discretion' then becomes in all respects like any other domestic sub-contractor. The clause goes on to allow either employer, architect or contractor to add further persons to the list post-contractually, subject to consent from the others. This still does not force the contractor to accept any particular name.

If the available list drops below three names sometime before there is a binding sub-contract, again names may be added, this time by agreement, which has the same effect as before. Alternatively, at this stage the contractor may choose to carry out the work himself or sub-let it in the way first described. Again the contractor is not forced to accept any one person and it is not stated which option is to prevail. It appears to be whichever is implemented first. If so, the contractor may secure the unassailable right to do the work himself, even if two persons remain on the list. If he wishes to sub-let in this case, it is effectively the same as if he were to seek to add names to the displaced

list, as consent is still required. The clause is not very helpful, however good in intent.

There is still no contractual provision in this instance for the contractor to be granted extension of time or be reimbursed for loss and expense if the procedure runs into trouble, despite the greater activity from the employer's side. His remedies are just as troublesome.

SUB-CONTRACT TERMS

The standard form available for optional use for a domestic sub-contract under the JCT contract is the DOM/1 sub-contract, while that under the IFC contract is the IN/SC sub-contract. They respectively follow closely in all respects relevant to present concerns the wording of the forms for nominated and for named sub-contracts looked at hereafter, except that there is no involvement of the architect in actions and agreements. All of the forms related to the JCT main contract are considered in detail in the present author's *Building Sub-Contract Forms*.

Nominated sub-contracts

Nominated sub-contracts lie at the far end of the spectrum from their domestic cousins, there being greater interaction with them from the employer's side, both pre-contractually and later. Named sub-contracts lie somewhere between, but are taken last to ease comparison. Some broad differences between the nominated and named varieties may be discerned from Figure 7.1.

Nominated sub-contracts are subject to more control by the architect over all the factors of quality, programme, design and price described above. Quality is usually the overriding factor, with design either required or not. The other two tend to come in because they are difficult to leave out, although this is managed with named sub-contracts.

JCT clause 35 regulates the position in some detail and relies on a number of sub-contract related documents, as named in it. It limits or even removes several ways in which the contractor can act on his own initiative, among these being:

(a) The contractor does not price nominated work in his tender, he simply includes a given prime cost sum and prices any attendance stipulated.
(b) The choice of sub-contractor rests with the architect, who obtains tenders and instructs the contractor which one to accept, subject to some right to demur and the obligation to agree subsidiary detail. There is the possibility of the contractor himself tendering for nominated work in a suitable case.
(c) The final sum payable is effectively agreed between the sub-contractor and the quantity surveyor, although the contractor is involved procedurally over the whole account and directly over any items of payment which are in dispute with him from either direction.

(d) Payments at all stages, including retention, are controlled by the architect and related to amounts agreed by the quantity surveyor. This extends to the possibility of direct payment of the sub-contractor, if the contractor defaults, subject to the counter-possibility of the contractor setting off charges which he may have.
(e) While the contractor is responsible for keeping the sub-contractor to programme and otherwise organising how he fits in, the architect is crucially involved in questions of delay and extension of time and when practical completion occurs.
(f) Determination of the sub-contractor's employment prematurely is closely monitored by the architect, both over reasons for its occurrence and the terms resulting.
(g) Replacement of the sub-contractor by re-nomination is undertaken by the architect, although the contractor usually receives reimbursement of the difference in amounts payable.

Despite these elements, the clause maintains that there is no privity of contract between employer and contractor due to the basic position established or to actions taken within that framework. Contractors often state that 'the nominateds' are not 'their subbies', but the legal position is sound. Even so, employers and architects need to watch their actions carefully, to avoid creating some implied relationship leading to effective privity and responsibility. There is a direct relationship over design by the sub-contractor, but this is created and moderated by a special agreement outside the sub-contract arrangement.

AUTHORITY FOR NOMINATED SUB-CONTRACTS

JCT clause 35.1 deals with the right of the architect to introduce a nominated sub-contract. The ways of doing this are by:

(a) The use of a prime cost sum included in the contract bills or specification, this has been mentioned and is the main method, in itself straightforward as it gives the maximum warning of intentions.
(b) A variation instruction or the expenditure of a provisional sum, either of these being less predictable by the contractor.
(c) Agreement between the architect and the contractor, by definition unexceptionable once the agreement has been reached. No rules are given over this, to allow complete flexibility and not to attempt to force anything.

The second option is the one needing care. In the case of a variation, the right of the architect to select a sub-contractor, which is what is in question, is limited by two characteristics, both of which must apply. The first is that the work must be additional to that in the contract documents, which by inference is to preclude the architect from taking work priced by the contractor himself and giving it to a sub-contractor. The second requires the additional

work to be of a similar kind to that already in the contract and allocated to nominated persons.

These two characteristics go with clause 13.1.3, which specifically excludes from the definition of a variation the nomination of a sub-contractor to perform 'work of which the measured quantities have been set out and priced by the Contractor' in the contract documents. The latter clause forbids the architect taking out work originally included and giving it to another, but in itself strictly does not negate him giving additional work of the same kind to another, contrary to the spirit of things and to practicality though this might be. The present clause does not positively allow him to do this, by virtue of its limitations, and he has only such powers as the conditions give him.

The architect is thus limited to 'such additional work . . . of a similar kind' and 'not further or otherwise'. This must be interpreted as referring to work of the same basic type, such as more suspended ceilings or mechanical engineering installations, when such work is already the subject of prime cost sums. In such a case, it could not reasonably be stretched to mean terrazzo paving (not included as a prime cost item) as being further internal finishings, in the same broad category as suspended ceilings. Given mechanical engineering installations in the first instance, but no plumbing, it would be not unreasonable to bring at least comparable plumbing work within the scope of a nomination. Highly distinctive sanitary work might push matters to the limits. There is some room for doubt here and need for tolerant interpretation.

In practical working situations, the distinction between a variation instruction extending an existing sub-contract and one introducing a new one might constitute the watershed over kinds of work. But, in principle, the clause does not exclude the introduction of a new sub-contractor, rather it exists to facilitate this happening.

With all this recorded about variations, the stark fact is that no restrictions are placed upon the architect when instructing the expenditure of a provisional sum. This sum may have been quite an inexplicit insertion in the documents, such as a sum for 'tank room complete', so that the contractor had little warning of the precise type of work required. In these conditions, the architect can introduce nominated sub-contractors for work not so covered in the original contract. This includes work for which he does not have the authority when dealing with a variation, anomalous though this may be. Clause 13.1.3, mentioned above, has no bearing on provisional sums.

Given work of a different kind from any originally envisaged, of a specialised nature and arising in the context of a variation, it is best for the architect and the contractor to agree under the last option that it be dealt with by nomination. The alternative is for the contractor to perform it himself or to seek consent to him sub-letting it. Both agreement and consent are not to be unreasonably withheld under the respective provisions, so that a first-round deadlock on a *quid pro quo* is possible, assuming that the contractor is not equipped to do the work himself. With the provision in clause 35.4.1 for the contractor to object (again reasonably) to a particular sub-contractor, it is

unlikely that a deadlock will exist except over money, and here an agreement on a nomination could take account of the contractor's margin in a special case. Responsibilities over delay or disturbance here could vary, according to the detailed pattern of events.

JCT clause 35.2 allows the alternative of the contractor himself tendering for work included in the contract as the subject of nomination. While it hedges procedures about rather fussily, it does not produce problems in interpretation or practice.

There are two procedures for nomination, these usually being distinguished outside the contract itself as the 'basic' and the 'alternative' methods. The intention is for the former to be used for the larger or more complex sub-contracts and the latter for those which are less demanding. Some of the later provisions in the JCT clause are obligatory only when the basic method is used, but the two obligatory nominated sub-contract forms are effectively identical.

Both procedures start inside the contract at the point when the architect has obtained tenders and has decided which person he wishes to nominate. In fact, the alternative method under clauses 35.11 and 35.12 does little but require the contractor to enter into a sub-contract with whoever is nominated within 14 days of his receiving the instruction. There are no defined tender documents, no specified flow of information and no drop-out mechanism, as in the basic method procedure.

By contrast, the basic method requires the use of Tender NSC/1 and of a definite exchange process between the contractor and the sub-contractor designate. The key elements are:

(a) The architect sends tender documents to the contractor, with a preliminary notice of nomination.
(b) The contractor proceeds to settle detailed points with the proposed sub-contractor within 10 working days. If he is successful, the architect nominates the sub-contractor.
(c) If the contractor is unable to reach agreement within the period, he is to seek further instructions from the architect.
(d) If the proposed sub-contractor withdraws before nomination (which carries acceptance with it), again the architect has to instruct the contractor.

This whole process is often criticised on the grounds of its complexity, quite apart from the desirability of nominated work. But it is essentially normal good practice codified, a necessity arising out of frequent lapses in its application in the past. Even in the alternative method some of the activity is still needed, while the documents optionally available for domestic sub-contracts are close in all essentials, giving comparability in operation.

The procedure is always at some risk in that the architect obtains a tender which leaves some elements with financial implications to be agreed between

the contractor and the sub-contractor after a tender sum has been given. This risk is minimised by the requirement for the architect to fill in quite a bit of detail about the contract and the terms under which the sub-contractor will be operating, before he sends NSC/1 with other information to tenderers. It is therefore essential for the equivalent information to have been included in the main contract, so that it is the basis of the contract sum.

A special case is that of the sub-contract programme duration. This usually arises out of the contractor's own programme, with the possibility that he may require the sub-contractor to operate within an uneconomically short span, so leading to a higher tender or haggling when it is received. The higher price is not always easily detected. The best safeguard is to consider main contract and sub-contract tenders together, so that programme effects can be sorted out before any commitment. If sub-contracts are not available then, the alternative is to examine the contractor's programme to see if it is adequate over sub-contracts. Even though the programme is not a contract document, the times for significant sub-contracts could be embodied in the contract.

Because each sub-contract may be different in, for instance, its call upon temporary facilities on site, there will be some margin for uncertainty, which is the reason for allowing the interchange between contractor and sub-contractor. While the architect will not wish to concede extra reimbursement for elements which should already be included in either the main or the sub-contract tender, he should remain alive to the possibility that there may be some genuine gap. Even more, there may be a situation in which it is good commercial sense to accept a lower sub-contract tender, even though this is at the price of some extra payment to the contractor, perhaps for a facility or some hoisting. The standard framework may need to give occasionally and it is at these points that the architect may be giving 'further instructions' within the 10-day period allowed. He may be asked for these earlier and should comply sooner if at all possible.

Equally, if the contractor validly objects under clause 35.4 to the proposed sub-contractor, or if the tenderer will not settle terms or withdraws, the architect has to act by instructing the contractor under clause 35.23. This may simply mean starting on another tenderer, but it may allow of some attempt to lure the earlier tenderer back by a concession, according to why he has withdrawn.

The importance of all this wheeling and dealing is not just that some money is being negotiated, but that time is running out on the parties. Nomination is treated as an instruction so that, as with other instructions, the contractor may be entitled to extension of time or reimbursement for loss and expense, if the instruction is late. The critical question is what constitutes lateness on his part or the architect's, in these circumstances when three persons are interacting?

In the first place, nomination instructions are no different from any other, in that the contractor has to request them 'in due time' under clauses 25.4.6 and 26.2.1 (see Ch. 9). This means that he is responsible for assessing dates

when he needs sub-contractors on site within his programme and, more difficult perhaps, how long they need from nomination to get there. It is up to the architect to decide the earlier dates for obtaining tenders to suit. In principle, all of this is straightforward. It can only be helped to work by close co-operation between architect and contractor, allied to preliminary enquiries of likely sub-contractors, if unusual time-scales are involved.

All of this is prior to when clause 35 itself starts, is quite direct in application, results in an instruction to treat with a proposed sub-contractor, but is ahead of the actual nomination instruction. This depends on the outcome of the negotiations, which may be affected in several ways:

(a) The tender may be unsatisfactory to the contractor, because the architect has invited it on an inadequate basis or has failed to tie up the details which are properly his concern before passing it to the contractor. If this leads to delay, a late nomination instruction may in turn lead to extension of time or loss and expense reimbursement.

(b) The contractor may be awkward over elements of agreement or simply take too long. Here, he has no cause for favourable treatment. In an extended case at a critical juncture, he could eventually run into liquidated damages.

(c) Conversely, the sub-contractor may cause delay. While the architect has selected the person, he probably cannot be held to guarantee that he will not delay at this stage, although he should take whatever action is needed if the 10-day period is in jeopardy. The case of *Rhuddlan* v. *Fairclough* (discussed below) may be relevant here. This was decided in the different circumstances of re-nomination, so that the architect was held not to have guaranteed that there would not be even a reasonable delay in obtaining a replacement sub-contractor.

There is plenty of room in these instances for questions of fact to be introduced, while the clause is silent about any inefficiencies in agreement, as distinct from complete failure to agree. The 10 days do serve to keep people on their toes and to trigger remedial actions, but it is highly desirable to allow as much extra margin as possible in the programme of activities. For the architect to be faced with accepting a poor deal because time has run out, is unfortunate at the least.

Also within the contract provisions, there is mention several times of Agreements NSC/2 or NSC/2a between the employer and the sub-contractor. These have to be entered into alongside the rest of the activities, the latter being optional (at the architect's discretion) under the alternative method of nomination. Their effects are generally more important at later stages, although they do give the facility for the architect to order fabricated work and design direct from a potential sub-contractor ahead of nomination, so gaining programme time. Should the nomination not go ahead, there are provisions for payment. Some related sorting out in the main contract will then be needed.

During the nomination process, a proposed sub-contractor may drop out for some reason and this may cause quite a disturbance or delay, as noted. If a nominated sub-contractor drops out *after* nomination and particularly during the execution of his work, the effects are more complex for both progress and the contractual aspect.

The reasons listed in JCT clause 35.24 are:

(a) *Default of the sub-contractor*: the reasons given in sub-contract clause 29.1 being:
   (i) unreasonable suspension of the sub-contract works;
   (ii) unreasonable failure to proceed with the sub-contract works;
   (iii) serious failure to remove defective work or materials;
   (iv) sub-letting without consent or not paying fair wages.

(b) *Insolvency of the sub-contractor*.

(c) *Default of the contractor*: the reasons given in sub-contract clause 30.1 being:
   (i) unreasonable suspension of the main works;
   (ii) unreasonable failure to proceed with the main works.

The wider questions of determination itself, of these reasons and of the financial and other consequences are considered in Chapter 16. In outline, in the first case, the contractor has to carry the architect with him over whether the default apparently justifies determining the employment of the sub-contractor, before he effects a determination. In the other cases, the architect is presented with a *fait accompli*. In all cases, he has to act to obtain another sub-contractor, that is he must re-nominate.

It was in doubt under the JCT 1963 contract whether the architect had an obligation or even right to re-nominate, when a sub-contractor had been lost. That contract provided in clause 11(3) that 'The Architect shall issue instructions in regard to the expenditure of prime cost and provisional sums' and in clause 27(a) that 'prime cost sums . . . shall be expended in favour of such persons as the Architect shall direct', leaving the question of what happened to find successors open. The principal areas of uncertainty were:

(a) Who was to select a replacement sub-contractor.
(b) Who bore the difference in cost between old and new sub-contractors.
(c) Who bore any delay costs or loss and expense flowing from the disturbance.

A test case was brought and reached the House of Lords on clause 11(3), to clarify the position over a relatively small amount as the additional price of a replacement sub-contractor. In *North West Metropolitan Regional Hospital Board* v. *T. A. Bickerton & Son Ltd* (1970), it was argued by the employer that the architect had discharged his responsibilities once and for all by the original nomination instruction, and that the contractor was responsible for

completing the works upon the failure of *his* sub-contractor at no extra charge
to the employer. The case was decided against the employer on both points.
From this it appeared that the architect must re-nominate as a duty, while
the contractor need not and must not find a successor, as this would infringe
the architect's right of nomination, which remained alive. The question of
resultant costs of delay or loss and expense was not in issue and was not
decided, although later cases have dealt with these, as stated below.

As a result of this decision, the JCT introduced its 1980 provisions. The
Tribunal (and the RIBA, as copyright holders) received quite an amount of
criticism judicially and otherwise at the time, although in fairness the ICE
and GC/Works/1 contracts were equally deficient in these areas and were
quietly revised to deal with the problems, in somewhat different ways.

Subsequent cases have also been related to the 1963 JCT form, but have
a bearing on the 1980 form. In *Percy Bilton Ltd* v. *Greater London Council*
(1982), another House of Lords case, a sub-contractor had become insolvent
and the contractor had acquiesced in his repudiation, but brought his action
over the delay element, which had three strands:

(a) Reasonable and inevitable delay in obtaining and nominating a new
    sub-contractor.
(b) Further delay due to the employer's dilatoriness in this last matter.
(c) Yet further delay due to the extended time required by the new
    sub-contractor to complete.

It was held that the sub-contractor's default was not a 'delay on his part'
within the meaning of what is now JCT clause 25.4.7 (see *Westminster* v.
Jarvis (1970) discussed in Ch. 9). Further, the employer was not by any
express term responsible for the sub-contractor's repudiation or obliged to
maintain a sub-contractor continuously available to the contractor. Loss of
a properly accepted sub-contractor was one of the risks of sub-contracting
work.

It was commented that the contractor had not raised any 'reasonable
objection' to the nomination of a replacement sub-contractor who required a
longer period to complete than did the original. It appears that his case might
have been helped if he had, and if he had not acquiesced in the repudiation
initially (see *Rhuddlan* v. *Fairclough* below). In the circumstances of the
Bilton case, the contractor won extension of time and relief from liquidated
damages only in respect of the second cause of delay listed. Under the JCT
1980 form, again the contractor would receive an extension of time for the
second cause of delay, as this would be the direct result of an instruction
of the architect, producing (as it happens) a re-nomination. The first cause
would still remain his risk, as the next case indicates.

In *Rhuddlan Borough Council* v. *Fairclough Building Ltd* (1983), the
position went further. Here, a nominated sub-contractor defaulted and there
was a repudiation, leaving work partly done and defective. The architect
spent several months in trying to get as good a deal as possible for the

employer in terms of the new sub-contract price and its basis. He nominated a sub-contractor whom the contractor declined to accept. Two key reasons were that the work in the re-nomination excluded the remedial work, so that the contractor would be left paying for it, and that the new sub-contractor's period ran to beyond the main completion date. The contractor accepted that he would have to concede to the employer the amounts already paid through him to the first sub-contractor for work now defective, the cost of remedial work however being several times this amount. In the end, after further delay, another sub-contractor was nominated.

It was held that the architect was reasonable in seeking an advantageous price for the employer and taking a reasonable time in doing this, even though it was causing delay to the contractor. But the contractor was not obliged to perform remedial work when the sub-contractor had not completed his work and it remained the latter's responsibility. The contractor was therefore entitled to a re-nomination which included the remedial work as part of the price. (JCT clause 30.6.2.1 (amended 87) allows the deduction in the final account of the amount already paid to the sub-contractor for defective work as such.) Further, because of the difficulties, the contractor was entitled to an extension of time to cover the additional sub-contract time over and above that due to the original delay in re-nomination.

Debate over whether the architect (or in the actual case, the supervising officer) had actually to instruct the contractor to determine led to *James Longley & Co. Ltd* v. *Reigate and Banstead Borough Council* (1982), which related to the previous Green Form sub-contract. It was held that he was not, so that the employer was not liable for delay and disturbance flowing from his inaction. The case is described in Chapter 16 in relation to determination, and its impact is modified in the current contracts. The effect of JCT clause 35.24 is therefore that the architect is to issue an instruction to the contractor when the latter notifies a default by a continuing sub-contractor, over whether to determine or not. The architect may also instruct the contractor to come back to him for a further instruction. This postpones matters, while the sub-contractor may mend his ways. Whenever the architect agrees with the contractor, the architect must instruct a determination, after which the contractor has an option as to whether he actually determines.

As all instructions under clause 35 qualify potentially for extension of time, the time before re-nomination would appear to be eligible for inclusion in the calculations, contrary to the foregoing cases related to the JCT 1963 form. However, there is no entitlement to loss and expense on this count. This leads to the need for a careful balancing of the various factors in a complex case. When determination occurs due to the sub-contractor's insolvency, there is no architect's instruction prior to that of re-nomination, so that an extension is not available. When it is the sub-contractor who determines for the contractor's default, the position is similar, as might be expected, while the payment provision is different (see Ch. 16). JCT clause 35.24.9 (amended 87) provides, following *Rhuddlan*, for the architect to have a reasonable time within which to re-nominate.

Named sub-contracts

As nominated sub-contracts are peculiar to the JCT 1980 form, so named sub-contracts are virtually peculiar to the IFC 1984 form. There is in fact just one reference to 'naming' in JCT clause 35.1, as a means of identifying a nomination as an alternative to using a prime cost sum. In practical terms, this can refer only to a nomination arising out of a provisional sum, and has been ignored under earlier headings.

The process of naming is akin to that of nomination, in that the architect puts a specific person to the contractor for acceptance. Also, if the sub-contractor drops out during progress, the architect is involved in selecting and naming a substitute and the amount payable by the employer may change as a result. The likeness goes little further. The sub-contractor is otherwise like a domestic sub-contractor, with the contractor pricing the work competitively in his own tender. As Table 9.1 indicates, there is no special treatment of the sub-contractor himself over dealing with such matters as interim and final payments, extension of time, loss and expense and completion or failure to complete on time. He 'is' the contractor for these purposes. Only when he provides design to the architect is his position distinct, and this is over a matter properly outside the present contract itself (see Ch. 5).

NAMING PROCEDURE

IFC clause 3.3 gives two methods for introducing a named sub-contractor: a detailed inclusion in the contract documents, or a provisional sum expended wholly or partly in favour of such a person. Either way, only one person is actually put to the contractor, the architect having carried out the earlier work of inviting tenders and making the ultimate selection.

The more likely method is the naming of a single person at the stage of the main contract tendering. The architect has to use defined documents, including a form rather similar to NSC/1: Tender and Agreement NAM/T. Its most intriguing section is that for listing the tenderers for the main contract. While this is there so that sub-contract tenderers are warned as to who may be their main contractor, and so can register any objections early and save time and complication later, the added complications of broadcasting the list of main tenderers do not need elaborating! There would appear to be no fundamental objection to leaving the space blank and clearing with the sub-contractor whether the main contractor is not desired, or only desired on different terms, as soon as the latter becomes known. This, after all, is what happens in reverse with nominations under the sister form.

The resulting tender in all its detail about price and stipulations is to be made available to the main contract tenderers, who include the price with their own additions for other factors. What the contractor prices will depend upon the basis of the contract: it may be a bill of quantities, a specification or some other description of works. It is essential that it is so drawn up as not to conflict with what the sub-contractor priced or to be discrepant with

it. This is important, even though the sub-contract tender documentation has to accompany the main invitation.

Within 21 days of entering into his own contract, the contractor under clause 3.3.1 is to enter into a sub-contract with the named person. This may mean some quick action, especially if 'entering into' covers some implied action, such as a letter or just starting on site. There is the possibility that the two parties to the proposed sub-contract may run into an area of disagreement over the particulars given in the sub-contract tender, as the sub-contractor is not under a fixed obligation to contract. At the extreme, the sub-contractor may not be willing to enter into the sub-contract at all, if his own tender has been lying with the architect for some considerable time and other work is to hand. The moral is that the sub-contract tenders should be obtained just before the main contract tenders, with a requirement that they be kept open for a sufficient time to complete the process. If they are 'dated', confirmation should be obtained that they still apply, with any amendments.

The clause recognises that the best-laid plans may suffer in the usual way. If therefore the contractor is unable to sub-contract on the terms provided by the sub-contractor, and on which the main tender was based, he is to inform the architect, who in turn has three options:

(a) *To change the particulars to remove 'the impediment'*: by implication, this will mean a financial change, and usually in one direction only. It may be sensed that this is another area where undesirable collusion could occur, given the wrong participants.
(b) *To omit the work*: this leaves the possibility of placing it as a direct contract, which may temper the tendency to operate unfairly under (a), but is counterbalanced by the contractor's right of reasonable objection under clause 3.11. If suitable, the work may simply be left out of the project.
(c) *To substitute a provisional sum for the work designated for the named sub-contractor*: this postpones the final decision and means that the work may not go to a named sub-contractor at all, under the rules for provisional sums.

The first two options result in a variation, to be valued accordingly, and possibly leading to extension of time and loss and expense, as the clause states directly. As the action all occurs quite early in the programme, it is to be hoped that the effects will be minimal. If the architect seeks fresh sub-contract tenders, it is possible that a reasonable time spent doing this would not qualify for either of these redresses, on the basis of the decision in *Bilton* v. *GLC* discussed in relation to nominated sub-contractors. While its broad effects may be seen as quite possibly transferring to named sub-contractors, there is the distinction that that case related to failure of a sub-contract already in being (where it was observed that the employer could not be responsible for constantly maintaining a sub-contractor in being at all costs) and resulting delay and not to delay in the setting up of one initially, with the architect still in a primary position in the action.

Further, the possibility of seeking fresh tenders is not specifically mentioned in the clause, which refers only to an instruction to 'change the particulars', something rather less than one to 'change the sub-contractor', it might be thought. The only clear way of introducing a different sub-contractor is under the third option. The architect still has to act to instruct the expenditure of the provisional sum, where a delay may also produce these effects, owing to a late instruction. The likely applicability of *Bilton* v. *GLC* remains the same in this situation. The position with each option will be governed by when the sub-contractor work is needed, and this may be late rather than early.

Nothing is said about what happens if the 21-day period is overrun without a valid sub-contract being entered into and without any delay to progress as a whole resulting. Clearly, there is no case for the contractor receiving extra time or payment, and it would appear that there are no consequences upon which the employer may act over the technical breach which exists.

Most often, a procedure like this will run without hitches. If they do occur, they are likely to be due to the triangular pattern of activities between architect, contractor and sub-contractor. The time when most is known, but distributed among all concerned, while least is committed, is that of the main contract tendering period. Desirably for the employer, the tenderers should endeavour to remove any problems during tendering, but are unlikely to do so when other more pressing aspects concern them and later adjustment is available. It would be possible to make some system of resolution a condition of tendering, as effectively happens when domestic sub-contractors are named under JCT clause 19.3. This is not likely to commend itself to the one sub-contractor in the present case, when he already has the job virtually in his pocket. It would eliminate some problems but retain others, such as allowing the sub-contractor to call the tune and allowing the identity of all tenderers to be known to a third party.

When the named sub-contractor is identified by way of a provisional sum, it becomes necessary to value the financial effects under clause 3.7. This should be reasonably straightforward, if the 'control' figures have been made available in the contract bills or other analysis, set against the original sub-contract tender.

NAMING ANOTHER SUB-CONTRACTOR

While 're-nomination' is an accepted term, even if slightly inaccurate in its implications, 're-naming' does suggest something unintended – perhaps a conversion from heathendom! At any rate, the topic falls within clauses 3.3.3 to 3.3.6, which also deal with determination (taken in Ch. 16, as also for nominated sub-contractors).

The reasons justifying a determination, or at least appearing to do so, are substantially those occurring under the arrangements of the JCT form. These have been listed above in relation to nominated sub-contractors and, again, they are discussed in Chapter 16. In this contract, there is the specific

debarring of the contractor from himself accepting a repudiation of the sub-contract.

While the JCT clauses envisage only the possibility of a re-nomination, the present clause 3.3.3 has three avenues available:

(a) Naming another person to perform the work or such part as remains.
(b) Instructing the contractor to perform the work (or presumably any remainder), with the possibility of him sub-letting.
(c) Omitting the balance (or presumably the whole) from the contract, although perhaps having it executed by a direct contractor.

Whether the presumptions indicated are justified, is a matter for doubt, as the precise wording supports the distinctions shown without the bracketed portions above. There is little reason which can be put forward for tying affairs up in such knots, especially when it runs against what has been done over a hiatus in the original appointment of a sub-contractor. If the distinctions are upheld, it restricts the alternatives open to the architect to (a) or (b), if sub-contract work has not been started on or off site, or to (a) or (c), if it has been started.

In relation to the cases discussed under the nominated position above, the present arrangement generally follows the same pattern. However, several extra elements are introduced, presumably in the light of the decisions which were handed down in the cases after JCT 80 was published, or of a review of that contract. Thus in the first option above, naming another person, clause 3.3.4 designates the instruction as leading to extension of time when this is justified, but specifically excludes reimbursement of loss and expense. In the second and third options, the contractor making his own arrangements or the work being omitted from the contract, he is entitled in principle to both these recompenses (see the case study in Ch. 22).

These specific provisions cut across the concept of the architect having a reasonable time in which to secure a new sub-contractor or otherwise act, say by delaying an instruction to the contractor to make his own arrangements until possible sub-contractors have been explored and eliminated. Extension of time, for instance, starts to run from any qualifying delay occurring. This is still a matter which has to be established in the particular circumstances, so that some specific effect on critical activities is needed. By contrast with the nominated situation, delay on the part of an outgoing named sub-contractor over his own sub-contract period does not lead to extension of time.

If the architect has been unable to find someone to name, the contractor is not obliged to sub-let. The architect should consider carefully whether he would wish the contractor to perform the work himself, having once used the named sub-contractor system presumably to secure control. On the other hand, there is at least the possibility that the contractor will not be able to find someone either, or not someone acceptable at any rate, while he may not be able to perform the work directly. This is an acute problem when the work involves special components obtainable from the original source only, but it is not unique to the naming system. The result may be redesign and

the delay which goes with it or omission of the work, if this is practicable, or perhaps both. In the worst instance, existing work may have to be removed and replaced.

CHAPTER 8

Certificates and payments

Status of certificates
Dissatisfaction over certificates
Deductions from certified amounts
Ownership of materials and goods

The topics of this chapter are linked, because all payments to the contractor and many to sub-contractors depend upon the issue of an architect's certificate. Not all certificates deal with payment, however, as some deal with approvals or the deciding of contractual issues between the parties. The cases in which the architect may or must issue a certificate are strictly limited and a complete list of certificates of all types under the JCT 1980 and IFC 1984 contracts is given in Table 5.2. They may be set beside the architect's instructions, as his other major way of communication during progress, in addition to drawings. Only certificates covering payment are treated here.

The main areas of dispute over certificates, and particularly those governing payment, are:

(a) Whether they are properly authorised, correctly issued and on time.
(b) Whether they have been subject to any undue influence from the employer.
(c) Whether the contents are entirely in order, including the principles and amounts certified.
(d) Whether the employer can modify the effects, such as by making a reduced payment.

These matters and others concerning certificates are dealt with more widely and in detail in various works, such as the present author's *Building Contracts: A Practical Guide* and *Building Sub-Contract Forms*, as they affect the employer, the contractor and sub-contractors. This section is limited to the more contentious elements, as they bear on the purpose of this book, by being incidental to other disputes or perhaps bringing them on.

Status of certificates

The authority for issuing certificates is covered by the clauses in Table 5.2, while any stipulations about their contents are within the clauses. Those

relating to payment, in JCT clause 30 and IFC clause 4, are particularly detailed and should be consulted where there is uncertainty.

It would appear that the contractor is entitled to have work certified for payment, as soon as it has been performed and a certificate is due. This is so, even if this is well ahead of what evenly distributed progress would indicate, just as he is entitled to finish early and be paid off. Equally, he may run late with his programme and receive a greater reimbursement for fluctuations. The programming aspects of this are mentioned in Chapter 4 under 'Payment' effects.

What an interim certificate does not do is to give final sanction for inclusion of any item within it in the final certificate, as was demonstrated as far back as *Tharsis Sulphur & Copper Company* v. *McElroy & Sons* (1878). There, the interim inclusion for payment of some work did not formally establish a right to final payment, in the absence of a proper architect's instruction for the work to be done. The architect in question appears to have been negligent in ever including the work, so far as can be told at this remove. A similar lack of finality will exist when amounts are included on account for loss and expense due to disturbance of regular progress, for which no architect's instruction is issued – understandably! It would be imprudent, at the least, for an architect to include amounts when he had not decided in principle that loss and expense were due, but it does mean that he may include approximate amounts and later revise them downwards, if needs be. The broad issue of including such amounts and the contract authority is set out in Chapter 15, while *Croudace* v. *Lambeth* in Chapter 12 should be noted.

The other side of this consideration is that, when the architect has issued a proper certificate, the employer must usually honour it under JCT clause 30.1.1.1 or IFC clause 4.2, even if unhappy over its apparently high amount. This was the issue in *Killby & Gayford Ltd* v. *Selincourt Ltd* (1973), where the Court of Appeal held that the JCT 1963 contract was mandatory over the time margin for payment (as is the current version), that there was no suggestion of defects in the extra work to give a counter-claim, and that the defendants had produced no evidence to show that the work was not properly instructed. The need for the employer to raise his query direct with the architect was evident.

However, in *C. M. Pillings & Co. Ltd* v. *Kent Investments Ltd* (1985) the employer was judged as entitled to challenge the accuracy of a certificate in arbitration, the contract being in the JCT prime cost form. The estimated final cost exceeded the original estimate by over 100 per cent, as a result of hundreds of variation instructions. The contractor claimed that he should be paid and then the accuracy checked. The employer's case was accepted in view of the large discrepancies and the apparently casual attitude of the architect, alongside the possibility of arbitration over whether a 'certificate is not in accordance with this Contract'. This is rather parallel to a sensibly quantified set-off under a sub-contract (see below). The Court of Appeal referred to its judgment in *Ellis Mechanical Services Ltd* v. *Wates Construction*

Ltd (1978), where the employer had 'on balance . . . raised a bona fide arguable contention'. The decision is not helpful to contractors, any more than that in *Lubenham* v. *South Pembrokeshire* mentioned below.

Cases of this type point up the importance of the architect keeping the employer in the picture over the way that events are moving financially, to avoid clashes or worse. This is especially so when there are matters of the nature of loss and expense, which the employer may not see coming, as he should see the cost of variations, at least when these are substantial and then track back to his initiation of what has happened.

Dissatisfaction over certificates

CONTRACTOR'S REMEDIES

The remedies of the contractor vary according to the cause, if he is dissatisfied with matters relating to a certificate. One of the least satisfactory aspects is over what is included. While the provisions are quite definite about this and while limited approximation is to be expected, the contractor has no specific remedy to promote realism, other than arbitration, if the valuation for a certificate is grossly low, or indeed if this keeps on occurring. On this matter arbitration may take place immediately under the JCT form, as it may on any matter under the IFC form. Unless he decides on nuisance tactics, the contractor is unlikely to use arbitration, or even threaten it, except for a very large discrepancy.

In the early stages of a substantial variation situation or especially a loss and expense situation, the possibility of under-inclusion of a provisional allowance is high. When uncertainty is running strong, the contractor has no realistic remedy, other than to provide details as soon as he can. This is no excuse for the architect not trying to make reasonable inclusion, bearing in mind the possibility of reducing the amount later, as indicated by *Tharsis* v. *McElroy* above, and balancing this against the risks in over-inclusion.

Even if there is an improper deduction from a certificate, the contractor can do little more than seek arbitration or to have the position rectified in the next certificate. The latter option was stated in *Lubenham Fidelities & Investment Co.* v. *South Pembrokeshire District Council and Wigley Fox Partnership* (1986), where the contractor (actually a bondsman completing through sub-contractors) had determined his employment because the architect had purported to deduct for defective work (which should not have been included, presumably) and for liquidated damages when the completion date had not been passed. While the architect had been negligent, the contractor had no right to determine and so was in breach and responsible for the employer's losses.

Equally unsatisfactory is late issue of certificates: no specific remedy is available, other than repeated complaints to the employer. The absence of a certificate was, however, no bar to payment in the special circumstances of *Croudace* v. *Lambeth* (see Ch. 12). Over late payment by the employer,

the provisions are clear: the contractor may determine his employment under the contract, subject to observing the procedure over notices. This is a most drastic remedy, and so unlikely to be used except in the most drastic situation. It is also no use when late certification follows practical completion, the final certificate being the ultimate situation and a common one for delay in settlement.

In a loss and expense situation, as distinct from a variation one, there is the possibility of the contractor under the contracts being quoted, recovering financing charges incurred during the period of delay between notification and certification as direct loss and expense. This is distinct from the general position that interest cannot usually be applied to business debts, without special contract terms, a position which applies in building contracts as much as others. There is no certain legal authority for recovering financing charges incurred through late or inadequate certification in general. It may be that the attitude of the courts is changing here, in that there is more readiness to allow at least simple interest on some classes of late payment. Cases discussed under 'Interest and financing charges' in Chapter 15 may be consulted, with the mention of the courts 'distinguishing' cases. An extension of their principles to inadequate or late certification, including that arising from late preparation of the final account, is at least possible.

The remaining aspect to note is that of the employer trying to interfere with a certificate or influence the architect over it, a serious act because the architect is supposed to exercise his functions impartially between the parties. Again, the remedy available is determination, present mainly as a deterrent, but more likely to be used in this situation. The contractor needs to steer a careful path here between what is miscertification and what is the result of interference. In *R. B. Burden Ltd* v. *Swansea Corporation* (1957), the contractor had determined on the latter ground, while the House of Lords found that it was only the former (after a history of prior mistakes), so that the contractor was incorrect in determining.

SUB-CONTRACTORS' REMEDIES

Directly, sub-contractors have no remedies over certificates, as they are not parties to the main contract. Only nominated sub-contractors receive any special treatment in certificates, but they are in the same basic position outlined above as the contractor himself, over lack of inclusion of their amounts in whole or part.

The contractor has an obligation under a clause of each sub-contract, for example clause 22 in the nominated sub-contracts, to 'obtain for [the sub-contractor] any rights or benefits of the Main Contract' where they apply to the sub-contract. This all-embracing but nothing-specifying provision perhaps requires him to press the employer over matters of variation instructions, etc. affecting sub-contractors, when there are irregularities. In the case of domestic or named sub-contractors, the relationship between main and sub-contract payments is not fixed by what the architect has certified, and the contractor

is due to pay irrespective of whether he is being paid some related sum. He is not entitled under the standard forms to operate 'pay when paid'. These sub-contractors therefore have to press the contractor in isolation from the main contract position.

Sub-contractors of any variety have a right to suspend their work after due notice, for example under nominated clause 21.8, if the contractor has not paid them, and to continue suspension until they are paid. In the case of nominated sub-contractors, this may also mean when they have not received direct payment from the employer, which is discussed below. This may effectively become a weapon against the employer in their case, as the contractor will be entitled to an extension of time if the suspension is due to the employer failing to operate the direct payment provisions properly, when these are obligatory upon him. Named and domestic sub-contractors also have a right to determine if they are not paid, this being a weapon against the contractor, as he decides what to pay them, even if the dates are related to the main contract dates.

Deductions from certified amounts

EMPLOYER'S RIGHTS

The right of the employer to make deductions, or set-off, from certified amounts for counter-charges, mentioned in JCT clause 30.1.1.2 and IFC clause 4.4, is founded in the common law right. Counter-charges, by definition, are in respect of something other than what is in the certificate: they are deductions from its total and not adjustments of it. In fact, the architect may not deduct these amounts when arriving at the amount stated as due in a certificate. They remain with the employer under the contract wording, even though the architect may well advise him of his rights.

As such, the deductions exist unless the terms of the contract expressly forbid them, or there is a necessary implication to that effect. They may extend, for example, to amounts for remedial work which the employer has performed when the contractor will not do the work, this not being itself work within the certificate. This example and its terms are made specific by the contracts. So too is the right to deduct liquidated damages when, and only when, the architect has properly certified that completion is overdue. Proper certification was emphasised in *Token Construction Co. Ltd* v. *Charlton Estates Ltd* (1973). These instances follow the common law right, but there is the implied qualification that the employer cannot make frivolous unsupported deductions. He should show reasonable quantification of what he contends is his due, as is expressly provided in the sub-contract arrangements mentioned below.

CONTRACTOR'S RIGHTS

There are two basic situations in which the contractor may deduct from sub-contract payments: where he himself has suffered a corresponding

deduction from a certified amount and where he has some contra-account on which to recover. In dealing with a named or domestic sub-contractor, he acts entirely on his own, in that the sub-contractor has no recourse to the architect. When a nominated sub-contractor is involved, the position is more complex.

This is because of the obligation of the contractor under nominated sub-contract clause 21.3.1.1 in general to pay on to a nominated sub-contractor precisely what he has been paid, as the settlement of the sub-contractor's account. This amount is set against the prime cost sum in the contract, and so the decision on the amount payable effectively rests with the architect and the quantity surveyor. If the contractor fails to pay in this way, he may face action by the architect implementing direct payment of the sub-contractor. When the employer has exercised his right to deduct from a main contract amount because of a sub-contractor's item, there should be no difficulty, unless the employer has overlooked letting the architect know about his action.

When the contractor has made a deduction for some reason of his own, he should ensure that the architect is aware of the reasons, so that the possibility of direct payment (discussed below) is minimised. Among these reasons may be unliquidated damages for delay, of which the architect will be aware, as he has to be involved in the granting or otherwise of any extension to a nominated sub-contractor. If the architect is not convinced of the adequacy of the contractor's reasons, and especially if the sub-contractor complains to him and he checks the position, he may still implement direct payment.

The other reasons why a contractor may deduct from a sub-contract amount are several, and are common whatever the type of sub-contractor. The contractor may have rendered some service by way of attendance, etc. which is reimbursable. Only the amount, rather than the principle, may be in dispute. Alternatively, there may be a question of loss and expense (provided for in, for example, nominated sub-contract clause 23 and not such as to be passed up to the employer) or damage to other work by the sub-contractor, with the reinstatement by the contractor or another sub-contractor. Here, both principle and the contingent amount may be in dispute. In all of these instances and provided there is something more than a frivolous deduction, the architect should make haste slowly over any direct payment action. He should certainly not be drawn into the rights and wrongs of the issue. At most he, or the quantity surveyor, may wish to check that the deduction is not at an absurd level, suggesting that the issue is being used as a pretext for delaying payment.

The question of quantification mentioned above was highlighted by the legal cases mentioned under 'Set-off in sub-contracts' below, and has become part of the provisions of the two 1980 JCT nominated sub-contracts in clause 23.2.2. It is also present in the corresponding domestic sub-contract and in the 1984 IFC named sub-contract and domestic sub-contract. These documents all make it a pre-condition of the right of the contractor to deduct. This remains true even when the deduction originates with the employer, although then

the details should be readily available. A perusal by or for the architect may be useful for the reasons just advanced. Usually, it is sufficient to leave the matter to the adjudication procedure provided in the several sub-contracts to resolve any gross injustice.

Sub-contractors for their part, when faced with contra-accounts which relate to other sub-contractors or the employer, should continue to act and pay through the contractor, as they have no privity of contract with these other persons. The exception occurs when they have made a direct arrangement with another sub-contractor over a private issue.

SET-OFF IN SUB-CONTRACTS

The position over set-off or counter-charging sub-contractors is in essence as given above, so that separate discussion is not needed. However, there have been a number of legal cases on the theme affecting sub-contractors directly, of which two may be mentioned, as their vibrations are still sometimes felt.

Dawnays Ltd v. *F. G. Minter Ltd and Trollope and Colls Ltd* (1971) was a successful appeal by a sub-contractor for legal action to be allowed to proceed over a matter of money withheld by the contractor for delay. The defendants contended that arbitration under the 'Green Form' of sub-contract (predecessor of the JCT nominated sub-contract) should be followed, which would have led to long delay until after practical completion. It was held that cash flow was vital to the industry (almost, it appeared, more than to most!). More importantly, it was held that counter-claims for sums, relatively vague and unagreed in amounts, could not be deducted from sums due. These had already been paid to the contractor for paying on to the sub-contractor. Specifically, it was held that the words 'any sum or sums which the Sub-Contractor is liable to pay to the Contractor' in clause 13 of the existing form meant any sum or sums ascertained by proceedings or otherwise agreed, rather than those where the legal liability was not disputed, but the amount was vague.

Several cases followed from this and the expression 'Dawnay principle' gained currency. Some doubt arose over elements of the decision, shown in the following case here, although this did not formally reverse it.

Gilbert Ash (Northern) Ltd v. *Modern Engineering (Bristol) Ltd* (1974) related to a deduction by the contractor from an interim payment to a nominated sub-contractor as set-off for breach. The sum was slightly less than what was calculated by the contractor, but was not agreed by the sub-contractor. It related to bad workmanship and delay which were not disputed in principle. The sub-contract form was not the Green Form, but specially produced, and allowed the contractor 'to deduct . . . or otherwise to recover the amount of any *bona fide* contra account and/or other claim'. It was held that the contractor was entitled to make the deduction under the wording, even though not agreed, and that the then main JCT form did not remove this right as between employer and contractor. Several collateral

points emerged as *obiter* during the judgment of the Lords:

(a) A right to set-off at common law or in equity existed but could be contracted away by a party, although it had not been done in this case.

(b) The terms of the main contract did not exclude a set-off there by the employer, although one was not in question in the case.

(c) While the Dawnay case was not being reviewed in the judgment, it would appear that were a case following it to come before the House in the future, it would be held by a majority (if not all) of the present judges to have been misdecided by the Court of Appeal in disallowing a set-off. This was despite the strong view taken in that case of the words 'is liable to pay'.

DIRECT PAYMENT OF NOMINATED SUB-CONTRACTORS

Alone among sub-contractors, the nominated variety may be paid direct by the employer in some circumstances. One instance is for work, etc. performed before nomination, which is not likely to lead to dispute, except over accounting detail. The other arises after nomination in the limited case of the contractor failing to discharge an amount already included in a certificate, so that it remains unpaid, or more precisely cannot be shown to have been paid, by the time that the next certificate is due to be issued. There is neither right nor duty to pay sub-contractors direct, instead of paying them through the contractor, however strong the fear that the contractor will not pass monies on. Payment can be made only after default by the contractor. The main stipulations and results of JCT clause 35.13 may be summarised:

(a) The employer has an option whether to exercise this power except that, when there is an employer/sub-contractor agreement in force, he must exercise it as one of the terms of the agreement. Sub-contractors under the 'basic' method of nomination are therefore automatically given this extra protection, as an agreement is obligatory.

(b) An architect's certificate stating the amount of the non-payment is required before the employer may act.

(c) The amount is to be paid to the sub-contractor at the same time as the corresponding certificate is honoured. It is to be deducted by the employer from 'any future payment otherwise due', so that it falls into the category of set-off, rather than being something which the architect can use to reduce the amount to be certified. Certificates will therefore continue to show the unreduced amounts.

(d) The inference of 'any future payment' is that the employer may make the deduction in more than one bite, if there is not enough due at one time, or if he is seeking to support an ailing contractor, when deduction is optional. When there is not enough available as 'otherwise due' to allow a complete deduction without the employer being temporarily out of pocket overall, he is never obliged to pay more than is available – and should not.

(e) Within these main provisions there are subsidiary rules about retention and about apportioning the available funds when more than one sub-contractor is owed money.

(f) If insolvency of the contractor is coming about, the whole apparatus of the clause ceases to have any effect, as it might well transgress the legislation by giving one creditor or more a privileged position as against others.

The provisions exist almost entirely for the benefit of nominated sub-contractors, as part of their VIP treatment, as it appears to be. As indicated, neither named nor domestic sub-contractors have any such safeguard. The only obvious benefit to the *employer* is that he may be able to avoid a desirable nominated sub-contractor suspending work, or even repudiating his sub-contract if driven too far. It is not in the interests of the employer to face disruption of the programme, even when he has assured remedies at hand. A smooth run is better, so long as the price is not too high.

Again, the employer should be wary of operating these provisions when there are negotiations going on between contractor and sub-contractor. There may be contra-accounts for extra facilities provided or for damage to other work or materials, with the principle or amount in dispute. This is why the clause requires an architect's certificate as the trigger to action by the employer. Provided this is available, the employer may make a deduction from the main contract payments, without fear that he is transgressing under his contract, even though the architect may be open to criticism if he has not taken enough care. In calculating the amount, the employer should be advised to deduct retention from the original gross inclusion, as this is part of the fund for nominated sub-contractors and is still held back from the main payments. He should not deduct cash discount, as this is due to the sub-contractor as recompense for late payment.

In the case of all other types of sub-contractor, the employer should not make direct payments at all. Again, he may be entering areas of dispute about which he knows nothing. He certainly risks paying twice, as the contractor is always entitled to be paid for work performed by a sub-contractor in the absence of an unusual provision like that for nominated sub-contractors. Under the named and domestic sub-contract forms, the sub-contractor has the extra weapon of determination available in the provisions.

Ownership of materials and goods

This is a particularly difficult area when dealing with payments during progress. All that can be done within the present limited scope is to warn of the more problematic issues which arise, centring around the question of transferring ownership from one party to another. Detailed information requires consultation of specialist legal sources.

All standard contracts and sub-contracts provide for payments to be made for materials and goods which have been delivered for incorporation into

the works. The contractor or sub-contractor may rely on these provisions as giving him a right to be paid, provided that he complies with requirements about timing of deliveries and storage, etc. Usually, there are also provisions for payment for similar items off site, these being available for use by the architect entirely at his discretion, so that the contractor or sub-contractor cannot rely on them. They are most commonly used when there are severe problems over space on site, or when advanced, extensive prefabrication is occurring. Not all of these provisions are legally watertight in all the situations which arise.

The basic problem over ownership and payment is that no one can confer a better title than he himself possesses. If therefore the employer pays the contractor for materials properly on site and supplied by another, he usually obtains a good title as and when the contractor pays for them, but not necessarily before. In particular, if they are a sub-contractor's consignment, property does not pass until the sub-contractor has been paid by the contractor, as there is an agreement for works and materials and not for sale of goods. The period of risk is while the payment chain is being completed, if it starts from the wrong end, as it often does when merchants are offering credit which exceeds the time for honouring certificates. The most common risk is that of the contractor becoming insolvent after himself being paid and before paying a sub-contractor. The issue has been around for a long time, but was brought to a head for the construction industry comparatively recently.

The earlier form of the issue centred on the position between employer and the liquidator over materials for which the employer has paid. It was held in *Re Fox ex parte Oundle and Thrapston Rural District Council* v. *The Trustee* (1948) that the trustee in bankruptcy had no claim to materials on site which had been paid for in interim certificates under a predecessor of the JCT form, containing similar provisions to the present clause 30.2. These materials had not been in the reputed ownership of the contractor, that is there was a presumption of ownership by the employer. On the other hand, materials paid for but at the contractor's yard were in the reputed ownership of the contractor, in the absence of proof otherwise. This doctrine of reputed ownership does not apply when liquidation of a company occurs. The predecessor of JCT clause 30.3 was introduced to give protection here, although it has weaknesses over sub-contractors (see in, for instance, the present author's *Building Sub-Contract Forms*).

A development of the situation came in *Aluminium Industrie Vaassen BV* v. *Romalpa Aluminium Ltd* (1976). A supplier incorporated a 'retention of title until payment' in a contract for sale of goods, which admittedly suffered from complications in translation from the Dutch and otherwise. It was held that the clause was valid against the buyer, who had not only taken delivery, but had converted some of the goods by manufacture and sold some on to others. The goods or proceeds were in trust until the seller had received payment in full. Without the clause, the legal position would have been reversed. This indicates one area of severe difficulty. The Bibliography may be consulted for further information.

In 1979, there was the case of *Humberside County Council* v. *Dawber Williamson Roofing Ltd*. This was brought under the old Blue Form sub-contract, which preceded the present range of standard domestic sub-contracts. The sub-contractor delivered roofing slates, the employer paid the contractor for them, the contractor went into liquidation, and the sub-contractor had not been paid. The equivalent of JCT clause 16.1 was in the main contract. The employer prevented the sub-contractor from removing the slates as his own property and used them for completing the works, arguing that he had paid for them and they were his property for this reason and by virtue of the clause. It was held that the employer had to pay the sub-contractor for the materials and other damages. Title did not pass from sub-contractor to contractor under the sub-contract by any provision in it, as it was a sub-contract for works and materials. The notice which the sub-contractor had had of the main contract terms did not import the ownership provision into the sub-contract. The contractor had no sufficient title to transfer: he had not paid for the materials, nor had they been fixed.

Terms now exist in the current revisions of the JCT main and sub-contract forms to overcome these problems for the employer and protect him. These appear broadly effective, although not free from weaknesses. They of course reduce the protection available to sub-contractors, when they are in force.

Debate over the position of the quantity surveyor in preparing valuations and of the architect in issuing certificates is inconclusive. It would appear that, strictly, they should check the status of every brick or pipe lying on site, before including it. When the chain of payment may extend back through three or four persons, the matter becomes impracticable. The implicit attitude seems to aggregate as 'press on and hope for the best'. The situation is not entirely unique to the construction industry. To protect themselves, some consultants have suggested warning employers that they are implementing the requirements of the contracts, but that these may put the employers at some risk. Whether employers would be held then or otherwise, in any action over professional negligence, to be aware of this fact remains to be established.

It certainly is necessary for the terms of contracts and sub-contracts to be observed carefully, especially over payments for materials off site, and despite flaws in those clauses. In the case of Scottish contracts, these clauses do not satisfy the distinct legal position in Scotland, and the alternative contracts of purchase available there must be used.

PART 3

Delay and disturbance

CHAPTER 9

Causes justifying extension of time or reimbursement of loss and expense

Some principles
Causes leading to extension of time only
Causes leading to extension of time or loss and expense

This chapter sets out the various causes or reasons which may lead to extension of time or loss and expense under the JCT and IFC contracts and their related sub-contracts. This is done here before considering the wider aspects of the law and contract clauses and their various effects in later chapters, to bring together the causes which are given in each contract. Most of these causes are the same, even though there are differences of emphasis or effect due to the contract in which they occur. They may thus be compared across the range of contracts most conveniently, and also be referred to from later chapters, as these are read.

The contracts and sub-contracts use the term 'event' or 'relevant event' to mean something which leads to extension of time and the term 'matter' or 'relevant matter' to mean what leads to reimbursement of loss and expense. The forms taken into account are:

JCT 80 main contract forms (in any edition)
IFC 84 main contract form
JCT 80 nominated sub-contract form NSC/4 (NSC/4a being identical for all present purposes)
IFC 84 named sub-contract form NAM/SC
Domestic sub-contract form DOM/1 (used optionally with JCT 80)
Domestic sub-contract form IN/SC (used optionally with IFC 84)

The clauses concerned in the first four of these are tabulated for outline comparison in Table 9.1, the clauses for the two domestic forms being the same as those in the corresponding nominated or named version for all practical purposes. Clause numbers are not given in commenting upon the various events or matters, but may be traced by reference to this table, which also gives clause numbers relating to determination as discussed in Chapter 16.

Table 9.1   Comparison of relevant events and matters

Event or matter		Extension of time				Loss and expense			
		JCT 25.4	IFC 2.4	NSC 11.2.2	NAM 12.7	JCT 26.2	IFC 4.12	NSC 13.1.2	NAM 14.2
Force majeure	[D]	1	1	1	1	—	—	—	—
Weather conditions		2	2	2	2	—	—	—	—
Loss by perils	[D]	3	3	3	3	—	—	—	—
Civil commotion, etc.	[D]	4	4	4	4	—	—	—	—
Delay nominated firms		7	—	7	—	—	—	—	—
Statutory powers		9	—	9	—	—	—	—	—
Shortage of labour		10	10*	10	9*	—	—	—	—
Shortage of materials		10	11*	10	10*	—	—	—	—
Statutory bodies		11	13	11	12	—	—	—	—
Forecast quantities		13†	—	—	—	—	—	—	—
Deferred possession		13*	14*	14*	13*	—	—	—	7‡
Suspension of work		—	—	13	14	—	—	—	8‡
Instructions regarding:									
Discrepancies, etc.	[D]	5	5	5	5	3	7	3	6
Variations, etc.	[D]	5	5	5	5	7	7	7	6
Postponement	[D]	5	5	5	5	5	5	5	5
Antiquities		5	—	5	—	(34)	—	—	—
Nominated firms		5	—	5	—	—	—	—	—
Named sub-contractors		—	5	—	5	—	7	—	6
Opening and testing	[D]	5	6	5	5	2	2	2	2
Late instructions, etc.	[D]	6	7	6	6	1	1	1	1
Work not in contract	[D]	8	8	8	8	4	3	4	3
Materials from employer	[D]	8	9	8	8	4	4	4	4
Ingress and egress	[D]	12	12	12	1	6	6	6	5

Note: The JCT and IFC main contracts and the related nominated and named forms are given. Each domestic sub-contract (not given) has the same numbering as the corresponding sub-contract. Slight differences between the clauses could lead to different effects on occasions.

[D] These causes may also lead to determination under the main contract forms (see Chapter 16). There are other causes for determination.

(34) This cause is given in clause 34.

* These causes are optional and must be specifically included to be active.

† This cause occurs only in the approximate quantities edition.

‡ These causes appear to be included in error in the sub-contract.

Causes are listed in the order in which they are discussed in the text.

Some principles

CAUSES AND EFFECTS

The expression deliberately used above is '*may* lead to extension of time or loss and expense'. It is still necessary to demonstrate that an actual effect of delay or loss and expense has been caused by the item identified. The simple occurrence of a specific item cannot alone lead to a concession to the contractor

or sub-contractor: it must produce effects of a suitable nature and sufficient magnitude at the right time and place, so that some adjustment of time or money is needed under provisions which serve to lighten the contractor's or sub-contractor's responsibilities under an entire contract.

Equally, an item may lead to either extension of time or loss and expense, without the other: they are not inexorably linked in such a way that both must be conceded when one is proved to be justified. Most obviously, this is shown by the longer list of items leading to extension of time, compared with that of items leading to loss and expense reimbursement in all the forms. It is also demonstrated by the general proposition that time can be extended without disturbance that costs money, while there can be disturbance within a programme which is not extended overall, this latter being the appropriate effect for extension of time to be granted. Often the two effects are linked, but the proof that one has occurred is not enough to show that the other follows. Certainly, there is no unbreakable legal link, as the existence of two clauses in each document suggests. The distinction was rehearsed particularly clearly in *Henry Boot* v. *Central Lancashire Corporation*, discussed for other specific reasons below. The point is important enough to be repeated in several later chapters.

EVENTS AND MATTERS

It has been noted that only events which result in an overrun of the final completion date, and not those causing some delay contained within the total programme, can be used to justify an extension of time. Similarly, matters must cause actual loss and expense to lead to reimbursement. The point is self-evident when put so baldly, but much energy can be wasted if a clear view is not taken in a given instance. Further, it is only in relation to the events and matters actually specified that the architect can act at all, any others being either completely the contractor's responsibility or those constituting breach on which he should approach the employer himself, even if he chooses to do so through the architect.

The clauses covering extension of time contain almost identical sets of events, which divide into two conceptual categories:

(a) Events which are the responsibility of the employer or the architect on his behalf. These may be lapses or deliberate acts taken in recognition that they carry potential repercussions. As they have this status, the employer is protected by their inclusion from losing a defined, if extended, completion date.

(b) Events which are not usually the responsibility of either party, so that they are effectively 'neutral'. As these events have this status, it is the contractor who is protected from what he would otherwise bear under an entire contract. Occasionally, it is not entirely the case that the contractor does not have a margin of responsibility for some of these events.

The first category contains those items which are also matters possibly leading to loss and expense. The third possible category of event, covering items for

which the contractor alone is responsible, is not included within the ambit of the clauses, as might be expected. The salient differences between the lists in the two groups of contracts and sub-contracts, JCT and IFC, questions of drafting and sequence aside, are:

(a) Nominated sub-contractors and suppliers occur only in the JCT group, while named sub-contractors occur only in the IFC group.
(b) Antiquities and the exercise of statutory powers occur only in the JCT group.
(c) Deferment of possession of the site occurs only in JCT (amended 1987) and in the IFC group.
(d) Inability to obtain labour or materials is an optional event only in the IFC group.

Subject to these considerations, the various events and matters from the contracts and sub-contracts may be taken together, arranged under the two conceptual categories mentioned above and otherwise following the order of JCT 80 where there is any difference. The interpretation of each cause is in view, as the possible interaction of more than one is reserved until Chapter 11.

If any clauses within one of the forms are likely to be considered for special amendment in a particular contract, the present are strong candidates for change, when they do not appeal to one party or the other at some point. This may be understandable, and even justifiable in some circumstances, but it causes problems over the fluctuations provisions when there is an overrun of the completion date, in view of JCT clause 38.4.8 and its equivalents. An ill-considered change of wording is especially likely to fall foul of the *contra proferentem* rule in these sensitive areas of the contracts.

THE CONTRACTOR AND SUB-CONTRACTORS

The comparable clauses in the main contracts and the sub-contracts for events and matters are very similar, because they are dealing with the same basic causes. They can therefore be discussed once, whichever level of the contractual relationship is in view, over their main effects and subject to some overriding comments here. Usually the reference is to the contractor for simplicity.

Some events or matters are mentioned in exactly the same terms in each set of clauses, such as adverse weather and discrepancies in documents. Others are qualified in sub-contract clauses as happening to either contractor or sub-contractor, such as late architect's instructions, because what happens specifically to the contractor may affect sub-contractors in their progress by way of a follow-on. Sometimes sub-contract clauses also refer to the contractor's directions. These nuances are not mentioned in each instance, but should be borne in mind. Even when the point is not made in a clause, a follow-on effect may occur, so that a sub-contractor is affected because the contractor has been thrown out by an event or matter. Such a sub-contractor is entitled to put forward a notice in these cases under the clauses concerned.

Within the sub-contract clauses, there are also extra provisions to any in the main contract clauses. One is the additional question of suspension of work by sub-contractors, which still counts as an event, but which does not run up to main contract level to allow the contractor the possibility of an extension of time.

The other provisions are concerned with 'act, omission or default' of either contractor or sub-contractor. In the case of extension of time, they can only refer to the contractor, whereas in the case of loss and expense either party may cause the problem. This is not because a sub-contractor cannot delay the contractor, but because the appropriate remedy must be entirely in loss and expense, as the sub-contractor cannot give the contractor an extension. If the contractor takes proper action to progress a sub-contractor, he may gain an extension from the architect when the sub-contractor is *nominated*, but this is outside the terms of the sub-contract (see JCT clause 25.4.7 hereafter).

The default situations are not spelt out in the sub-contract clauses in the same detail as are those governed by events or matters, because they are always breaches, potentially more variable and not to be restricted to a few causes which modify the contractual position of entirety in a defined way. They are not discussed separately for this reason, but can be of importance. The procedures embodied in the clauses are as relevant over them as over the other affairs, although the detail given varies between nominated and other sub-contracts.

While more strictly a concern of later chapters, it may be stressed here that it is up to sub-contractors to remember that they are responsible for taking their own action under their sub-contracts, by way of notices and so forth to secure extensions of time and reimbursements for themselves. Even though these may be affairs to be pursued with the architect on their behalf by the contractor, it is not the responsibility of the contractor to remind sub-contractors to act, or even to put forward his own ideas of what is due. It may be that he does not know with any precision or, in the extreme, that he does not know at all that there is a case.

In the case of named and domestic sub-contracts, the amount agreed in time or money does not relate directly to what the architect and the contractor agree, which may not isolate it, even though a money amount is loss and expense and strictly should be the 'direct' amount. The contractor has to come to an agreement which he should ensure includes sub-contract elements, and then deal with his sub-contractors afterwards if necessary. If possible, he may find it useful to settle with sub-contractors first, so that he knows where his base line for settlement with the architect lies. Alternatively, he may want to see how the main settlement is going before actually finalising with sub-contractors. This is the standard dilemma over agreeing rates and all such features of final accounts.

In the case of nominated sub-contracts, the architect is to be involved directly in agreements and effectively to make them. This in practice gives such sub-contractors a more obvious spur to act initially, in that the architect

has to be introduced and will wish to look at all aspects together to form a balanced assessment. They may thus 'miss the boat' if they delay. Other sub-contractors may feel that they have a little more leeway, because only the contractor is involved in the settlement. Often it works like this in practice, but sub-contractors should remember that the timetable set out in sub-contracts can run against them, if they delay unduly and the contractor settles without taking account of their representations. He will not take kindly to granting what he cannot recover, and the provisions are on his side.

Causes leading to extension of time only

To emphasise the distinction in the heading, the term 'event' is used throughout this section.

'FORCE MAJEURE'

This continental expression is the nearest thing to 'etc.' in the list. It refers to an uncertain area of exceptionally severe events. It is a difficult peg on which to hang a request for an extension, since in its extreme form it is likely to amount to frustration, while in less than the extreme form it may be impossible to demonstrate at all.

WEATHER CONDITIONS

The conditioning term in this event is in the other two words of the clause 'exceptionally adverse'. The thrust of this is that the contractor must allow in drawing up his programme for the routine run of adverse weather which all but permanent underground dwellers must be expected to know about in these climes. He must know about rain, frost, snow, ice, continuous sun and wind running through long periods of any year and abounding above what is otherwise normal in certain positions of exposure and so forth. He must also anticipate a measure of any of these somewhat outside the strict limits.

What he cannot allow for is an exceptionally severe incidence or duration of adverse weather, or weather which is completely misplaced. He has quite a difficult task here to prove his point, as anyone acquainted with the weather patterns of the United Kingdom will be aware! To establish whether there has been a distinct aberration from the norm, it is necessary to go to the meteorological records for the region covering a prolonged period, at least a decade, and to establish a statistically significant deviation, not just something rather severe for the time of year.

It was held in *Walter Lawrence & Son Ltd* v. *Commercial Union Properties (UK) Ltd* (1984) that the applicable test was the exceptional nature of the weather and not how exceptional was the delay produced. Further, it was held that the contractor was not obliged to programme 'in the strict sense', so that reasonable allowance for expected conditions was what was to be

made. Interaction with the contractor's own delays in this case is mentioned in Chapter 11.

It will of course depend on the stage of works, such as whether there is a lot of earthworks, wet trades, cladding, roofing or work under cover going on, as to the effect produced. This is also a good example of an event where the responsibility of the contractor to mitigate the extent of any delay is high. He is responsible for protective work of various sorts, often by express provisions of the specification or preambles clauses, although this does not mean that he must necessarily press on in all weathers irrespective of the cost involved. Equally, the instructions of the architect to suspend work which the same clauses may confer, do not necessarily give a right to extension of time, although here the position is entwined with the provision over extension due to postponement. Such clauses should be so worded that the architect is acting to stop the contractor ignoring weather conditions and the specification, but is not introducing a definite postponement for other reasons. The instruction should then require the contractor to suspend work to comply with the specification.

LOSS OR DAMAGE BY PERILS UNDER JCT CLAUSE 22 OR IFC CLAUSE 6.3

The loss or damage here relates to the works themselves and to unfixed materials on or adjacent to the works. It does not cover damage to adjoining property, through which the contractor may have a negotiated access, although here the employer may be liable for an extension of time under the 'ingress or egress' provision below. Perhaps more pressing for the contractor, it does not cover loss or damage to materials off site, even when they have been paid for by the employer, or to his plant, accommodation or other temporary items. If any of these contingencies also lose him time, the risk is entirely with him, so that he cannot secure an extension.

The perils leading to the possibility of an extension are the same under the original 1980 and 1984 contracts and under the 1987 revisions, which latter substitute the term 'Special Perils' (see Ch. 16). The full range covered by 'all risks', as in the insurance clauses themselves, therefore does not apply here. If they are to lead to a determination, they must not be due to the negligence of the contractor, sub-contractors, etc.

As with a number of the events, there is no corresponding matter available in this instance in the clauses covering loss and expense. Both parties are advised to consider their insurance cover against the categories of risks and results which are not within the contract scope, and for which cover is possible over each party's own delay costs, as it is not over some other events under these clauses. The contractor may find himself running into liquidated damages here. Alternatively, the employer may lose his right to recover liquidated damages.

CIVIL COMMOTION, ETC.

The various elements given here are effective at any stage in the production

process leading up to the delivery of materials and so on at the works. There is therefore considerable scope for this event to come into play, provided its effect can be demonstrated, which is the more difficult side of it. Damage due to civil commotion is covered by the preceding event.

DELAY ON THE PART OF NOMINATED SUB-CONTRACTORS OR NOMINATED SUPPLIERS

The primary nature of this event is delay in the execution of work by one of these persons. The clause affects the usual responsibility of a contractor towards an employer for whatever sub-contractors or suppliers do or fail to do. It is discussed in relation to sub-contractors alone initially, as they present more facets, while suppliers are taken by comparison in closing.

Nominated sub-contractors

The clause allows the contractor to secure an extension and avoid damages when a sub-contractor has defaulted in the manner stated, provided the contractor has done everything reasonable in the circumstances to mitigate the effects. If therefore the contractor has taken appropriate action, he is not liable to the employer. But further, the sub-contractor has no liability to the contractor, as the latter is released. He is already without liability to the employer directly, as there is no privity of contract. This is a most odd provision when left like this, without the extra arrangements mentioned below. It is made more so by the uncertainty attaching to the expression 'delay on the part of'.

The provision received consideration by the House of Lords in the case of *Westminster Corporation* v. *J. Jarvis & Sons Ltd and Another* (1970), which was brought on the same wording in the JCT 1963 form. A nominated sub-contractor completed piling work and left the site. The piling was found to have been carried out with defective concrete and remedial work caused substantial delay. The contractor sought extension of time, arguing that there had been delay 'on the part of' his sub-contractor, which 'he had taken all practicable steps to avoid or reduce' (meaning in this instance that he could not have done anything about it). The main argument was around whether such delay could arise when once the sub-contractor had finished work, apparently satisfactorily. The defects came to light when an excavator nudged a pile cap, which crumbled away. It was held that this did not constitute delay within the meaning of the clause. The case was fought effectively between the employer and the sub-contractor, with the contractor hardly represented in the action, as he had little at stake.

From the judgment several deductions appear to follow about the naked clause itself:

(a) The term 'on the part of' is not to be interpreted as equivalent to 'caused by'. It must be limited to delay in performance by the sub-contractor himself and not be extended to include delay which is the consequence of any default, such as poor work. In the circumstances in

the actual case (and these are always critical), the resultant delay came after the sub-contractor had completed. Specifically, it was held that the term did not apply to *any breach* of contract or to *complete failure* by the sub-contractor to perform his obligations because of repudiation, insolvency or other determination of the sub-contract.

(b) It would appear likely that delay caused during the sub-contractor's activity, owing to his defective work or some cognate matter leading to him being late, would qualify as being 'on the part of', provided it delayed him and the contractor in turn. If it delayed the contractor without any interposed delay to the sub-contractor, say by affecting large areas of the contractor's work and little of the sub-contractor's, it would appear to be 'caused by' and so not likely to qualify.

(c) Provided the contractor operates a procedure suitable in all the circumstances to 'take all practicable steps' to limit delay, the clause removes the employer's protection against the sub-contractor's default in being late in completion. This may recognise a degree of special relationship existing in nomination, but exposes the employer totally.

(d) The corollary of this is that the sub-contractor can protect himself against liability for damages by proving two things: that he was in default and that the contractor took 'all practicable steps', which he then ignored or could not match. This is obviously a fall-back position from proving that he was not in default: either 'I am innocent' or 'I am doubly guilty'.

(e) The contractor can remain fairly passive, so long as he chases the sub-contractor in the first place. Either the sub-contractor responds and delay does not occur, or he does not respond and the contractor is covered against damages, although he still has to act against the sub-contractor over the cost to himself of the delay.

This catalogue presents a quite unsatisfactory position for the employer. One answer would be to delete the clause entirely, and this would not lead to problems of cross-dependence of other clauses. It is presumably included at all to give some reassurance to contractors when accepting nominations of performers of uncertain quality, and so may not be lightly removed, apart from the reactions of tendering sub-contractors.

The standard answer is the use of one of the employer/nominated sub-contractor agreements, NSC/2 or NSC/2a, according to which method of nomination is being used (see Ch. 7). Indeed if the basic method is used, NSC/2 is obligatory, although under the alternative method the agreement there is optional. Both of them are strongly desirable at all times for a number of reasons of cumulative strength. For present purposes, they give the employer the right to secure recompense from the sub-contractor for the liquidated damages which he has had to forgo when the contractor receives an extension of time. Like all such rights, it is worth as much as the substance of the sub-contractor in meeting his liability. Further discussion and legal cases are given in Chapter 7, under re-nomination procedures.

A nominated sub-contractor who does not delay, but who is affected

by the delay of a second such sub-contractor, is in a position similar to the contractor. If the contractor receives an extension of time, so does the affected sub-contractor, to whatever degree is appropriate. Conceivably, he might receive one when the contractor does not. The architect is to be implicated in the granting of any extension for a nominated sub-contractor, with this covering even the situations in which the contractor is at fault and not receiving an extension himself (see Ch. 11). Among these would be that in which the contractor has not taken all steps to avoid or reduce the other sub-contractor's delay.

In view of the multi-level dealings between architect, contractor and sub-contractor, the contractor needs to pay particular attention to the procedural aspects considered under sub-contracts in Chapter 11.

Nominated suppliers

In principle, the effects of delay on the part of nominated suppliers is the same as that of nominated sub-contractors, so far as the contractor is concerned. The related subsidiary document is the Standard Form of Tender by Nominated Supplier, which is strictly optional, although something close to it is always necessary to fit with the requirements of JCT clause 36.4.

It is for the architect to set up matters by obtaining tenders on this form to protect the employer. A critical provision is that delivery is to be 'in accordance with any delivery programme agreed'. Beyond this, the document is silent in its original version. It does not involve the architect in the post-contract phase in giving his opinion over programme matters, or provide for how the supplier receives any equivalent of extension of time. It does, however, provide an equivalent to NSC/2 and NSC/2a which *inter alia* covers an indemnity by the supplier to the employer over loss of liquidated damages and over loss and expense, when the supplier is at fault. JCT 80 (amended 87) gives a fairly limited selection of causes for varying the programme, which are carried into the revised form of tender.

As between contractor and supplier, the position is regulated more widely by the general law. Much will depend on the precision with which the delivery programme is laid down and any extra clauses which the parties to the supply contract are able to introduce or exclude.

EXERCISE OF STATUTORY POWERS

This event is included only in the JCT contract, intended as it is for larger projects. Its scope is both wide and restricted.

Its width arises from the unbridled reference to 'any statutory power'. This is, however, tempered in several ways. It is an 'exercise after the Date of Tender', so that the contractor has to foresee and make allowances when tendering, as usual. It is an exercise 'by the United Kingdom Government' and not by some nationally owned body, which may of course introduce policies that affect progress in some way. There may be fine points of distinction here, when the government influences policy by its own pressures fairly directly

applied. Further, it must be an exercise which 'directly affects the execution of the Works', rather than some less direct effect, such as an order applying to builders' merchants. These indirect effects may be covered by the events in the next clause.

Whatever the action, one effect is that it restricts 'the availability or use' of labour, so that the contractor may not be able to obtain it at all or may not have free disposition of what he can obtain, say by an imposed limitation on working hours. The other effect is 'preventing or delaying' the contractor's securing of essential materials, fuel or energy. Delaying here is the equivalent of restricting use in the case of labour, as both stretch out the supply for the contractor.

In the case of materials, and to a smaller degree labour, there is some possibility of the architect instructing variations to overcome the problem of delay by introducing different materials or techniques. This he does not have to do, but realistically he will consider the option when some serious delay is in prospect. Often there is little that can be done. This is an instance in which the contractor's obligation to give warning of problems under the procedures for extension of time has very direct point. If he fails, it is more than a lapse in procedures when avoiding action could have been taken. However, the onus of proof that there was a reasonable way round the delay will be on the architect.

The materials, etc. must be those which are 'essential to the proper carrying out of the Works'. Usually any materials which the contractor plans to use, and which are likely to hold up progress by their absence, will be those which have been specified sufficiently precisely to prevent him making any substitution on his own initiative. If he has any latitude, he must use it, as he should not receive any extension when the possibility of ameliorating action is open to him. This will be so whether or not he can obtain a substitute at equivalent cost. If these comments are true of permanent materials, they are even more likely to be true of fuel or energy, where the option of switching to an alternative is often more readily present. This might mean using a dearer type of concrete batching or placing system, or a change from work on site to yard or the reverse.

In all of these cases, there is some reasonable limit to what the contractor should be expected to do, although this will vary with the seriousness of the delay or the level of expense involved. It would be ludicrous to expect a change to hand-mixing of concrete for a project of any scale at all, whereas an interchange between site and ready-mixed concrete may be reasonable. If a site does not permit of a large batching plant, this will affect what is reasonable in that direction, while a change from fossil fuels to electricity will be affected, but not necessarily ruled out, by whether complex plant has already been set up on site.

INABILITY TO OBTAIN LABOUR, GOODS OR MATERIALS

The two clauses relating to this group of events are given as optional in the IFC contract and its sub-contracts and an entry must be made in the related

appendix to render them effective. It would be possible to include one and not the other, or to have them applying in one document and not the other. The latter would lead to unevenness of treatment, and should be resisted by the party adversely affected.

When the clauses apply, the criterion for an event to qualify is the same as under the immediately preceding clauses about government action, that is the elements concerned must be 'essential to the proper carrying out of the Works'. All that applies there is true here also, although the absence here of any mention of fuels and energy is important. For example, shortage of petrol without statutory action causing it, does not qualify for an extension of time.

The immediate event is the contractor's 'inability . . . to secure' labour or materials. Again, 'inability' does not mean 'inability at more or less the same cost', so that the possibility may have to be faced of inducement or importation of labour with attendant higher costs, if the local supply is taken up by some major contract. There is no power in the contracts for the architect to agree to extra payment in these circumstances, and no obligation on the employer to meet such amounts. For his part, the contractor has to weigh the additional costs against his possible liability to liquidated damages, quite apart from goodwill.

While this quite hard line may be correct in principle, it may be wondered whether it holds in the case of a smallish local contractor for whom the operation of engaging and importing labour from any distance would fall into the category of being beyond his ability. The same might apply to obtaining materials from national markets. Perhaps for such a firm it is reasonable for the architect to lower his sights somewhat in applying the provision. This is again a matter of degree and one which may lead to consideration in drawing up a tender list according to the urgency of the project.

There are two qualifications to the contractor's inability, which underline these points. One is that there must be 'reasons beyond his control', which would be a likely term for the courts to imply, even if it were not express, to give 'inability' substance. The result is perhaps tautological, but avoids uncertainty where it is often felt. The other is that the inability must be such that he 'could not reasonably have foreseen at the Date of Tender'. He should not contract to perform the impossible, but should warn of anything in this field. Otherwise, he will be held to have anticipated the problem and to have made allowance in some way for it.

WORK IN PURSUANCE OF A BODY'S STATUTORY OBLIGATIONS

There are situations in which the contractor may engage a local authority or statutory undertaker to perform work under a sub-contract, when this clause does not apply. If then the sub-contract is domestic, no extension of time is due whatever happens, while if it is nominated or named, the position is affected accordingly and is discussed in Chapter 7. These positions hold even if the contractor has no choice over whether to have the body as his sub-contractor.

There are other cases for which these clauses are intended in which the body is acting, not as sub-contractor, but in the role given it by statute. When this occurs, the contractor may find himself impeded by the simple performance of the work concerned, or by some lapse in its performance. The work may or may not be on his site, although it may be the provision of some service to the site. It must be 'in relation to the Works', and not just causing some hindrance while completely extraneous.

There are areas of uncertainty here, as the position of a statutory body in relation to the contractor is not always clear. In *Henry Boot Construction Ltd* v. *Central Lancashire New Town Development Corporation* (1980), work was allowed as provisional sums in the contract bills for statutory undertakers to perform and delay occurred. It was held, despite the inclusion, that the undertakers were employed directly by the employer as 'artists and tradesmen' under the 1963 JCT contract, so that the employer was liable to suffer both extension of time and loss and expense. Had they been statutory undertakers performing their statutory duties under what is now clause 6.3, only extension of time would have been available to the contractor, as the present clause provides. This decision has been criticised on several counts, but remains the law at present.

QUANTITIES NOT REASONABLY ACCURATELY FORECAST

This event applies only under the JCT approximate quantities forms. It covers the situations in which delay is due to performing more work than could have been expected or work of a different character from what has been described. There are two other relevant provisions in the contract:

(a) The articles of agreement refer to 'Drawings and Bills of Approximate Quantities showing and describing, and intending to set out a reasonably accurate forecast of, the quantity of the work to be done'.
(b) Clause 13.1 gives the contract bills as stating the quantity and quality of work included in the tender price (equivalent to the contract sum), but makes no reference to the drawings.

The second of these means that the work included in the *price* is precisely what is given in the bills alone, so that the descriptions and unit rates are established as applying for remeasurement and valuation purposes. The former means that two sets of documents must be consulted to establish the somewhat broader indication of content which affects the programme.

The reference to drawings and bills is untidily worded, but is so made that *both* document types show, forecast and so forth the quantity of work to be done. As the works are only 'substantially designed', according to the non-contractual headnote to the contract, exact correspondence between the documents is not to be expected, but each should be 'reasonably accurate' in allowing the contractor to set up a realistic programme and then be able to implement it without surprises. It becomes a matter of technical judgment whether a difference in quantity or character within the overall quantity

leads to an extension. To an extent it will hinge on whether the contractor has the resources to expand his capacity, if needs be, and so to be using his best endeavours to maintain the programme.

The combination of provisions mentioned gives the contractor some protection against gross inadequacy in the quantities and misleading drawings, by comparison with the developed scheme. It also aids him against excessive variations which it is not easy to segregate, although strictly the provision over architect's instructions covers this aspect. The routine valuation provisions, including those over preliminary items, deal with financial effects, so that there is not a corresponding loss and expense matter. If information and instructions are issued so as to cause disturbance, the relevant clauses cover the position.

There is no reference to what happens if the drawings and quantities substantially overplay the extent of work required. The contractor has the same time to do less, if he wishes, and the employer has to accept this as part of the risk of using approximate quantities. Strictly, there is no 'omission' as such of work when the design is finalised, so that no reduction of an existing extension can be made.

DEFERMENT OF POSSESSION OF THE SITE

This is a relevant event only under JCT 80 (amended 87) and IFC 84, but only when JCT clause 23.1.2 or IFC clause 2.2 is stated in the appendix to apply. It is similarly included in the sub-contracts to the IFC contract, but apparently in error, as it is superfluous.

The clauses allow the employer to defer giving possession by a period as stated there, but not more than six weeks. Whether the effect on the contractor's programme will be a straight deferment of the same amount, will depend on how closely before the date of possession he actually receives the notice of deferment and how advanced his own preparations are. He may, for instance, have orders placed which are fitted into a supplier's own schedule and which will be displaced by an undue amount if once they lose their place. Alternatively, he may welcome the extra breathing space.

If the deferment is agreed with the employer on the signing of the contract, often the completion date will be moved at the same time and usually by the same amount. This case does not fall within the clause, which can relate only to post-contract events when the architect is charged with fixing a revised date for completion.

Under the earlier unamended JCT contract, failure to give possession is a breach entitling the contractor to the usual remedies. In practice, he may well be happy to negotiate in such a way as to give a result similar to that under the later contracts, although he does have the additional lever available.

SUSPENSION OF WORK BY SUB-CONTRACTORS

This event occurs only in the sub-contract forms and is applicable to all sorts of sub-contractors over extension of time, provided the appropriate

standard sub-contract form is in use in the case of domestic sub-contracts. It is given in clause 14.2 of the sub-contract forms to the IFC contract as a matter leading to reimbursement of loss and expense also, but there is no equivalent in the other sub-contract forms. It could be a difficult provision to have, as it extends the power of the sub-contractor in a situation in which the default is hard to place, by giving him recompense over a matter which he triggers off. Its inclusion looks like an error of drafting.

In respect of extension of time then, the event entitles only the sub-contractor to an extension, as might be expected. He is the person aggrieved by non-payment, which is why he may institute suspension. This he may do when the contractor has failed to pay him or, alternatively, when the employer fails to pay him direct on the contractor's default. A number of considerations arise over the procedures for suspension, as are discussed in Chapter 8.

Even though this event lies entirely between the contractor and the sub-contractor, the action of the architect under JCT clause 35.14 is still needed for a nominated sub-contractor to obtain a valid extension. The architect is not implicated under any of the other sub-contract arrangements.

Causes leading to extension of time or loss and expense

As already indicated, the two remedies are not necessarily linked, although the cause *may* be common. To distinguish what is said in this section from that preceding, the term 'event or matter' is used throughout.

COMPLIANCE WITH ARCHITECT'S INSTRUCTIONS

This event or matter is to be distinguished from that under 'Design questions' below, where delay in the issue of instructions is in question. Here the instructions are issued in proper time, but their nature leads to prolongation of the contract period. Alternatively, variations of design or of obligations and restrictions may lead to reduction of an extension in suitable cases.

Design questions

Discrepancies, divergences or inconsistencies (treated slightly differently as between events and matters) may be discovered at a late stage just before the work concerned is to be performed, with the result that corrections take some time to work out before being instructed, or to put into effect after that. Even worse, they may not be found until some part of the troublesome work has been done, so that the correcting instruction inevitably leads to some disturbance of sequence. This is of course subject to the contractor giving warning on such issues as soon as he can, which includes him checking over information as he receives it for the more obvious points.

There is room for difference of opinion here as to when the contractor should find any mistake, not only difference between architect and contractor

on a particular project, but between any two architects or contractors when faced with a similar inconsistency and a delay in bringing it to the architect's notice. While the contractor is held to be a person skilled in the process and technicalities of building, the intricate and sometimes innovative nature of much construction does mean that not everything can reasonably be discerned in time. The problem is accentuated by the preparation of some drawings by sub-contractors, so that the contractor is receiving information in different formats. If the architect has not fully co-ordinated this information, it is not always fair to hold the contractor responsible in his position of long-stop. The sub-contractor's responsibility is a separate issue, as mentioned in Chapter 5.

Variations are not something which the contractor should be requesting – and very few really look for them! On the other hand, he does have a duty, by virtue of the wording for the event or matter concerned, to seek instructions timeously over the expenditure of provisional sums, provided he can tell what they are for, from the sometimes enigmatic descriptions attached to them in specifications and bills. When the instructions come for either type of item, they may cause significantly more work, or lead to work which needs longer to execute owing to its sequencing, setting time, labour-intensive nature and so on. They may also lead to alterations to executed work, which the contractor could not have foreseen in this case. Procedures over variations and provisional sums and their evaluation are dealt with in Chapter 6.

Programme effects

Postponement by its very nature holds things up. But like all the other events, it must extend the end date to lead to extension of time, and this often means a very substantial postponement, either in time or quantity of work affected, and so affecting the critical path of the project.

Antiquities are recognised expressly only by the JCT contracts, and incorporated by reference into their sub-contracts, but the contractor would need to seek instructions over them under the IFC contract, so that a similar position should arise. The distinction between such objects as a Stone Age toothpick and a full-scale heathen temple is critical to the delay that is likely, especially when the archaeologists become involved, armed with powers to arrest progress for long periods. This is an event or matter that no employer should yearn to see occur, despite the quite short time attributed to it in the case study of Chapter 19, to ease illustration of the main points at issue. It is the one case in which the JCT clause dealing with the procedure also deals with the question of loss and expense, rather than including it in the main loss and expense grouping.

Nominated sub-contractors and suppliers, named sub-contractors

Only in the case of nominated sub-contractors and suppliers and named sub-contractors, is the architect empowered to give instructions. Domestic sub-contractors are entirely under the contractor's control, once they have

been approved. Even for the permitted categories, the present reference is to instructions *about* these persons, rather than to instructions given *to* them through the contractor, which are included for present purposes in those given to the contractor. Instructions about them are broadly about their appointment and cognate affairs, as listed in Table 5.2. They must be distinguished from other related actions by the architect, such as 'directing' the contractor over payments to nominated sub-contractors and 'certifying' over completion of their work. These and their consequences do not fall within the present scope as events or matters. (See also 'Delay on the part of nominated sub-contractors and suppliers' and 'Suspension of work by sub-contractors' in this chapter.)

An effect is most likely to occur when the architect instructs a change over nomination or naming arrangements when these are proceeding. This is to be distinguished from a late initial instruction, which falls into the general category of late instructions taken below. The case of *Rhuddlan* v. *Fairclough* set out in Chapter 7 indicates some of the distinctions of responsibility here, particularly that the contractor will probably not receive an extension or reimbursement when the architect is acting with reasonable promptitude, but having regard for the proper commercial interests of the employer.

Instructions over named sub-contractors are covered in the lists of events and matters by references to IFC clause 3.3, and 'to the extent provided therein', which warrants some repetition here. That clause and those related to it give these situations:

(a) *Clause 3.3.1*: there are three options if the contractor cannot enter into a sub-contract initially:
   (i) changing the particulars included in the contract documents and relating to the named sub-contractor, leading to the possibility of either remedy;
   (ii) omitting the work, with the further option of engaging a direct contractor, but in either case leading to the possibility of either remedy;
   (iii) substituting a provisional sum, leading in its expenditure and only then to the possibility of either remedy.

(b) *Clause 3.3.4*: by referring back to clause 3.3.3, after determination of a named sub-contractor's employment, for reasons not the fault of the contractor, this covers three options:
   (i) naming another person, leading to the possibility of extension of time only;
   (ii) instructing the contractor to make his own arrangements, leading to the possibility of either remedy;
   (iii) omitting the balance of work, with the further option of engaging a direct contractor, but in either case leading to the possibility of either remedy.

These options should be set against the comments in Chapters 7 and 16 over the appointment of named sub-contractors and arrangements after determination. Comments made about delay by the architect under the topic of re-nomination in Chapter 7 are also applicable here if, as appears likely, the courts were to take a similar view over delay in a re-naming situation. The differences in the present patterns are self-explanatory, but should be noted closely.

As between the nominated and named sub-contracts, the references in the lists of events and matters are the same, but as between the two lists in each sub-contract there is a distinction. The event is given as 'compliance by the Contractor with the Architect's/Supervising Officer's instructions . . . deemed to include compliance by the Sub-Contractor', while the matter is given as 'the Architect's/Supervising Officer's instructions . . . and the Contractor's directions consequent thereon'. No reason for the distinction can be deduced, it being hoped that the nuances involved will not lead to dispute. As always, actual delay or loss must occur.

As between the main contract and the sub-contracts, another distinction exists. While the main contract gives the various patterns listed above, the sub-contracts simply state that compliance with or the issue of 'instructions . . . under clause . . . 3.3.1 [or] 3.3.3' constitute the grounds for a remedy being possible. The distinction introduced by IFC clause 3.3.4 when another person is named is thus not applied, so that there is the possibility of loss and expense being available to the sub-contractor, but not the contractor, in such a case.

Opening up work or testing work or materials

The architect has the right under JCT clause 8 or the more complex IFC clause 3.12 to instruct that any opening up or testing shall be performed by the contractor, whether or not anything has been specified in the contract documents. The liability over cost of direct work is discussed in Chapter 5, the contractor usually being reimbursed when the items are not found to be faulty, unless the cost of testing and replacement is specially covered in the contract sum. This latter approach is suited only to such routine and regular matters as testing concrete cubes and runs of installed pipework. However cost is actually dealt with, the possibility of extension of time or reimbursement goes with the question of liability in principle, so that the contractor is protected if he is in the right, but vulnerable if in the wrong. With the routine tests specified in the contract documents, the contractor is able to make proper allowance in his programme and avoid delay or disturbance. Any which occurs he should bear, even though the precise wording says otherwise. A major item of defective work here can give rise to quite unanticipated results, which he would also have to bear.

LATE INSTRUCTIONS, ETC.

This, it may be suspected, is the most frequently invoked event or matter,

unless it is beaten over extension of time by that of adverse weather, rather less justified on some occasions.

Information concerned

The list given in the clauses covers several 'necessary' items, meaning items without which the contractor cannot proceed at certain points, as distinct from such matters as variations which he can well do without to finish his work! Of these, 'drawings, details and levels' refer to post-contract information under JCT clauses 5.4 and 7 and IFC clauses 1.7 and 3.9, but not to contract documents. The latter are to be provided 'Immediately after the execution of this Contract' in the JCT instance, and at an unspecified but reasonably early stage under the IFC arrangement. They are not items for which the contractor should have 'specifically applied in writing', as under the present clause, but constitute the bedrock data without which the contractor will not know what to do at all.

The present list, by contrast, covers the supplementary information which is needed to develop the scheme into the construction phase. Oddly, it does not mention the 'descriptive schedules or other like documents necessary for use' under JCT clause 5.3.1.1, which in turn the IFC contract does not mention anywhere. It would appear that these may be classed as 'necessary instructions' under this clause or perhaps, by forcing the usual terminology, as 'details'. Certainly, the contractor cannot proceed without information like ironmongery, finishings and decoration schedules, which in the main convey data which cannot sensibly be given on drawings and can be included in bills of quantities only with difficulty.

Under the drawings and specification contracts, JCT or IFC, far less information should be needed, as indicated in Chapter 5. If much is, there may be unstated variations or errors being corrected, with the possibility of redress over time or money. Under any of the contracts, it is always necessary to apply for instructions over the expenditure of provisional sums, which are likely to involve drawings, etc. in their own right.

A list of all items for architect's instructions under the two main contracts is given in Table 5.2, where those which are 'necessary' in the sense described may be identified. While variation instructions are not themselves 'necessary', incompleteness or uncertainty introduced by them may create a need for other and necessary instructions.

Applying for information

While there is no clause requiring the contractor actually to apply for any missing information, or even to notice that anything is missing, this clause hedges the position about in respect of any consequential delays. However, the principle of the contractor being the expert in construction applies here, presumably to the same extent as about errors in the design and warnings over them considered in Chapter 5.

Over the categories of information to which it refers, the clause requires that the contractor shall have 'specifically applied in writing', so cutting out the possibility of him simply saying something like 'please send me everything I do not have'. This is fine, in so far as the contractor notices some point of uncertainty when he applies his distinctive analysis to the problem of actual construction, using different criteria from those of the architect or the quantity surveyor, working pre-contractually. But it leaves doubt over those errors of a more subtle character and, in the present context, over those which do not reasonably come to light until almost the moment of execution. Even more onerously here, the contractor is required to apply for information which neither he nor the architect can be in any doubt is necessary, such as the whole construction of a tank room covered by a provisional sum.

The key difficulty about the clause lies in the timing requirement. The contractor's application must be made 'neither unreasonably distant from nor unreasonably close to' when the information is really needed. The latter part of this expression obviously protects the employer from a later completion date or added expense, simply because the contractor has neglected, accidentally or otherwise, to apply until it becomes impossible for the architect to supply the information in time. It places the onus on the contractor, although the problem in operation still centres in the points raised in the immediately preceding paragraph.

Equally, the former part of the expression is to guard against the contractor putting up requests which are unduly early and which are then used as a pretext for claiming delay or disturbance. It may be queried whether the wording adds much, as the contractor has to demonstrate that actual deferment of the completion date or loss and expense has occurred, so that an unreasonable allegation of when he would require information should be undermined at that stage. But the effect of the clause is also to remove any validity from a single, comprehensive list of known requirements which the contractor may draw up and put forward early in the contract period, supported by dates when they are needed. In fact, strictly he cannot ask for anything early, which is not a great help to the architect in planning the overall work of his office either. The best solution appears to be for the contractor to put in his early all-purpose list and then to confirm individual requirements as they arise, taking account of any changes in the programme meanwhile. His early list will have no express contractual validity here, any more than has the master programme (unmentioned anywhere in the lists of events or matters), but may be admissible evidence when there is a dispute, if other data are inconclusive. More records are always better than less.

This is the view taken in *Stanley Hugh Leach* v. *The London Borough of Merton* (1985). The contractor had provided two programmes, at and soon after commencement on site, which he argued were requests for necessary information under the JCT contract. This was held to be in satisfaction of the requirement, provided that the dates specified met the criteria of 'not too late, not too early', as they did. This may be regarded as eminently sensible, although it does not meet what the clause is actually saying.

Challenged instructions

It is obvious that any instruction of the architect, the validity of which the contractor queries under JCT clause 4.2 or IFC clause 3.5.2, cannot be a 'necessary' one for the purposes of the present clause. A delay of any consequence, caused by following the procedure of either of those clauses, is in practice likely only if the alleged instruction is issued closely before it should be implemented. There may then be a case that the contractor has not received instructions which he has effectively asked for, by querying their status.

The contractor is under no express obligation to hold work while the procedure is operated, although it will be prudent to do so and avoid a complaint that he has exacerbated any difficulty. Usually things will be cleared quickly by a straightforward exchange of letters. Should he delay his query until the last minute, he will lose himself any cause for redress. If, however, the architect is slow in replying, but then gives an adequate substantiation, the contractor may find his programme set back. This would appear to fall under the present clause. If the matter is taken immediately to arbitration, as it may be, a delay is the more likely to occur. If so, the question of who bears the effect of the delay should go with the award, so that the contractor would secure an extension or reimbursement only if he won in the reference.

Even without arbitration, the outcome for extension or payment will be affected by whether the architect is able to substantiate his instruction, or whether the contractor appears to have acted frivolously in raising his challenge.

WORK NOT PART OF THE CONTRACT

It is sometimes the practice for the employer to engage persons to perform work under direct contract with him, at the same time as the works under a building contract, or even to perform work with his own organisation (see Ch. 4). Both options are mentioned in the clauses. Provided this work is physically distinct from that of the contractor, there is not likely to be a risk of conflict between the two sets of activities.

JCT clause 29 and IFC clause 3.11 give the employer, not the architect, the right to introduce other persons, so long as he has had a mention of their work included in the contract documents. His own presence is not specifically catered for, except by placing a different interpretation upon 'employed' from that usually given in contracts. In the JCT clause, there are requirements about giving rather more detailed information. The employer may also introduce during progress persons not mentioned earlier, unless the contractor has some good reason to object. Without the clauses, the employer cannot act to deny the contractor the uninterrupted, sole possession of the site, which should otherwise be his under the contract.

For present purposes, the contractor may become entitled to an extension or payment, if he is impeded more than he might have deduced from the data

in the contract documents. This may occur if the detail given is inadequate or misleading, if no warning is given at all in the documents, or if the direct contractor fails to perform as expected. The last instance gives meaning to the inclusion of the simple 'execution of work' in the clauses, as well as relating to the direct contractor's 'failure to execute'.

In the second case of no warning, the contractor is entitled to make his consent to the entry of another to the site subject to conditions, rather than just to say 'yes' or 'no'. He might therefore require an extension of time or premium at the outset of negotiations, as a condition of allowing the direct contractor on at all. While he cannot refuse consent unreasonably, he would appear to be on fairly firm ground in stipulating his own ideas over an extension or sum before consenting, within sensible limits, and not having to rely on the architect's 'opinion' or 'ascertainment' (see Chs 11 and 12).

MATERIALS OR GOODS PROVIDED BY THE EMPLOYER

This event or matter parallels that just given, by dealing with items which the contractor is to fix, and similar points can be seen without need for particular comment.

There is no clause in either contract dealing with the employer's right to supply, as this does not involve any question of disturbance of the contractor's possession of the site. Suitable clauses should be included in the contract documents to cover questions of accounting, wastage and other issues outside present discussion. There should also be a programme for delivery or, better, a procedure for the contractor to schedule deliveries as he needs them. This should cover such points as requesting materials at dates that are reasonable, on the lines of what has been discussed over details and other information during progress. It is not apparent how straightforward supply by the employer (which is what is actually mentioned), as distinct from lateness, etc. can lead to delay. The situation envisaged by the clauses may also arise during progress, by the employer having then 'agreed to supply' particular items.

There are sometimes pressing reasons for the employer to supply materials, as when he can obtain very large special discounts, or he is himself the manufacturer or sole distributor, or long lead times mean ordering before the contractor is appointed. Usually, there is everything to be said for him avoiding this sort of complication, which can so easily lead to a hitch and so to delay or disturbance. He should not be drawn into promising to obtain materials which the contractor finds are in short supply unless, again, he is in a particularly strong position. This has to be balanced against the possibility of a delay leading to extension of time under later parts of the present clauses. Often the contractor can be pointed in the right direction, without incurring any responsibility for the timetable.

FAILURE OF THE EMPLOYER OVER INGRESS AND EGRESS

These are rather problematic clauses, in that their subject-matter is not dealt

with distinctly in other clauses, while there is a potential overlap with the provisions about obligations and restrictions mentioned under the provisions about variation instructions, but again not defined further (see Ch. 6). This is due to the mention of access in the other clauses, as a matter subject to possible restriction. Here the main thrust is that the employer is making something extra available, by allowing access through land, etc. other than the site but for which he is responsible. Inasmuch as this access, or alternatively this way out, may not be given at all times (so he has 'to give [it] in due time'), there is an element of restriction over it. The reference in both this and the variation clauses is to at least part of what is set out somewhere in the contract documents, subject to the complications of wording noted in each case.

In the present clauses, the main part is clear, provided it is ensured that any notice of an event or matter is related to the correct clause to avoid any confusion. In practice, the effect should be the same, but clarity can only help in this difficult procedural area. Reasonably, there is a limitation to such land, etc. as is 'adjoining or connected with the site'.

Although the statement about such an area in the contract documents may be quite explicit about when it is to be available, there is also the possibility of the contractor needing to work out when within his programme he is going to need it, if it is not continuously available. His use of it may therefore be dependent on the giving of a suitable notice, which then becomes a condition precedent to his right of use and so also to any question of an extension or payment. The need for some form of notice may also arise out of some extension already granted which has thrown the employer's timetable and grasp of events out of gear. In this case, the contractor may not be liable for some of the uncertainty element, but he should act carefully to avoid refusal because of inadequate notice.

Less clear is the reference to 'failure of the Employer to give such ingress or egress as otherwise agreed'. It is not easy to construe this as meaning giving ingress or egress in the circumstances of a shift in the programme as just outlined. It appears more natural to place on the words a meaning of something agreed completely *de novo* post-contractually. If so, the whole thing is by way of variation of the contract provisions, although not precisely covered by the variation clauses themselves. Leaving this lack of precision aside in the present discussion (but see Ch. 6), it follows though that an extension of time is envisaged, because of a failure of the employer to carry out something which itself is part of a variation agreement. Whether the variation itself resulted in an adjustment by way of extension or even reduction, as might be more appropriate if it is possible (see earlier discussion on variation omissions in Ch. 6), affects the logic of allowing anything here. If the contractor has received an additional way in or out quite gratuitously, it is difficult see how his time will be extended by losing it, unless it is because he has rearranged his programme to rely on this gift. A disturbance is more conceivable. Some care is needed in arranging these post-contract changes to give precision of intention.

Remedies for breach of contract

Damages for breach of contract at common law
Standard provisions equivalent to damages in building contracts
Liquidated damages
Costs of claims for extension of time and loss and expense

This chapter is included primarily to outline a number of principles of the background law. These affect the application of the remedies available beyond the contract terms, but also give substance to the provisions of the contracts themselves. They relate particularly to damages and so to the theme of loss and expense taken in later chapters, but also include the question of liquidated damages in this chapter. It must be emphasised that these are principles which are full of complexities and are treated at length in legal works, because of the cases which have led to their elucidation and continuing development. The present treatment is given to set out some pointers, which should be followed up elsewhere if the need arises.

Secondarily, this chapter serves to indicate that there are more available remedies when one party is in breach than what is set out specifically in standard contract forms, or indeed in any contract as written. What is included over the two major areas of extension of time and loss and expense for disturbance of regular progress exists to regulate affairs by providing a first point of reference and action. In the case of extension of time, the provisions given will usually delineate the boundaries of action fairly closely, as may be seen from discussion in Chapter 11. Those over disturbance of regular progress are also usually the major consideration: they exist to be used when no other provisions within the contract provide reimbursement, as the clauses state. But they are also by the same token without prejudice to, and so do not exclude, other remedies, meaning arbitration and legal proceedings.

It is thus open to an aggrieved party to go to other remedies if dissatisfied with his treatment. Most commonly, this is likely to be the contractor reacting against decisions of the architect or the quantity surveyor, or against some entrenchment of the employer, but it could be the employer doing the reacting, as both architect and quantity surveyor are there under the contract to act impartially between the parties.

The expression used in JCT clause 26.1 and IFC clause 4.11 in relation to recompense for disturbance of regular progress is 'direct loss and/or expense'. It is generally held, for reasons set out below, that this gives amounts

similar to those which would arise by the award of damages in the courts. It has just been indicated that the existence of clauses like these does not remove the possibility of the contractor seeking damages as an alternative to payment for loss and expense under them, or even as well when he is not satisfied with what he has already obtained under them. There is also the possibility of issues arising which are common law breaches, while not also falling within the ambit of the clauses. These must be pursued at law if the employer is unwilling to meet them by negotiation, so as to include the resultant settlement within the final account by specially authorising the architect and quantity surveyor. It is also possible that not all of the matters in the clauses would constitute breaches in all circumstances.

Damages for breach of contract at common law

NATURE OF BREACH OF CONTRACT

A breach of condition at law is a major breach, to be distinguished from a breach of warranty, as discussed in Chapter 3. What is termed a 'condition' within standard or other written contracts is not necessarily a condition in the immediate sense, which is restricted to legal nature and importance. There is a growing tendency for the courts to distinguish conditions and warranties, not by abstract definition of their statuses in particular instances, but by the extent of the effects of their breach. However, every breach of condition or warranty leads to the possibility of an action for damages.

In addition, when the breach is of a condition and so fundamental in its effect, it may entitle the aggrieved party to treat the contract during or before progress as repudiated by the other, so as to bring it to an end, or to treat the precise and apparently binding terms of the contract as overruled. The courts are careful to restrict recognition of fundamental breach. Thus in a case in which such breach was alleged over the non-availability of a hired ship due to the defendant's fault for 20 *weeks* out of a total hire period of 24 *months*, it was held that there was not fundamental breach, as the plaintiff could still obtain a large part of the hire benefit (*Hong Kong Fir Shipping Co. Ltd* v. *Kawasaki Kisen Kaisha Ltd* (1962)). On the other hand, the installation of defective pipework which led to the complete destruction of a mill by fire was held to be fundamental (*Harbutt's Plasticine Co. Ltd* v. *Wayne Tank & Pump Co. Ltd* (1970)). Here in fact, work had been completed, but the decision overruled an exemption clause in the contract, put forward originally by the defendant.

It is also possible in these circumstances for the party treating the contract as repudiated to select the alternative of suing on a *quantum meruit* basis instead of damages, that is usually for expenditure incurred. This may be more advantageous in the right circumstances, but can only be pursued in extreme circumstances. Thus, in *Davis Contractors Ltd* v. *Fareham Urban District Council* (1956), it was held that an extension of the contract period from 8 to 22 months did not frustrate it and allow a *quantum meruit*. The

contract to erect a number of houses as envisaged could still be performed and was not frustrated in its nature, whatever the problems and costs introduced by the extended period, while the potential hazards which had come into reality were not beyond the contemplation of the parties. This of course did not deny the contractor whatever reimbursement was open to him under the contract.

In general in contract, it is possible for an injured party to seek specific performance or an injunction as an alternative to damages over breach. The former is unlikely to be granted, as it would be difficult to oversee to make it effective, while the latter is seldom relevant, especially against the employer.

SOME PRINCIPLES OF DAMAGES

These principles are similar, but not identical, whether the action is in contract or tort. The purpose of damages under contract is to put the injured party back into the position he held before breach, so far as it is possible to do this by pecuniary means. The aim therefore is to compensate that party for loss, and not to inflict some penalty on the other. It is what the one party has suffered, and not what the other has gained, which is relevant. This applies whether there is non-performance in part or whole, or misperformance of some part, although what the relevant ingredients of the damages are will vary. The broad parallel may be noted with *liquidated damages*, discussed below, over compensation rather than penalisation.

Direct and consequential damage

The compensation afforded by *damages* is in respect of *damage* sustained. The test over damage is that of its remoteness or otherwise, where the position is that it must not be so remote, or consequential, as not to be direct, in the terms of the contracts being considered. A direct loss is one which flows from the cause without the interposition of some other cause. Several broad variations may be seen:

(a) 'A' causes 'B', an element of loss, without intervening cause. The loss is direct.
(b) 'A' occurs and is followed by 'B', another causal event. 'C' then occurs as loss, as it would not have done in the absence of both 'A' and 'B' occurring in that order. 'C' is only an indirect or consequential result of 'A'.
(c) There is the same sequence of events as in (b), but 'C' would have occurred in a less intense form, if 'B' had not occurred. The reduced form of 'C' is thus direct, but the compounding of it by 'B' is a consequential and inadmissible element of loss.

These stark examples are minimal in their illustrative power. Within construction, the situation often arises when there is a loss by delay due to one cause and further loss by defects due to another. If only the delay can be laid at the employer's door in terms of reimbursement, its costs should

not be inflated by the extra costs due to the presence of the defects, which have arisen independently of the prime cause of delay. Their conjunction is fortuitous and has led to excess costs which should be settled separately where they lay.

As one judge has remarked, 'The word "consequential" is not very illuminating, as all damage is in a sense consequential'. However, in *Millar's Machinery Co. Ltd* v. *David Way & Son* (1934), it was stated that the word had come to mean 'not direct'. This was quoted in *Saint Line Ltd* v. *Richardsons, Westgarth & Co. Ltd* [1940] where a clause excluding 'any indirect or consequential damages' was under review. It was held that loss of profit on the use of a ship, wages and stores and fees paid for superintendence were all direct and recoverable. Similarly, in *Croudace Construction Ltd* v. *Cawoods Concrete Products Ltd* (1978) loss of productivity, delay costs and meeting indemnity costs to a sub-contractor were all held to result directly and naturally from failure to deliver on time and from defects in the items delivered.

Contemplation of the parties

This principle of directness of loss is then moderated according to the knowledge held or which reasonably should have been held by the parties about the loss likely to flow from a breach, especially the defendant in an action. A narrower view of what might be assumed to have been in the contemplation of the parties is taken in contract than in tort, so that reasonable information is required to be available about the possible nature and extent of loss flowing from breach, in the absence of crystal-clear knowledge. How serious the loss may be in amount is a distinct matter, and here there is room for much wider variation in information.

The basic case is that of *Hadley* v. *Baxendale* (1854), concerning failure to deliver on time a replacement shaft for a mill, which in consequence was out of production, so causing loss to the owner. It was held that the plaintiff could not succeed: the defendant was not reasonably to have known that no spare shaft was held by the mill, as might have been thought in accordance with general practice. There was no indication to the contrary in the order for the shaft. The critical section of the judgment reads:

> Where two parties have made a contract which one of them has broken, the damages which the other party ought to receive in respect of such breach of contract should be such as may fairly and reasonably be considered *either arising naturally*, i.e. according to the usual course of things, from such breach itself *or* such as may *reasonably be supposed* to have been *in the contemplation* of both parties, at the time they made the contract, as the probable result of the breach of it. (Emphasis added)

The two branches of the decision relate to damage which arises in the normal course of affairs, and to that which arises in special circumstances. The latter is only admissible when assessing damages, if the defendant was

specifically aware of the circumstances when contracting. In a later case, *Victoria Laundry (Windsor) Ltd* v. *Newman Industries Ltd* (1949), the two branches were rolled up into one, forming the first of the three propositions given in the judgment:

(a) Recovery is limited to 'such part of the loss actually resulting as was . . . reasonably foreseeable'.
(b) What was then 'reasonably so foreseeable depends on the knowledge then possessed by the parties . . . [especially] the party who commits the breach'.
(c) Two classes of knowledge may be possessed, 'one imputed, the other actual', the former relating to what is reasonably foreseeable, the latter to what must be specially made known when contracting.

The point at issue in the case was distinct from that in *Hadley* v. *Baxendale*, in that there were two levels of profit involved. One was that attainable on normal business, but lost by late delivery of a boiler. This profit was recoverable, as the plaintiffs had made it plain that they were 'most anxious' to put the boiler into use 'in the shortest possible time'. It was held that the defendants must have known the implications of these statements in relation to taking on work, by their own experience in engineering. The second level of profit was that in prospect from some 'highly lucrative' contracts. This, it was held, the defendants could not have foreseen unaided, so that damages were to be limited to an assessment of normal profit for the type of contracts concerned.

Later still, in *The Heron II* (1967), the House of Lords modified this position by stating that the criterion was not whether the damage as such should have been foreseen, but whether both parties should have had the probability of its occurrence within their contemplation. At this point, contract is narrower than tort, where a position more akin to possibility rather than probability applies. The liability is not, however, to be limited by whether the actual consequences, as distinct from their probability, are more serious than could have been reasonably contemplated. It may well be that damages are out of all proportion to the contract amount, as happened in *Harbutt's Plasticine* v. *Wayne Tank* above, where a fairly small defective installation led to destruction of the whole building into which it had been fitted.

Extent of damages

It is the duty at law of a person sustaining damages to do all that is reasonable to mitigate his loss, that is to reduce its impact by suitable countermeasures. He must not allow loss to build up unheeded over a period, if he could stop it or reduce it early on. It may be that his act of mitigation itself introduces extra costs which he may have reimbursed, again subject to them being reasonable. A net saving should therefore be in view, although what is done may turn out with hindsight to be more expensive. The key issue is

whether proper judgment was exercised over matters as they appeared in the circumstances prevailing at the time. Several illustrations of the problems are given in Chapter 16 and in case studies in later chapters.

Standard provisions equivalent to damages in building contracts

LIQUIDATED DAMAGES

These provisions wear their communal heart on their sleeve. They are a prior arrangement to cope with one form of damage, that flowing from delay in completion by the contractor, but not usually delay by a sub-contractor. By virtue of their special character, they present a number of distinctive features and are dealt with separately later in this chapter.

They are used only as a means of recompensing the employer over delay by the contractor, whereas the next form of recompense is used solely to recompense the contractor or a sub-contractor.

DIRECT LOSS AND EXPENSE OR DAMAGE

Within the particular sphere of building contracts, there is an important distinction between a contract performed, even if with difficulty, and one broken off, that is determined. Taking the contractor's aspect, when a contract is performed but with some element of breach from the employer's side, the measure is loss and expense incurred by the contractor in performing his obligations. When he is unable to perform, as in a determination, the measure is what he might have expected to obtain from the contract and has been unable to realise. In later chapters, this leads to a distinction over profit forgone and overheads laid out in each situation. The question of financing charges to cover delayed payment is also discussed.

The term in standard contracts for the former case of breach within the continuing performance of a contract is 'direct loss and/or expense'. This echoes, and means, the concept of direct rather than consequential loss when damages are under consideration. It means that care has to be taken to segregate those matters, as the clauses term them, which are or are not the responsibility of the employer at main contract level, or those matters which are or are not the responsibility of contractor or sub-contractor at sub-contract level. Only these, or a share of the total situation, are the responsibility of the party concerned. 'Loss' is usually related to some return on resources which the contractor is unable to realise, and 'expense' to additional outlay incurred. Fortunately, no segregation of these elements is required, as the practical distinctions are not always easy to sustain. For instance, when productivity of plant drops, a loss of return on existing resources, there is often also the need to spend more on additional plant, an added expense.

The term in standard contracts for the latter case of breach, that at determination, is 'direct loss and/or damage'. This carries the same essential meaning, although it is used within the provisions in such a way as to distinguish

some elements of loss from others. These distinctions are brought out in the respective chapters.

Liquidated damages

An extensive body of legal decisions and discussion underlies the use of liquidated damages, a device by which the damages payable upon a defined breach of contract are calculated in advance and made a term of the contract. The parties have thus agreed to their inclusion at the level stated. Upon the breach occurring, it is then a case of the party in breach paying the sum in question, without the need for legal proceedings to discover whether there is a liability and, if so, how much is due. Needless to say, this simplicity is an understatement of reality.

PURPOSE AND LEVEL

The usual purpose of liquidated damages in main building contracts is to provide against late completion of the works by the contractor (a note on sub-contractors is given at the end of this section). In standard contracts, this is their sole purpose and they are usually stated as so much per week or other period. It is therefore assumed that any such period within a total overrun has the same effect on the employer in terms of his loss, any inaccuracy here being outweighed by the simplicity of the system and the ease and promptitude of collection. Inaccuracy may relate to the need to forecast or to different disturbance effects, according to just when they occur and for how long. The figure inserted also gives the contractor a clear measure of what he has to forgo for a given delay on his part. He may even decide whether or not it is worth his while to catch up at a particular stage of the programme!

It is not possible to include just any figure in the contract, at least not one that is too high. If the sum is demonstrably high, it will be treated by the courts as a penalty, a sum put *in terrorem*, so that it will be set aside, even though included with the agreement of the contractor and whether or not he knew at the time that it was unreasonably high. This distinction was established in *Re Newman, ex parte Capper* (1876), while *Law v. Redditch Local Board* (1892) established that a single sum in respect of a breach of any scale or character was unenforceable because of its very uncertainty. It remains, however, a question of fact in the actual situation under any contract whether an amount is a penalty or not. The test is whether it is a reasonable pre-estimate of anticipated loss at the time of entering into the contract, as distinct from the actual loss which flows from the breach when it occurs. If it is held to be so, and the matter may be tested, then the courts will not interfere to set the amount aside. If it is set aside, unliquidated damages will be substituted by the courts; the employer does not lose his right to damages, only the unduly high level that he sought.

It may be noted that the effect of reasonable prior calculation, based on

the evidence available at the time of entering into the contract, may work in the interests or otherwise of either party if conditions change. For instance, a contract to build a filling station may have the level of liquidated damages related to a given volume of business which is likely to be lost if the station is late opening. Upgrading of the road by which it stands may increase the traffic, and so the takings, dramatically. Conversely, construction of another road may siphon off much of the existing traffic and cut takings. In either case, the level of liquidated damages is not affected by hindsight, but remains as contract, if this was reasonable at the time.

VALIDITY AND COUNTER-DEFENCES

The test is reasonableness, as so often, and not precision. This latter indeed it may not be possible to attain, given all the imponderables of a venture. It is no defence against the application of a provision for liquidated damages that the calculation was beset with difficulty and necessarily approximate. The principle is still: was it done with reasonable care and judgment? If so, it stands. Because this is a calculation of *damages*, it must be related to the employer's loss and not to what, if anything, the contractor may save by not finishing on time. The employer's loss also does not bear a fixed relation to the contract sum, as the purpose of developments varies so much, although some broad correlation is to be expected on general economic principles of value, cost and return.

It is important that the contractor should be fully aware of the purpose of the project, and so of how reasonable the level of damages is, more particularly when this level is apparently high. Although he agrees the sum in that he knows what is going into the contract, he also knows that the sum may be set aside as a penalty, if it is too high. If therefore he has not been adequately warned of the purpose, and so indirectly of the likely return on the project, he may assume that his liability is not as drastic as it appears. According to the precise facts, he may be held to be excused from liability, if his ignorance warrants it, following the principles in *Hadley* v. *Baxendale* and other cases discussed above.

Apart from the matter of penalty, several defences against enforcement of liquidated damages exist, especially over the procedural niceties of granting an extension of time. These are discussed in the context of the standard contract provisions in Chapter 11. There is also the general question of the employer failing to meet his obligations under the contract and so causing delay. If he does, in the absence of any modifying contract provisions, he then places time for completion at large, so that the contractor may finish within a reasonable but not excessive time, and so that the liquidated damages provision becomes ineffective. For this reason, standard contracts regularly include a number of events which are in essence a lapse or even a positive act on the part of the employer, and which lead to an extension of time being granted. Without these provisions, the employer would lose his right to damages (even unliquidated damages) because he has at least contributed

to the delay. An extension of time of clause is as important to the employer in these circumstances as it is to the contractor, who also needs some of its other, more neutral provisions.

Even this outline suggests that clauses for liquidated damages and extension of time are inserted for the benefit of both employer and contractor, at least in the form in which they occur in standard contracts. In non-standard contracts, if they are inserted for the benefit of one party, they risk being construed *contra proferentem*, that is against the party putting them forward, as happened in *Peak Construction Ltd* v. *McKinney Foundations Ltd* (1970). Here, the employer was dilatory in settling problems which had arisen out of defective work by a nominated sub-contractor. The employer sought to rely on an event leading to extension of time given as 'other unavoidable circumstances'. It was held that the employer's delay was not unavoidable, while the form was described as containing 'the most one-sided, obscurely and ineptly drafted clauses in the United Kingdom', which is probably an accolade without equal and not highly to be prized at that!

Provided a standard contract is a consensus document, that is one agreed by a group representing both sides to contracts, this type of risk is not present. While the JCT forms are safe on this basis, those emanating from another body, such as the ACA forms, may well not be.

However, amendments or incautiously inserted provisions may remove the employer's protection. In *Bramall & Ogden Ltd* v. *Sheffield City Council* (1983), the liquidated damages provisions were construed *contra proferentem* and held to be unenforceable, even though the employer was recognised to be operating the provisions in a reasonably fair manner. He was declared not to lose his right to seek common law damages. In the JCT appendix, a sum had been inserted at a rate per house for each week of late completion. There was a single completion date and no sectional completion supplement included. To circumvent the problem, the employer advanced the argument that a total sum for liquidated damages over the whole contract should be calculated from the available data and this then apportioned under the routine partial possession provisions, even if those optionally available for sectional completion were not present. This argument was not accepted, on the basis that it gave a single sum which would have become a penalty if the employer had not taken possession progressively.

SUB-CONTRACTS

In building sub-contracts, it is not usual to provide for liquidated damages, but for an amount payable equivalent to loss or damage and to be calculated after the event. This is because the effects of a delay per week may be quite varied in the context of interacting site operations, according to the total length of delay and just what stage the contractor and other sub-contractors have reached. It may render the contractor liable to the employer for liquidated damages or to other sub-contractors for disturbance costs, or both, as well as causing disturbance costs for the contractor himself. Usually affairs are rather more

clear-cut for the employer at main contract level, so that liquidated damages are considered appropriate there.

Costs of claims for extension of time and loss and expense

A contractor (and the same is true of a sub-contractor) may choose to expend some amount of effort in drawing up a claim over one of the major contingencies which the standard forms recognise. Alternatively, he may engage a specialist to draw up a formal claim document or to give advice on how to present a claim in negotiations, either because of lack of capacity or because of special need of expertise. Whichever way this particular enterprise is undertaken, he is not entitled to receive payment in the settlement for doing it.

The reasoning here is that the contracts do not require him to prepare such a document or to engage outside assistance. They go so far in the main contracts as to require him to provide the architect or, in the case of loss and expense, the quantity surveyor with limited information in support of a notice or application from which the person acting may calculate the contractual entitlement. The principle is similar in sub-contracts, although the sub-contractor (except when nominated) will be dealing with the contractor alone, which may colour his approach to settlement. The information under the JCT main form, as an example, is:

(a) *For extension of time*: particulars of expected effects, an estimate of the expected delay and further information from time to time to keep the architect up to date.
(b) *For loss and expense*: information to enable the architect to form an opinion in principle on the application, and details of loss and expense as are requested and necessary for the architect or the quantity surveyor to ascertain the amount.

It is then the responsibility of the person dealing to perform the calculations and grant the extension or settle the amount. It is true that this gives a rather simplified picture of what the contractor has to do in presenting even what is necessary as a bare minimum, while often he may consider that his case will be better served by presenting as cogent a document as possible. But, just as with the actual final account (of which a loss and expense amount is but part), so with these other exercises, he is due to make an allowance somewhere to comply with his contractual obligations. While he anticipates the final account, he perhaps does not anticipate these other contingencies, at least not in any precision, but he should prudently make an average allowance in tenders at large.

The matter has been highlighted in *James Longley & Co. Ltd* v. *South West Thames Regional Health Authority* (1983), where the contractor was generally successful, but was not allowed the original fees incurred in drawing up a claim. He had, however, incurred subsequent fees from the same source

for preparation of expert witness submissions for arbitration, and these were admitted. This follows the usual pattern that costs in presentation in arbitration or court are admissible and follow the award or judgment.

Some slight modification of the position may have come about as a result of *Tate & Lyle Food and Distribution Ltd* v. *Greater London Council* (1982). There it was indicated that additional 'managerial and supervisory resources' expended as a result of the actions of the defendant 'can properly be claimed'. In principle it would appear that these may include costs of assessing loss and expense, if not of preparing a full-scale claim. The actual case failed on this point because the plaintiff put forward a flat percentage, rather than an analysis of expense incurred, but not on the principle involved (see further in Ch. 15).

The position of the contractor in seeking reimbursement is made rather tougher by the procedures in the current JCT documents. These allow for progressive notification and preparation of claims for extension of time and loss and expense, more explicitly than do earlier forms. The emphasis is upon the contractor giving notification and then either the architect or the quantity surveyor performing the actual calculations, as discussed in following chapters.

CHAPTER 11

Delay and extension of time

Late completion
Procedures for extension of time

This chapter is concerned solely with the ways in which the standard contracts and sub-contracts listed in Chapter 9 deal with delay and its effects. Some preliminary remarks serve to introduce the subject in this context, most of them being expanded during subsequent discussion:

(a) Delay is treated only so far as it leads to failure to achieve the completion date and not in its effects on the programme before completion.

(b) No direct connection is established between delay and disturbance of regular progress, as one can occur without the other, common though it is for both to be caused by the same set of circumstances.

(c) On the entirety principle (see Ch. 2), delay is assumed to be the responsibility of the contractor, so leading to him having to pay liquidated damages, even if the delay is not necessarily his fault, unless the contract specifically provides otherwise.

(d) When the contractor is not to be responsible for delay, the contract provides for him to receive an extension of time, but still no reimbursement for the delay in isolation from any other disturbance effect, and even then only for some causes (see Ch. 9).

(e) There are stipulations over the timing of granting extensions and over related procedures, to lessen the possibility of either party suffering through the laxity of the other, or having events manipulated against his interests.

(f) A list of reasons for granting extensions of time is given, outside which the architect cannot step when exercising his power to grant extensions (again, see Ch. 9).

(g) Little consideration is given to possible overlaps between causes of delay, whether or not these are such as to lead to extensions, although these will be taken into account in calculating extensions.

Quite a number of issues lie dormant within these basic points and fall to be examined in this chapter and others. In anticipation, it may be said that the tidy contractual positions given by the contracts are often disturbed in practice by such things as the interaction of several causes of delay – to say

nothing of the failures of the participants to carry through the procedures laid down. It is therefore useful to remember the basic legal positions set out in Chapter 10, while moving to the detailed contractual situations and on into some of the practical problems, which are what disputes are so often about.

Late completion

MAIN CONTRACT WORKS

JCT 80 and IFC 84 deal with liquidated damages under the main contract very similarly. The former has clauses for this purpose, followed by a clause on extension of time, so that the latter is presented by inference as a means of overcoming the former. IFC 84 reverses the order, so that the contract date and its adjustment are treated first, and then what happens if the resulting date is overrun.

The requirement of JCT clause 24.1 and IFC clause 2.6 is for the architect to issue a certificate stating that the due date, extended as it may be, has been overrun. This is to be done quite baldly; there is no call to express an opinion over where the blame lies. It leaves the possibility of revising the date under the extension of time clauses and, if this leads to a sufficiently later date, removing any liability to damages. The possibility of an earlier date is also present under JCT 80, but not under IFC 84, as pointed out under the clauses concerned. In the case of IFC clause 2.6 only, there is a requirement for the architect to issue a cancellation of a certificate of late completion, if an extension of time renders it no longer correct. An amended certificate is then to be issued, if there is still a lateness in completing.

JCT clause 24.2.1 and IFC clause 2.7 then oblige the contractor to 'pay or allow' damages at the contract rate to the employer, but only after the employer (not the architect) has required this in writing. There is thus no automatic pressure on the contractor to pay without being asked. If the monies outstanding for the contractor and coming through under interim certificates are sufficient, the obvious course for the employer is to deduct amounts from these, periodically as the damages accrue and as the certified amounts allow. The architect may not anticipate this by himself making deductions from or in what he is certifying. The employer thus has a clear right of set-off.

Alternatively, he may ask the contractor to pay the amounts to him independently of any passage of certificates. If amounts due are inadequate, this may be the only clear course. It may be the most hopeful if the contractor appears likely to drop into insolvency, a state usually preceded by delayed progress. Once insolvency happens, though, there may be little to retrieve anyway. The alternative, while there is life, is to recover amounts as a judgment debt – the third option under the clauses, but not one to be preferred while the others are feasible.

The issue of an amended and later date for completion which cancels out the liability to liquidated damages means that the employer has to repay to

the contractor any sums already received. There is no requirement for the contractor to ask for these amounts and the employer will be in breach if he does not pay within a reasonable time, although none is specified. The contractor has no redress *within* the contract machinery, even the determination provisions (as the extreme weapon) do not help him, and he must rely on his usual legal rights.

If a JCT contract includes a sectional completion supplement, the level of damages will be lowered when this comes into play, while JCT clause 18 over partial possession introduces a similar position without a proper hand-over necessarily being anticipated when the contract is formalised. There are potential complications in each case, as illustrated by *Bramall & Ogden* v. *Sheffield* in Chapter 10.

SUB-CONTRACT WORK

The several sub-contracts deal with the sub-contractor's failure to complete in the following clauses:

NSC/4 and 4a	Clause 12
DOM/1	Clause 12
NAM/SC	Clause 13
IN/SC	Clause 12

They follow their respective main clauses fairly closely. All of them require the contractor to act by giving notice about failure to complete either the whole sub-contract works or any distinct section of it. All but one require this notice to be given to the defaulting sub-contractor, with whom the contractor alone deals. The exception is the nominated clauses in both versions, which requires the notice to be given to the architect.

The reason for this difference is that the architect has to be involved under JCT clauses 35.14 to 35.16 in the following steps:

(a) Granting an extension of time to the sub-contractor for a part or the whole of his works, even when the cause is default by the contractor himself.
(b) Certifying that the sub-contractor should have completed by the date currently applying for a part or the whole of his works.
(c) Certifying that practical completion of the whole of the sub-contractor's works has occurred.

These procedures are discussed hereafter. When the architect has come to a decision under each head he acts through the contractor, who passes the result to the sub-contractor.

The JCT-related forms contain a provision corresponding to that in the main form for the sub-contractor to 'pay or allow' any sum by way of loss or damage to the contractor. There is the proviso under the nominated forms that such sums are due only after the architect has exercised his functions.

However, the IFC-related forms contain no such provision. Provided that a sub-contract delay causes disturbance of regular progress for the contractor, the position is covered by clause 14 of the forms. To the extent that a sub-contract delay causes simple delay to the contractor, the position is not clear. The reasoning behind the omission is not certain.

Procedures for extension of time

BACKGROUND CONSIDERATIONS

The central purpose of extension of time is to keep a definite completion date in a contract, rather than to allow the original date simply to be replaced by a reasonable but uncertain date when there is some default by the employer which places time at large. This acts to protect the employer, so far as the causes for extension are in the nature of employer's defaults in the broad sense of the term. Some may be less than defaults, while others are usually included which represent 'neutral' matters which would otherwise put extra pressure on the contractor to counteract them to complete by the original date, and so a high allowance in his tender. None are intended to be defaults of the contractor.

But in any case, when the contractor is likely to receive an extension of time it is important that he should know this and its amount as soon as possible, so that he is certain over what date he is to aim for and can adjust his effort accordingly. This fact has been recognised in the earlier legal decisions over extensions of time and whether they lead to avoidance of liquidated damages. These were related either to non-standard contract conditions or to earlier standard conditions and need not be considered closely here. In particular, they sometimes revolved round whether an extension had to be granted before the existing completion date, original or amended, was passed to allow the contractor to have the certainty which has just been mentioned. Because of differences in wording, the cases of *Miller* v. *London County Council* (1934) and *Amalgamated Building Contractors Ltd* v. *Waltham Holy Cross UDC* (1952) were decided oppositely in this respect, the former against the right to grant such a late extension and the latter (on a forerunner of the present JCT form) in favour of the right.

Very largely because of these considerations and the ways in which the looser provisions for extension of time have been abused or ignored, the present procedural provisions have been introduced into the JCT contract. They aim to give certainty over procedures, as well as over when an extension may be granted. They have been subjected to an amount of criticism second only to that over the nomination clauses, but much of it is misplaced, as the procedures are largely what should be happening anyway. It is unfortunate when good practice has to become contractual. For the larger contract, they are needed, although to be regretted in the without-quantities variants. For the smaller contract, the IFC form embodies a more simple clause.

They must be seen against the provision in each contract that the

contractor is to use his 'best endeavours to prevent delay . . . and to do all that may reasonably be required to the satisfaction of the Architect to proceed'. The words mean that, at the very least, he must take action to prevent further delay and to contain the effects of what has already occurred or been set in train. He cannot sit back fatalistically and let affairs drift. Some would argue that 'best endeavours' mean recouping the effects so far suffered, when this is at all possible, and at considerable expense if needs be. This goes beyond 'prevention', but at least co-operation and resource are expected. The contractor stands to gain by some action, because he is incurring extra overheads without reimbursement when delay occurs without loss and expense as well. The point of a trade-off is illustrated in the case study in Chapters 19 and 20.

STANDARD CLAUSES, JCT 80

It is easier to take the longer JCT clause first and then to compare the IFC clause.

Applying for interim extensions of time

JCT clause 25.2 deals with the actions which the contractor has to take when there is delay. It operates 'forthwith', when 'it becomes reasonably apparent' either that a delay is occurring or is likely to occur. It is therefore better for the contractor to act whenever he has reasonable doubt about progress, rather than to wait until he has reasonable certainty about delay. It follows from the list below that the clause is not intended to operate by retrospective action by contractor or architect.

Failure by the contractor to initiate action can only be to his detriment, even though it does not lose him the possibility of an extension, in view of JCT clause 25.3.3. He may cause vital evidence to be lost, so that he receives inadequate extension – he should not work on the basis that confusion over what has actually happened is bound to help him gain more. But further, it may be possible for the architect to take action by way of instructions to reduce the delay, given enough warning that it is threatening. If this opportunity is denied him, then the contractor may face a reduced extension because he has not done what he can to mitigate the delay.

Like all such provisions, it requires the contractor to act in writing, here to the architect. There are several things which he has to say:

(a) Immediately, what are 'the material circumstances, including the cause or causes of the delay'. He particularly has to name 'any . . . Relevant Event' (perhaps therefore several), the term used to identify those causes which lead to an extension. It would appear that the purpose of the rather repetitive wording is to ensure that the contractor gives some specific detail, but also that he hooks it rigorously to the list of events. He might otherwise do one without the other and perhaps lead to confusion.

(b) As soon as possible, if practicable with the foregoing, particulars of the *expected* effects of 'each and every' relevant event. This means making

a segregation which the preceding clause does not require, as it is simply an early warning system. This may be a formidable task, if several events come together and overlap in effects, as is discussed hereunder.

(c) Again as soon as possible, but possibly not so soon as (b), 'estimate the extent . . . of the expected delay' in relation once more to each relevant event, but taking account of any other delay which is involved, concurrently or otherwise. This estimate is again difficult, but the contractor is not committing himself finally by it. It is for the architect to make the final decision, with this estimate as one factor to aid him.

(d) Thereafter, as is 'reasonably necessary' or when the architect 'reasonably requires' (hopefully the two are not in conflict?), further information to bring matters up to date.

(e) Parallel information to all of the foregoing for nominated sub-contractors concerned in the delay.

This list does give a lot of work, but properly followed it also nurses the whole question of delay carefully through in terms of the provision of data by the contractor. What sort of data will best meet these requirements is outlined hereafter.

The clause is related closely to the provisions of JCT clause 25.3, which gives what the architect has to do. Apart from the considerations given in introducing the above list, the contractor should note carefully that the architect has no obligation to act over granting an extension during progress of the works, unless the contractor takes steps to notify him of delay. Without this 'triggering' effect, the contractor may lose himself the benefits of early reassurance that adequate extension of time is coming his way.

Granting interim extensions of time

JCT clause 25.3.1 goes on to what the architect must do as a minimum in response to the actions of the contractor. His action is conditional upon that of the contractor and in particular upon receipt of 'any notice, particulars and estimate'. He is required to exercise his 'opinion' to grant a 'fair and reasonable' extension, which recognises the degree of inaccuracy inherent in the process, and not to agree an extension with the contractor. While he is to have 'regard to the sufficiency' of what the contractor has supplied, he is not required specifically to check it, approve it or in any other way negotiate upon the basis of it. How he uses it is his concern, although sensibly he will discuss with the contractor any clear point of divergence. Under JCT 80 (amended 87), the architect is specifically required to notify the contractor if he decides not to grant an extension. This is a reasonable practice under any contract.

As a moderating influence, at the end of the process now being reviewed there lies the possibility of arbitration (which does not have to wait until after practical completion in this case) when, no doubt, any coarseness in operating the procedures would be assessed. It is, however, the architect's opinion which

is required, both here and in the final revision of the completion date under JCT clause 25.3.3.

What the architect does have to take into account is twofold. Firstly, he has to decide whether any of the causal events adduced by the contractor are in fact relevant events as listed in JCT clause 25.4. He can act only within this framework and must ignore any other cause of delay, even if responsibility may be laid at the employer's door. Beyond the stated list, the contractor must look to direct interaction with the employer for any redress, either by special agreement or by legal proceedings.

Secondly, the architect has to consider whether the result of any qualifying event is that completion is 'likely to be delayed' beyond the date currently fixed for completion. If it appears that a delay will not extend the date, but simply cause some lateness within the programme, he can do nothing. This may seem harsh, but relates to the fact that the whole extension of time arrangement is to protect against liquidated damages, which relate to final overrun. There are several problems here (see also Ch. 10):

(a) Several small, separate and relatively innocuous delays can build up into a total delay sufficient to overrun the completion date, so that the architect must look beyond the immediate event or events, if needs be, to assess the complete picture. It is up to the contractor to give the broader picture when estimating the extent of delay under JCT clause 25.2.2.2, by leaning on the phrase 'whether or not concurrently' used there.

(b) Delays not falling within the category of relevant events may occur within the same time span, or have already caused such delay that achievement of the actual completion date looks unlikely. There is more than one school of thought on this issue, but much is likely to depend on just how and when things happen, or fail to happen. Some guiding principles are given at the end of this chapter.

(c) The completion date may have been passed already when the delay occurs, and this appears not to be within the scope of the unamended clause (by the words 'is likely to be delayed' or of those which follow). Legal decisions look both ways here: both the amended JCT clause and IFC clause 2.6 have provisions to remove the doubt and to allow an extension to be made.

The architect has to fix a new date, so giving an extension, and state which relevant events he has taken into account. This allows the contractor to query why any have been left out completely, so that he can narrow any field of complaint, perhaps as a prelude to arbitration. This date is to be such 'as he then estimates to be fair and reasonable', pointing to the final revision which comes after practical completion.

The extension is only interim in its significance and the architect has to act within a definite time. Usually, this is to be 'not later than 12 weeks' from receipt of sufficient information from the contractor to enable the architect to act, which means that it is in the contractor's interests to chase each stage of supply through promptly. Although the architect is not

specifically required to take account of what is supplied to him, he can hold out '[in]sufficiency' of information as a reason for not acting. This cannot be over mere technicalities, but only over major gaps which prevent him from forming his interim opinion and fixing a new date.

The modification to this time-scale occurs when there is less than 12 weeks between receipt of sufficient information and the completion date currently obtaining. Here the period for the architect to fix a revised date is shortened to that remaining up to the current date, to avoid that date being overrun without an extension. This would create doubt for the contractor and also trigger the possibility of the employer deducting liquidated damages, as he might even if he knew that an extension was pending.

But within this latter situation there is the possibility of the architect being faced with an unreasonably short time in which to calculate an extension, conceivably even just the day before completion is otherwise due, so that a term of reasonableness must be implied here. An extension of time granted just before the previous date was reached could hardly help the contractor to review his programme, which is the major consideration. Equally, a relevant event cropping up close to completion is not very likely to cause a substantial overrun, although there is a saying about things that have happened at sea. In principle, several situations can crop up, and no clause can be expected to legislate with practical precision for them all:

(a) Cases when the '12 weeks' rule applies, because the contractor acts in time.
(b) Cases when the '12 weeks rule' should apply, but the contractor does not act in time, so that the 12 weeks are not available to the architect before the existing date. If the contractor has been dilatory, he is caught by the 'as soon as possible' of JCT clause 25.2.2. If he has done what is reasonable, then the 'less than 12 weeks rule' applies, subject to comments just made.
(c) Cases when the 'less than 12 weeks rule' applies, with reasonable time for the architect to act, depending on the complexity of the issue.
(d) Cases when this rule applies, but time is inadequate.
(e) Cases when the event comes to light before the current completion date, but the data for calculating an extension are not to hand until after the current date has been passed. These should be avoided in most instances by the contractor working to the earliest dates practicable for providing information, bearing in mind that he is giving an estimate and other provisional information.
(f) Cases when the current date has been overrun when the event comes to light. These have been alluded to above as the most controversial.

Effect of instructions to omit work

While all the relevant events may lead to an extension of time, there is also the possibility of a reduction in work content occurring due to omission variations, sufficient to shorten the programme noticeably. JCT clause 25.3.6

states that no completion date is to be fixed earlier than the contract date, and this limits what may be done, but there is the possibility of omissions reducing a potential extension by some margin, even eliminating it. Within the clauses already considered, there lie elements to regulate the matter, although their wording does not lead to self-luminous interpretation.

One controlling factor is that the omissions must be of 'work' under the unamended clause, so that omissions of obligations and restrictions do not lead to any effect, even though they may have quite a drastic effect. JCT 80 (amended 87) rectifies the situation by including 'obligations', although still not explicitly mentioning 'restrictions'. A measure of special pleading may be needed here – by either party. A second factor is that only omissions instructed since the last fixing of a revised completion date can be taken into account: any preceding that fixing should have been taken in then. If that was not possible under the rules, they will have been lost for ever, as discussed below.

The third factor is in JCT clause 25.3.2 and allows the architect 'After the first exercise . . . of his duty' to fix an earlier date 'than that previously fixed under clause 25'. It gives the architect power to take sufficient account of omissions when fixing a *second or later* revised date to reverse the extension of time that might otherwise arise, or even to reduce the previous extension in the absence of any relevant event justifying an extension. It excludes any effect when fixing a first revised date, by virtue of its opening qualification and remains subject to the overriding provision that the original date is not to be cut down at any time.

A fourth factor is that the architect is to state when fixing a new date how far he has taken such omissions into account. This is in JCT clause 25.3.1.4 and is qualified as relating to 'instructions . . . issued since the fixing of the previous Completion Date'. There is in fact no explicit authority anywhere in JCT clause 25 for the architect to take account of omissions to reduce, but not reverse, what would otherwise be an extension period, although JCT clause 25.3.2 could perhaps be operated to achieve this. The present clause does not give the architect power to take anything into account when fixing a date, but simply requires him to make a statement about how he has done it. It seems necessary to rely upon some implication of a term to make the clause work in this respect.

Subject to this implication being made, the clause apparently contemplates taking in the effect of omissions instructed before the first fixing of a revised date, with this turning upon the words 'previous Completion Date'. 'Completion Date' is defined in JCT clause 1.3 as 'the Date for Completion as fixed and stated in the Appendix' (that is the contract date) 'or any date fixed under either clause 25 or 33.1.3'. The completion date accordingly includes a distinctly defined, if identical, date fixed when entering into the contract and also various versions of itself fixed thereafter. It appears therefore that 'the fixing of the previous Completion Date' includes the entry of the original date in the appendix, unfortunate though the contortions of the several clauses may be.

If this is so, the contractor is obliged to have any omissions, instructed before he applies for his first extension of time, taken into account when that extension is fixed. They cannot be carried forward to be set against later relevant events, however, but must be used up at the time and any excess ignored for ever. A similar position arises over omissions occurring before any later relevant event, as noted above. This opens up a number of ploys over the instruction of omissions and the timing of notices, etc. to secure a particular effect, which need not be detailed here.

Granting the final extension of time

JCT clause 25.3.3 (unamended) deals solely with the final extension of time and requires it to be made within 12 weeks of practical completion. The clause as amended in 1987 introduces wording to cover also the period before practical completion when the currently fixed completion date has been overrun, and is noted at the end of this section. The procedure is not dependent upon any documentation from the contractor, or at least any further documentation. Indeed, it could be dealt with by the architect when no earlier extension has been given and without the contractor knowing that it is coming. It is to be hoped that nothing quite so remote actually occurs.

There are three options given: a later date than existing, an earlier or the same date confirmed. The first may be the result of a comprehensive review of the history of the project and allows the architect to take account of better knowledge about extensions already given and the relevant events on which they were based. But further, he may take note of additional events, whether or not the contractor has drawn his attention to them. He has no authority to review any reductions of extensions based upon omission variations, the amounts of which he has had to state explicitly when granting any extension taking account of them.

The architect may, however, secondly take into account any omission instructions which he has issued since the last fixing of a date, whether that deferred or advanced the completion date. This is allowed to give an earlier date, but it would appear reasonable to use both the first and second provisions for reaching an earlier and a later date together and obtain a net adjustment. Strictly, the architect may do *either* one *or* the other, but each has to be 'fair and reasonable', which would be impossible to achieve if he could arbitrarily choose whether to give an earlier or a later date.

His third option is to confirm the previously fixed date. No details are given here, and the architect is free to take into account any factor that he sees as relevant. Reasonably, it should be a combination of the other two options, with the results cancelling out. There is no prohibition by silence on him reviewing reductions already made for omissions variations, as there is in the other options.

Several comments arise. The architect cannot review his previous decisions in a downwards direction, unless he does so under the cloak of the last option. This avoids the contractor working to a given extension, only to find after

he has met practical completion apparently safely, that it has been eroded and he has become liable for damages. If there is any genuine doubt, the architect understandably may give somewhat conservative extensions during progress, to avoid this situation and remain fair to the employer. He has to give as accurate extensions as he can, and again the contractor's estimates need stressing as contributing to this result.

Further, the architect has only one chance to firm up on his earlier efforts: he cannot go on revising his figures. He should therefore round up all the detail that he needs before he acts, but do so within 12 weeks of practical completion. This is no longer than he had during progress and finality is required, but he can now act with the benefit of hindsight, so that uncertainty over the future has gone.

Lastly, the unamended clause contains nothing to clarify whether an extension may be granted when the completion date has been passed, but practical completion has not been achieved, so that the contractor is currently at fault. It is widely held that one may not be granted and further that time will become at large against the employer if variations (perhaps quite critical) are introduced extending the time during this period, or if other 'non-neutral' events occur (see cases under 'Background considerations' above). The architect needs to keep on top of granting extensions in the closing stages to avoid being caught on a technicality by work running past the existing date. It is also likely that the contractor, being in default, could not obtain an extension for 'neutral' events. The clause as amended in 1987 empowers the architect to grant an extension during this period, without any restriction as to the type of event. This removes the doubt over the original clause, while still allowing him to act again during the 12 weeks following practical completion. It is also more generous to the contractor than the IFC clause.

STANDARD CLAUSES, IFC 84

IFC clause 2.3 reflects the simple project for which it is intended, by having less procedural detail.

The introductory wording is closely similar, as is its effect. The contractor has to give notice 'forthwith' and in similar circumstances, stating 'the cause of the delay'. This appears as effective as the longer requirement of the JCT clause in securing warning and some information, although this still means that neither contractor nor architect can afford not to act promptly, so prejudicing their position in coming to a proper solution. There is an obligation on the contractor to 'provide such information . . . as is reasonably necessary' to operate the clause at this and all its later stages. This covers supplementary statements, estimates and so on. It is again 'the opinion' of the architect which decides the amount of 'fair and reasonable' extension given, as soon as it can be calculated. There is no fixed period of 12 weeks from adequate data within which the architect must act.

The clause refers only to making an extension of time, and not to fixing a new date, these being effectively synonymous terms. Its third paragraph

allows the architect to make an extension 'At any time up to 12 weeks after the date of Practical Completion', which therefore gives an effect similar to that under JCT 80, covering the periods both before and after practical completion. The paragraph again covers the review of a previous decision and the case in which the contractor has not given any notice under the main procedure above. It differs by prohibiting *any* reduction of an extension of time already made, so that the comments made earlier about the architect being careful not to overstate an initial extension apply with extra force here.

There is silence over whether any reduction can be made to allow for the effect of omission variations. From the preceding paragraph it is clear that they cannot be taken alone or against delaying events (these are not termed 'relevant' in this contract) to lead to a reduction of an extension already granted. Further, there is therefore no authority for setting variations which are omissions against other types of events, such as delayed instructions. It is, however, reasonable to set their effect against addition variations which may be under review at the same time as a possible cause for extension of time. In the circumstances of execution to which they give rise, it may indeed hardly be possible to do otherwise when assessing their effects. In the smaller project envisaged for this contract, the whole question of such omissions is less likely to be significant in the programme.

A provision additional to the unamended JCT provisions is contained in the second paragraph of the clause. Like the amendment to the JCT clause, this deals with the doubtful area between when practical completion should have occurred and the possibly later date at which it does occur, by making it explicit that the architect can still make an extension of time due to events happening within that period. There is a limitation to those events which are grouped in Chapter 9 as the responsibility of the employer, rather than 'neutral', a limitation not in the JCT version. It thus does not protect the contractor as he is protected while still within the accepted time-scale, unless there is a later extension of time which shifts the boundaries of this grey area sufficiently.

STANDARD CLAUSES, SUB-CONTRACT FORMS

These provisions, variously in clauses 11 or 12 of the respective forms, follow closely on the related main contract clauses and, subject to these groupings, are similar to one another as well. They thus run through a pattern of notices, particulars and estimates, leading to interim and final extensions of time, hedged about with similar provisos.

It becomes the sub-contractor's responsibility to give notices, etc. and the contractor does not have to act at all if this is not done. This is no bar to the contractor seeking extension of time himself under the main contract, when the reason lies in the event which the sub-contractor has not raised himself. In fact, the contractor would be ill-advised to delay, as his own right to an extension may be prejudiced. He cannot say, 'The trouble lay in something which delayed my sub-contractor first and then later, and only in consequence

of that delay, delayed me.' When he sees what is going to happen, he must move to secure his own position.

This highlights the point that what delays the contractor may not delay the sub-contractor and vice versa. So far as there is a consequential or parallel effect, they will both need to give notice. Neither can rest on what the other has done or hide behind what he has not done. The respective forms place the responsibility on the party seeking an extension to go after it, however obvious the point might appear.

The sub-contracts differ in one respect which does not follow from the immediate differences in the main forms. In the nominated forms alone the contractor has to bring the architect in to decide whether an extension is due to a sub-contractor and, if so, how much it should be. This arises by virtue of JCT clause 35.14 which states, 'The Contractor shall not grant to any Nominated Sub-Contractor any extension . . . except . . . [with] the written consent of the Architect.' The sub-contract provisions require the contractor to refer any request for an extension from a sub-contractor to the architect to decide both principle and amount. In fact, this is a pretty tall order for the architect, asking of him far more detailed involvement with the project programme than is usually needed to deal with a main contract extension. He is unlikely to be able to deal with it without substantial detail from both contractor and sub-contractor, and substantial effort on his own part.

The architect's problem may be that, while he was engaged with the sub-contractor's programme at the tendering stage, it could well have moved on since, as it has been integrated with that of the contractor more closely, and as changes have occurred without any question of an extension arising. For example, to grant an extension fairly, he may need to know why the sub-contractor's whole programme shifted a month later, before one section of his work was displaced a further month all on its own, with only this latter up for extension.

It is probable that many architects are unaware of just how detailed a burden is placed upon them. As a duty, it is not limited to extensions of time arising out of the relevant events alone, but also those arising out of default by the contractor in his own performance, which carries with it default by domestic sub-contractors. There is a whole network of relationships into which the architect may be drawn by the main contract provision and its simple reference to the sub-contract. Delay by other nominated sub-contractors and by nominated suppliers is covered for the sub-contractor by a clause paralleling that in the main contract.

The reasons for JCT clause 35.14 being present are several. It indicates the closer link that there is between the architect and nominated sub-contractors, despite the lack of any precise contractual tie with the employer. He has been involved in their introduction and, up to that stage, with their programme. If they have design to perform, he too is involved with that. More directly from a contractual viewpoint, he has to operate JCT clause 25.4.7 over granting any extension of time to the contractor because of delay 'on the part of' nominated firms, both sub-contractors or suppliers (see Ch. 9).

It is that clause which gives the strongest reason for the architect being involved in granting sub-contract extensions of time. The contractor is entitled to an extension due to sub-contract delay only if he 'has taken all practicable steps to avoid or reduce' such delay. The architect has therefore to check what has happened and so come to know what is a fair extension, subject to the points just made.

To be entitled to an extension in principle, the contractor must have acted to avoid or reduce the sub-contractor's own delay, the delay 'on his part'. This should be distinguished from the delay which is caused to him by the sub-contractor's delay. Here he has to act to mitigate the effects, as with all relevant events, perhaps by reorganising his domestic sub-contractors (who have their own rights to extensions) to counter the impact. Failure to mitigate does not debar him from securing an extension for this particular event, but it may reduce its amount. In reviewing the sub-contractor's extensions, the architect also needs to look to this area of delay where there are not extensions of time.

OVERLAPPING CAUSES OF DELAY

When several causes combine to produce delay, some being relevant events and some not, the question of the allowable extension of time arises. The categories of causes may be summarised for this purpose as:

(a) Employer's responsibility leading to extension, such as due to architect's instructions (relevant sub-contractors may be included here for present purposes).
(b) Contractor's responsibility not leading to extension, such as poor programming or organisation.
(c) 'Neutral' causes leading to extension, such as strikes.
(d) 'Neutral' causes not leading to extension, such as failure of a domestic supplier.

Of these, (a) and (c) are 'qualifying' causes and so may be relevant events, while (b) and (d) are 'non-qualifying' causes for a potential extension. The guiding principles for calculating the duration of any extension when more than one cause occurs, are related to these two condensed groupings: qualifying and non-qualifying. Several of the possible combinations are shown in Fig. 11.1. They all relate to delay actually caused and making for delayed completion, and are based upon these propositions:

(a) A non-qualifying cause would have happened independently of an overlapping qualifying cause, so that the delay which it causes is held to be primary in effect.
(b) A qualifying cause should be held to be superimposed upon the effect of an overlapping non-qualifying cause, so that only the excess due to the qualifying cause is allowed in calculating an extension.
(c) Two or more overlapping causes in the same grouping, qualifying or non-qualifying, may lead to a different overall delay from that calculated

as their sum, and this different overall delay will usually be less than the sum, but perhaps more than the length of the greater single delay.

(d) A qualifying delay occurring after a non-qualifying delay, but affected in duration by the 'amended' time at which it occurs, is to be allowed at its actual length, longer or shorter.

For greater completeness, two versions of non-overlapping delays are shown first. There is also one illustrating the principle in the legal decision mentioned below. The order in which qualifying and non-qualifying causes occur has no effect on the extension granted, unless the qualifying cause actually falls after the due date for completion has passed, as discussed elsewhere in this chapter. The calculation of an extension of time is difficult to show with any realism in a book, because of the limitations on data, but its relationship to a network analysis is shown in Chapter 19. The diagrams in Fig. 11.1 of delay occurring in a programme of 40 weeks' original duration show these effects, following the notation in the figure:

(a) A qualifying delay of 10 weeks and a non-qualifying delay of 5 weeks: extension of 10 weeks.

(b) The same delays as in (a), but in reverse order: the same extension.

(c) A qualifying delay of 10 weeks entirely overlapping with a non-qualifying delay of 5 weeks: 5 weeks' extension. Had these values been reversed, there would have been no extension. See also (e) below.

(d) The same delays as in (c), but creating a further 2 weeks' delay by their interaction: 7 weeks' extension.

(e) Delays as in (d), but with the values reversed: 2 weeks' extension.

(f) Qualifying delays of 10 and 5 weeks respectively, overlapping but creating a further 2 weeks' delay by their interaction: 12 weeks' extension.

(g) A qualifying delay which alone would be 4 weeks, preceded by a non-qualifying delay of 10 weeks, and so displaced into a period in the programme when it becomes 7 weeks: extension 7 weeks. See the case following here.

In *Walter Lawrence & Son Ltd* v. *Commercial Union Properties (UK) Ltd* (1984), there was delay due to exceptional weather which occurred after other delay which was the contractor's responsibility. In consequence, the weather delay was more prolonged than might have been expected. It was held that the weather delay was to be assessed as it occurred and not as some putative shorter delay, as though the other delay had not preceded it. Wider application of this principle tends to support the larger actual extension for a contractor, rather than a reduced one, in a range of appropriate circumstances.

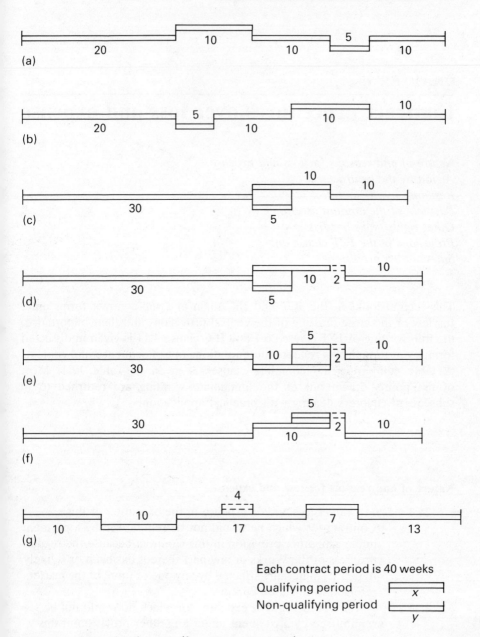

Fig. 11.1 Interrelated events (for comment see text)

CHAPTER 12

Contract procedures over loss and expense

Nature of and reasons for loss and expense
Action by the contractor
Response by the architect
Payment of the amount ascertained
Other rights and remedies
Provisions in the JCT clause only
Sub-contract provisions

This section looks at the JCT and IFC main and sub-contract forms only. In view of the close drafting of the central provisions and their importance, the full wording of JCT clause 26.1 and IFC clause 4.11 is given in dissected form, even though this renders the quotations out of sequence and context. A table comparing the complete clauses is given in Table 12.1. Most of the points drawn out of the immediate wording are returned to in subsequent chapters dealing with practical application.

Nature of and reasons for loss and expense

26.1   . . . direct loss and/or expense in the execution of this Contract for which he would not be reimbursed by a payment under any other provision in this Contract because the regular progress of the Works or any part thereof has been or is likely to be . . . materially affected by any one or more of the matters referred to in clause 26.2; . . .

4.11   . . . direct loss and/or expense, for which he would not be reimbursed by a payment under any other provision of this Contract, due to

(a) the deferment of the Employer giving possession of the site under clause 2.2 where that clause is stated in the Appendix to be applicable; or

(b) the regular progress of the Works or part of the Works being materially affected by any one or more of the matters referred to in clause 4.12, . . .

Table 12.1 Comparison of the main provisions of JCT clauses 26.1 and IFC clause 4.11 over loss and expense

JCT clause 26.1	*IFC clause 4.11*
If the Contractor makes written application to the Architect stating . . . that he has incurred or is likely to incur direct loss and/or expense in the execution of this Contract for which he would not be reimbursed by a payment under any other provision in this Contract . . . and if and as soon as the Architect is of the opinion . . .	If, upon written application being made to him by the Contractor within a reasonable time of it becoming apparent, the Architect is of the opinion . . .
. . . that the regular progress of the Works or any part thereof has been or is likely to be so materially affected as set out in the application of the Contractor . . .	. . . that the Contractor has incurred or is likely to incur direct loss and/or expense for which he would not be reimbursed by a payment under any other provision of this Contract, . . .
. . . because the regular progress of the Works or any part thereof has been or is likely to be so materially affected by any one or more of the matters referred to in clause 26.2; . . .	. . . due to

(a) the deferment of the Employer giving possession of the site under clause 2.2 where that clause is stated in the Appendix to be applicable; or

(b) the regular progress of the Works or part of the Works being materially affected by any one or more of the matters referred to in clause 4.12, . . . |
. . . then the Architect from time to time thereafter shall ascertain, or shall instruct the Quantity Surveyor to ascertain, . . .	. . . then the Architect shall ascertain, or shall instruct the Quantity Surveyor to ascertain, . . .
. . . the amount of such loss and/or expense which has been or is being incurred by the Contractor . . .	such loss and expense incurred . . .
. . . provided always that:	
1 the Contractor's application shall be made as soon as it has become, or should reasonably have become, apparent to him that . . . [progress is] affected as aforesaid, and	[within a reasonable time of it becoming apparent]
2 the Contractor shall in support of his application submit . . . upon request such information as should reasonably enable . . . an opinion as aforesaid, and	. . . provided that the Contractor shall in support of his application submit such information required . . . as is reasonably necessary for the purposes of this clause
3 the Contractor shall submit . . . upon request such details . . . as are reasonably necessary for such ascertainment as aforesaid.	

With the exception of (a) in the IFC clause, the two clauses are quite comparable and may be taken together.

The nature of the loss and expense is firstly that it is direct. This aspect is discussed in Chapter 10, but in essence means that what is allowable is much the same as would arise under an award of damages by the courts. It is therefore intended to put the aggrieved party back into the position in which he would have been if the breach had not occurred, so far as money can do this. In that it is direct, it does not allow for consequences which are indirect, that is which follow at a distance because there is some intervening event. Not all loss and expense occurring 'in the execution of this Contract' are reimbursable, as some may be due to other causes, including those which lie in the contractor's own inadequacies. Equally though, it also means that loss occurring outside the contract, but due to events within it, may be allowable on occasions. This is particularly true of loss of profit on lost business, discussed in Chapter 15.

The twin terms 'loss' and 'expense' mean that both a failure to receive and a necessity to expend may qualify. The 'and/or' conjunction simply establishes that either or both may be in prospect in any instance. It is self-evident at law that the contractor is not entitled to be reimbursed under this provision and again under another for the same reason. The expression relating to 'payment under any other provision' also means that the present loss and expense provision is the last port of call, after as much as possible of what is due has been met under, say, the variations clauses. This point is discussed in appropriate places in relation to the attractiveness of the several options to the respective parties, particularly in Chapters 6 and 19.

The mention of 'the matters referred to' covers the set of reasons described in Chapter 9. These are a smaller group than those which constitute relevant events for extension of time (see Table 9.1), there being no necessary connection between them on a given occasion. But it is equally true that only items set out in the present clauses produce an entitlement to recover loss and expense by using its machinery. It is permissible and necessary to resort to proceedings to obtain redress on other appropriate issues not listed.

The one extra reason in the JCT clause (amended 87) and the IFC clause (also given under extension of time) is that of delay in gaining possession of the site due to the employer's action. It is an optional provision, activated by an appendix entry, which the contractor should therefore ensure is made whenever it may be needed. Lack of an entry means that, as with the unamended JCT contract, there is a breach if delay occurs, so that the contractor has to negotiate or use proceedings to seek redress. The consequences should be fairly clear to identify when there is a straightforward shift of the whole programme, rather than a disruption within it.

If the delay is other than nominal, whenever the provision does not apply, the contractor may be advised to consider agreeing an amount in advance of proceeding with the contract, as a pre-condition to the waiving

on his part of a fundamental breach. In practice, this may be a question of expediency, according to which party is most concerned about not entering into the contract or by further delay, tempered by the amount at issue.

While no specific consequences are given following on this last reason for loss and expense, actual financial deprivation must of course follow for it to lead to any payment when once a contract with the provision is in being. This is also true of the other matters applying in both contracts, but a further criterion is introduced for all of these. This is that 'regular progress' is 'materially affected' by the matter concerned.

The latter phrase may be taken first. It is intended to exclude the small aberrations which occur within any programme for activities as complex and vulnerable as building works. It is not in the nature of things precise, but suggests an identifiable disturbance sufficient to step up the contractor's costs by more than the margin to be expected either way within routine fluctuations of output.

There is no absolute bottom figure in such a situation, nor one that can be measured as a percentage of the contract sum or any other amount. Given a small-scale matter affecting a restricted part of the works, as is possible under the wording, the actual loss and expense may be quite small, so long as the disturbance is material within the area concerned. This is especially so if sub-contractors are involved, with their more restricted interest financially, although it may be argued (unreasonably, it is suggested) that what justifies their claims against the contractor does not justify that of the contractor in the main contract context.

'Regular progress' indicates the element of disturbance. The contractor is under an obligation by JCT clause 23.1 and IFC clause 2.1 that he shall 'regularly and diligently proceed' with the works, as well as the obligation to complete 'on or before the Completion Date'. It has been indicated that what leads to an extension of time does not automatically lead to a loss and expense payment, while the converse is also true. Nevertheless, disturbance of regular progress can embrace at least two distinct characteristics:

(a) Work being performed in an uneconomic order and possibly piecemeal.
(b) Work being extended over time, perhaps by performance in a series
    of separated relatively piecemeal stages, perhaps by simple attenuation
    without breaks.

These characteristics are considered more fully in Chapter 14, but may be noted here as the necessary indications for the clauses to come to life. It may be said that the term 'disruption' carries a similar connotation to 'disturbance' for present purposes.

The other feature of the immediate clause, using the JCT wording, is that 'progress . . . has been or is likely to be . . . affected', that is there is either a recent effect or an element of futurity about the disturbance, or even both. This wording gives the possibility of two basic situations in which loss and expense will be entertained. The first is when it is already present when discovered, perhaps because it occurs suddenly, perhaps because it creeps up

through the operation of several factors, which individually seem harmless but combine to produce the disturbance. In a smaller instance, it may even be complete when first noticed. The second is when it can be foreseen, at least as an outline problem likely to occur, even if not quite certain in occurrence and maybe less in detail. By virtue of the proviso about giving early notice considered below, the contractor is required to deal with matters as in the second category whenever possible, if he is not to prejudice his chances of reimbursement.

Action by the contractor

26.1   If the Contractor makes written application to the Architect stating that he has incurred or is likely to incur direct loss and/or expense . . . [because of] any one or more of the matters . . . provided always that:

1. the Contractor's application shall be made as soon as it has become, or should reasonably have become, apparent to him that . . . the regular progress . . . [is] affected as aforesaid, and

2. the Contractor shall in support of his application submit . . . upon request such information . . . [for] the Architect to form an opinion . . .

3. the Contractor shall submit . . . upon request such details . . . as are reasonably necessary for such ascertainment . . .

4.11   If, upon written application being made . . . within a reasonable time . . . by the Contractor [over loss and expense] . . . provided that the Contractor shall . . . submit such information . . . as is reasonably necessary . . .

It is obvious that the JCT clause, as relating to larger or more complicated contracts, is more demanding. But also, in part, the IFC clause has been drafted to be less repetitive.

Both clauses require the contractor to make his 'application' in writing and to give *general* warning (see the cases below) that loss and expense have been incurred or are threatening, in the ways outlined already. This allows the architect to take any action which may be possible to reduce the effects of what is going on, in addition to the contractor taking his own ameliorating actions. It also allows the architect, or the quantity surveyor on his behalf, to keep records of what is happening, so that a proper assessment may be made of the loss and expense, in so far as site records can help. The position under both forms should be distinguished from that under the JCT 1963 form, referred to under 'Interest and financing charges' in Chapter 15.

If the contractor defaults in giving this notice, he may well prejudice his position by preventing information from being gathered. The school of

thought which says that it is best to leave everything over until a late stage when memories have faded, is risking a complete rebuttal, or at best a too modest settlement. As it is usually possible at least to foresee the likelihood of loss and expense, it is far better to give warning. The present contract routine is distinctly more precise than in earlier editions, and is to be welcomed. It also has the effect that it is not necessary for the contractor to give a series of 'updating' notices to cover a continuing matter, as was the case before.

The JCT clause is explicit that the contractor is to state the matter or matters causing his loss and expense, and this means that he must make a separate application for each matter which leads to distinct loss and expense. If, however, more than one matter occurs in close conjunction, with inseparable effects, he should then give them in the same application. This is sometimes referred to as a 'rolled-up' claim approach, since the case of *J. Crosby & Sons Ltd* v. *Portland Urban District Council* (1978) where it was ruled that inseparable matters might lead to inseparable effects which might be ascertained together, provided no duplication between them or other matters occurred.

This case was followed in *Stanley Hugh Leach Ltd* v. *London Borough of Merton* (1985), where the contractor had written a single letter lacking in detail and covering application for loss and expense covering both clauses 11(6) and 24(1) of the JCT 1963 form. The rolled-up approach was permissible when separation was not practical, and the contractor was not required to put in a moneyed-out claim, but simply to give notice of happenings. Even these might be well within the knowledge of the architect, as he had frequent contact with the site. This approach is not to be used when segregation is practicable, and it certainly is not to be used on the plea that 'it is too late now to do anything else: the records are not available'. JCT 80 and IFC 84 are drafted to rely on progressive data whether separation is possible or not.

The contractor is in a particular predicament when there is an incremental build-up of disturbance due to a series of individually minor matters, and he is uncertain whether to make an application. It may be best to wait until the situation is developing clearly, but no longer.

The alternative temptation for a harassed contractor is to put in an application every time that anything happens, be it even a revised drawing issue of the most minor variety. At the very least, this creates the atmosphere of 'little boy cries wolf', as he is soon not taken seriously. But worse, when his standard acknowledgement always reads as an application about loss and expense, he is giving no effective notice at all, as he is not specifying any precise matter. He is as much in breach of the clause requirements, as if he did not act at all when the real thing emerges.

Thus far, the two clauses are requiring similar action: an 'application' stating simply that loss and expense are present or anticipated and tracing the reason for this back to a matter or matters. There is no obligation on the contractor to put forward anything like a claim document; in fact this may well be impossible at such an early stage. The difference of emphasis is that the IFC clause does not require the contractor to act 'as soon as' there are,

but 'within a reasonable time of', danger signals. This is not quite so onerous, but should not lead to a damaging delay. It probably reflects the realities of life better and tones down the tendency mentioned in the preceding paragraph.

The application is really one for the architect to consider the overall situation, as set out under the next heading. He is the one to decide when to request supporting information to enable him to deal with the principle of the application and then with the evaluation aspect. These two elements are spelt out separately in the JCT clause, whereas the IFC clause is again less specific, but can be read just as demandingly.

It is always wise for the contractor to put forward as much properly detailed information as he can from time to time, and not to wait until he is asked. This issue is taken further in Chapter 17. When once he has applied, however, he is not obliged to take the initiative, so that he cannot be faulted for failing to supply data which have not been requested or warn of further developments, unless there is in effect some extra matter which comes up to exacerbate the situation, so requiring a fresh application. The strongest express obligation is that in JCT clause 30.6.1.1 and IFC clause 4.5 for the contractor to provide 'all documents . . . for the purposes of the adjustment of the Contract Sum', but these clauses are quite ambivalent as to whether this is to be done before or after practical completion. There is a weakness in the wording, by comparison with that over extension of time where the contractor is required to continue to give data without being asked, as well as any which may be requested. It is therefore prudent for the architect or the quantity surveyor, when acting on his behalf, to request details with as much precision as is suitable, and so activate the provisions of the clauses. This will be in addition to anything which either of them is obtaining by direct observation on site and, preferably, notifying to the contractor as being on record.

There are cases in which a contract gets so out of hand that the submission of individual applications and the segregation of the resulting records become an almost academic exercise. Until this impossible stage is reached, the formal procedure should be maintained, while even thereafter some tailor-made scheme should be instituted that will prevent the project veering off into little more than thinly disguised prime cost.

Response by the architect

26.1   . . . if and so soon as the Architect is of the opinion that the regular progress . . . [is, or is likely to be] materially affected as set out in the application of the Contractor . . . then the Architect from time to time shall ascertain, or shall instruct the Quantity Surveyor to ascertain the amount . . . which has been or is being incurred . . .

4.11   If . . . the Architect is of the opinion that the Contractor has incurred or is likely to incur direct loss and/or expense . . . then

the Architect shall ascertain or shall instruct the Quantity
Surveyor to
ascertain . . . the amount.

This heading and 'Action by the contractor' above are deliberately
chosen to indicate that the contractor must take the initiative, while the
architect acts only in response to the action of the contractor. Even if the
architect sees a very clear loss and expense situation boiling up, he need
not even suggest to the contractor that he should start affairs off with an
application, although desirably he should to avoid acrimony later and the
possibility of proceedings. Proceedings are the more difficult alternative to
what is effectively a negotiation, which comes about when the present clauses
are used.

It is always open to the architect to instruct postponement of all or part
of the works under JCT clause 23.2 or IFC clause 3.15 respectively, if he
considers that this will reduce the loss and expense being incurred. Except in
the clearest of circumstances, he is not advised to do this without consulting
the contractor fully.

While the two clauses are worded somewhat differently at this point,
their effect is the same. The JCT version requires the architect to form
an opinion about progress, while the IFC version requires him to form his
opinion about whether loss and expense have occurred for the reasons given
which are wider by the inclusion of delay in gaining site possession. It could
be suggested that the latter version raises the contractor's hopes rather more!
Until however actual ascertainment is accomplished, there is in the nature of
things no commitment to any particular sum, which may still turn out to be
zero.

Both clauses place the whole responsibility upon the architect for forming
an opinion on whether a case for disturbance exists at all, and this he cannot
shed, however much he may seek advice from the quantity surveyor or others
over matters of fact. In seeking such advice, he should endeavour to remain
uninfluenced by the consequences which are suggested.

The clauses also place the primary responsibility for ascertaining the
amount upon him. This arrangement is one of the most commonly criticised
aspects of these clauses, because the architect is saddled with being judge and
jury in matters which frequently arise out of his own actions or inactions, as
reference to the list of matters will show. It may be that the real cause lies
'further back' with the employer or with forces which even he cannot control,
but often it is the architect's own administration which is in question. In the
case of the ascertainment aspect only, the clauses do allow the architect to
instruct the quantity surveyor to perform this function, and it is to be hoped
that he will always require this. There have been calls for the inclusion of an
adjudicator within the contract system, to whom disputes could be referred.
This has its difficulties, but also considerable merit.

The architect's instruction to the quantity surveyor to ascertain loss
and expense must be made in respect of each matter which is notified, or

of each group of overlapping matters, unless he chooses to refer all such items to the quantity surveyor by a blanket instruction. He should sensibly refer a complete item, if he does so at all. Apart from the question of the architect's own potential conflict of interests or perception of the situation, the advantage of involving the quantity surveyor is that he has all the other financial affairs under his control and can avoid any double counting or gap. Once he does instruct the quantity surveyor to ascertain an amount, the architect relinquishes control and the quantity surveyor is empowered to reach finality, subject to his continuing need to refer back about any over-arching elements within the architect's opinion. Equally, the employer is bound by the results, subject to his final right to proceedings, even though employers are often consulted in practice during negotiations about loss and expense matters.

In *Croudace Ltd* v. *London Borough of Lambeth* (1984), under a JCT 63 contract, the contractor had given regular notices during progress of loss and expense and had made application for their amount within a reasonable time. The Council's architect had retired a few days after the application and no successor was appointed, nor was anyone else nominated under the contract for the purpose. The Council had annexed ascertainment to their staff and not to the private architect or quantity surveyor acting, but were then dilatory in dealing. It was held that the Council could not stay proceedings and seek arbitration (a delaying tactic), as there was no arbitrable dispute, and that the inability of the architect or quantity surveyor to ascertain was due to breach by the employer. Further, because of the breach, the absence of a certificate for an amount on account was no bar to the contractor recovering in the action.

A separate application has to be made about each matter as it arises. This means that the architect cannot take in further matters without the contractor first raising them, however obvious they are. This is to be distinguished from the position under the final settling of extension of time, when the architect may choose to take in fresh relevant events at his own discretion. He may well wish to nudge the contractor's elbow to save covering similar ground more than once, if the contractor is slow off the mark. It is also to be distinguished from the position under the JCT 1963 form, where it was necessary for the contractor to make a further application or more about the same matter, if some of its effects were still future when the first application was made. This is emphasised by the *Minter* v. *Welsh Health* case considered in Chapter 15.

Similarly, the architect or the quantity surveyor in evaluating the loss and expense cannot go beyond the matters already raised by the contractor. It is the contractor's responsibility to supply information of two sorts 'upon request': that needed for the architect to form an opinion, and that needed by him or the quantity surveyor to ascertain loss and expense. Strictly, he cannot make a further application via one of these supplies of information, but must do so separately. It is always tempting to throw in quite openly some further item when drawing up details supporting an earlier one, so

saving extra administration in what the contractor did not ask for in the first place. If the new matter directly follows on from the old, or overlaps with it substantially, it may be sensible to treat it as an extension of it. If not, it is best to formalise the position by seeking a fresh application.

No particular structure is required for any data which the contractor supplies on request. As these are qualified by 'reasonably enable' and 'reasonably necessary', the architect (or in the second instance the quantity surveyor) has a right within these limits to request information broken down in sections and generally laid out to facilitate his work, or to refer it back for emendation and clarification. There is no power to require the contractor to forward a complete claim document in elaborate style, of the type which has become so fashionable. Whether he chooses to put in the first statement of the position in such a document or something less formal, is his concern and largely a matter of psychology. The delay may count against the validity of his claim within the contract procedures. The format of such a claim is outlined in Chapter 23.

The clauses simply require the architect or the quantity surveyor 'to ascertain' the amount of loss and expense, aided by what the contractor produces on request. This suggests something of a prising out of detail to lead to a complete picture assembled like a jigsaw. While someone has to make the first move, there is often room for negotiation by stages, rather than a sweeping assertion waiting to be cut to pieces by 'the other side'. The term 'ascertain' has its problems in implementation, as discussed in Chapter 14. It gives the impression that the loss and expense are some fixed amounts lying somewhere waiting to be discovered in a purely objective manner. Life is not always so easy.

Payment of the amount ascertained

This is one of several provisions subsidiary to JCT clause 26.1 and IFC clause 4.11. It occurs as JCT clause 26.5, while IFC clause 4.11 contains it in itself. The former clause is the more explicit by referring to 'Any amount from time to time ascertained', whereas the latter says 'the amount thereof' only. In each case there is authority to add the amount to the contract sum. Under JCT clause 3 there is further authority to include the amounts of all adjustments of the contract sum in interim certificates. The IFC form does not contain such a provision, although both JCT clause 30.2.2.2 and IFC clause 4.2.2 allow inclusion of loss and expense amounts in certificates without deduction of retention.

The general philosophy of interim payment is that all amounts allowed may be included on a firm or approximate basis, according to how far the work, etc. and calculation have proceeded. JCT clause 3 allows inclusion 'as soon as such amount is ascertained in whole or in part'. The latter part of this may be interpreted to include 'some part as ascertained finally and accurately, or some part or the whole as ascertained approximately or

provisionally'. It is suggested that all of this enlarged reading is correct and also fair and reasonable. While the question of delay in making payments is an area of legal uncertainty, whatever its commercial dubiousness, there appears no contractual reason for failure to include amounts when once some fairly secure basis of approximation has emerged. It certainly cuts down on the level of financing charges otherwise entering on an ongoing basis into the calculation of loss and expense under the current contract forms. There is further discussion of the general withholding of amounts due in Chapter 8.

Other rights and remedies

JCT clause 26.6 and the last paragraph of IFC clause 4.11 recite that the provisions preceding them are 'without prejudice to any other rights or remedies which the Contractor may possess'. They might have added 'or which the Employer may possess', but do not, presumably because the whole of what goes before is for the contractor's benefit.

The effect of the present clauses is that they stand in order of recourse to available remedies as follows:

(a) *First*: to all other provisions of the contract over payment.
(b) *Second*: to clauses 26 and 4.11 variously for what is not
    reimbursed . . . under any other provision'.
(c) *Third*: to legal action or arbitration.

Provisions in the JCT clause only

There are two items peculiar to the JCT form. The first is an enigmatic reference to extension of time in clause 26.3, requiring the architect to state what extension he has granted for any of the relevant events under clause 25 which correspond to matters under clause 26, 'If and to the extent that it is necessary for ascertainment . . . of loss and/or expense'. This reflects the possibility that one extension of time may embrace several relevant events, so that segregation of the separate sub-extensions is not automatically given when the extension is granted.

Why this provision is made is not clear. As stressed in several places in this book, no inevitable connection between extension of time and loss and expense is to be assumed, as either can occur without the other. Even when an extension is granted and loss and expense are also due to be reimbursed, it does not follow that any prolongation costs will be measured by the extension granted. There cannot be any question of acceleration in view, as nowhere is the contractor required to make up lost time as mitigation of effects. In any case the present stipulation is in the context of ascertainment, not counteraction.

For the contract to imply some sort of connection here can only create confusion in the minds of its readers. It would appear better, and on wider

grounds sensible, for there to be a requirement in clause 25 for the architect to give a full analysis of any composite extension into its constituent parts, if the contractor should request this at any time. This would enable the contractor always to reassure himself or otherwise over what has been granted. It would also deal with the fact that the architect's statement in isolation for any one relevant event may make the extension appear more or less than it should be, when it has originally been compounded with other relevant events during calculation (see the mention of overlapping causes at the end of Ch. 11). The contractor may form a different detailed interpretation within the overall position, given all of the facts, and this is his prerogative if he wishes to do it for any purpose, but no immediate concern of the architect or the employer.

The second item peculiar to the JCT clause is the question of nominated sub-contractors and loss and expense in clause 26.4, which needs mention because of the architect's involvement, and perhaps the quantity surveyor's, under the sub-contract forms in those loss and expense issues which are not solely between contractor and sub-contractor. This issue is discussed under 'Sub-contract provisions' below, although any amounts which are the responsibility of the employer will be included in the nominated accounts and so come into the main reckoning. Again the puzzling question of extension of time comes into the provision.

Sub-contract provisions

The preceding sections are as relevant to sub-contractors as to the main contractor, but some additional aspects also apply. For these purposes, sub-contractors divide into two groups:

(a) Nominated sub-contractors.
(b) Domestic and named sub-contractors.

The point of the distinction is that nominated sub-contractors receive special attention in the main contracts when loss and expense are due to one of the given matters, whereas the other types of sub-contractors are not recognised by the main contracts for this purpose. There are, however, other causes of loss and expense which are effective solely between the contractor and all types of sub-contractors. These are treated in the sub-contracts, but are not mentioned in the main contracts.

NOMINATED SUB-CONTRACTS

The line and direction of communication set out in the JCT forms over sub-contract loss and expense are quite clear: the sub-contractor in all cases deals primarily with the contractor. Indeed, if the cause of loss and expense is not a 'matter' as defined under his sub-contract, he deals solely with the

contractor. Even when it is such a matter, he must raise it with the contractor, for the latter to pass on to the architect. It is not the contractor's responsibility when giving a notice of his own to make reference unprompted to any trouble of a nominated sub-contractor. He acts under main clause 26.4.1 'upon receipt of a written application made . . . under clause 13.1 of Sub-Contract NSC/4 or NSC/4a'. That clause requires the sub-contractor to take the initiative, just as much as must the contractor under main clause 26.1 over his own concerns.

Two distinctions may be noted here. One is by comparison with domestic sub-contractors, over whom the contractor at his own discretion includes any mention in his initial application, or defers it until later, and correspondingly gives his own presentation of figures in his own application and supporting details. This is so, even though these may be the same as, or close to, those of the sub-contractors, on the net direct loss principle and even though he still has no obligation towards the sub-contractor to include anything until approached.

The other distinction is by comparison with extension of time, when the contractor has to take account of delay effects on sub-contractors in any notice which he initiates. This is the effect of main clause 25.2.1.1, under which the contractor has also to notify any sub-contractor of what he is about. In the case of loss and expense, the contractor has no obligation to start off anything for the sub-contractor. The reason for the distinction is that delay can affect numbers of those on site, because activities interact, and so seeking an extension of time affects them all. Loss and expense are a more 'individual' affair, in that it flows immediately from the causal matter to the sufferer, and not from its financial consequences on another. One person may be losing while another is unaffected by the same matter: site work still proceeds, at least to a point.

It is therefore necessary for a nominated sub-contractor to take all the specified steps, as would the contractor over his own loss and expense. The steps in question are the same in all essential features and need no further elaboration. It is then the responsibility of the contractor to pass the sub-contractor's application on to the architect. If he omits to do this, so that the sub-contractor loses his right to payment by being out of time in applying, the contractor is in breach of sub-contract clause 13.1.1. The sub-contractor may then proceed against the contractor for this breach, but cannot seek reimbursement directly under the mechanisms provided within the sub-contract.

When the procedure is properly operated, it becomes the responsibility of the architect to ascertain the amount or to instruct the quantity surveyor to do so, just as for the contractor's own amounts. While the point is not express, the principle is for all dealings after the application to be dealt with through the contractor. In practice, as with other financial settlements with nominated persons, it is more expedient for negotiations to proceed direct, although the contractor should be kept informed. This is especially necessary if matters are overlapping with loss and expense amounts which

are entirely between contractor and sub-contractor, whatever the direction of indebtedness, so creating a three-way situation.

The resulting amount ascertained is included in the total set against the prime cost sum in settling the final account, so that the contractor has no real concern over its level, only over whether any extraneous amounts are still to come his way as a result of the three-way pattern.

Sub-contract clauses 13.2 and 13.3 deal with the cases of loss and expense caused by contractor or sub-contractor to the other, owing to 'any act, omission or default' of the one. They simply require the aggrieved party to give notice 'within a reasonable time' to the other and for 'the agreed amount' to be 'recoverable . . . as a debt' or, in the case of what is due to the contractor only, to be 'deducted from any monies due or to become due'. There is no provision for adjusting the sub-contract sum in either direction. Often settlement will be achieved by the most direct and suitable means available.

What is missing, by comparison with sub-contract clause 13.1, is any further detailed procedure (or indeed any detail), as under the main contract. Obviously, something must happen. In the case of claims by the contractor against the sub-contractor, some form of quantification has to be made to operate the set-off procedures of sub-contract clause 23, if this is invoked, as is most likely (see Ch. 8). Otherwise the parties must work out their own destinies. The pattern of dealings when the architect is involved gives a sensible guide to follow.

A procedure for the three-way case is not covered in the clauses, because it cannot sensibly be. In principle, the amounts which may occur can be separated into the following elements:

(a) Those between the employer and contractor, alone.
(b) Those between the employer and contractor, but passed up from the sub-contractor.
(c) Those between the contractor and sub-contractor, alone.
(d) Those between the contractor and sub-contractor, but passed down from the employer.
(e) Those between the employer and sub-contractor, under the employer/sub-contractor agreement if there is one, possibly reflecting amounts under (a).

It is up to those dealing to separate out the elements which they do not consider to lie within their own area of action, quite apart from responsibility, and pass them resolutely back, so that the relevant procedures apply to each element. The temptation to express an opinion or negotiate over some bordering issue should be studiously avoided, until a potential liability is identified, and even then it may well nigh create an unwarranted liability. The best way in practice may be for the three sets of negotiators (as they usually become) to meet and seek to allocate items in principle between them. This should be done without offering any trade-off if something is taken elsewhere, as this can have a nasty habit of rebounding later. The other side of this coin is to

agree a division 'without prejudice to review', if the various responsibilities are not entirely clear at the stage reached.

DOMESTIC AND NAMED SUB-CONTRACTS

Here the contractor alone deals with the sub-contractor concerned in any instance. As noted above, the architect deals immediately with the contractor and receives any representations about loss and expense due to 'matters' as from the contractor. These may well amount to similar sums, as they are intended to be settlements equivalent to common law damages, and so to reinstate the sufferer into the position in which he would have been apart from the disturbance. It is of course well known that claims settled at different contractual levels may differ in practice for an assortment of reasons, but this is to depart from principles or theory.

The two sub-contracts therefore deal with all loss and expense amounts of the sub-contractor in the same way, that is they do not provide separate clauses for 'matters' and for 'defaults, etc.', as do the nominated clauses, on the basis that the parties to the sub-contract must settle between themselves alone. They appear to differ between themselves over other points. Domestic clause 13.1 requires the sub-contractor to apply within a reasonable time and to submit information of effects and details of loss and expense, so paralleling the main contract. Named clause 14.1 has the reasonable time requirement, backed up by an 'information as necessary' requirement. These should not cause any serious practical differences.

A three-way claim situation is outlined in Chapter 21.

CHAPTER 13

Disturbance of regular progress

The nature of disturbance
Some factors related to disturbance
Patterns of disturbance

This chapter is concerned with the key reason why the contractor may become entitled to payment for loss and expense. The title is a convenient shorthand for the precise terminology:

(a) JCT clause 26.1 has 'direct loss and/or expense . . . because the regular progress of the Works or any part thereof . . . [is] materially affected'.
(b) IFC clause 4.11 has 'direct loss and/or expense . . . due to . . . the regular progress of the Works or part of the Works being materially affected'.

The clauses are considered in their entireties in Chapter 12, while other activities arising out of their operation are taken in later chapters. The term 'materially affected' has been discussed as meaning some substantial impact, greater than the comparatively incidental fluctuations due to ordinary external influences and internal inefficiencies which are experienced in all projects, and especially those which proceed in uncertain circumstances as on a construction site.

The clauses restrict rigorously the influences affecting progress which qualify as leading to reimbursement of loss and expense. They give the same list of matters, except that the JCT clause (amended 87) and the IFC clause add delay in giving the contractor possession of the site. All the matters are discussed fully in Chapter 9. They constitute just some of the larger list of items qualifying as relevant events, but it may be stressed yet again that an extension of time does not necessarily lead to payment for loss and expense for the same occurrence, or *vice versa*. There may also be other factors which entitle the contractor to recompense, but these must be pursued by common law remedies if there is resistance to payment: the clauses and their procedures cannot be invoked. These limits to what is being discussed in the present chapter should be carefully marked.

The nature of disturbance

Throughout the two contracts mentioned, the noun 'disturbance' is not used

as corresponding to 'materially affected', any more than are the two other nouns commonly coming into the reckoning. Of these, 'disruption' has the meaning of a more violent and thoroughgoing disturbance, but may be taken as synonymous with a disturbance of orderliness which reaches significant proportions. It is the term used in the GC/Works/1 form of contract, used by central government bodies.

The other noun 'prolongation' clearly refers to something distinguishable, so that the case must be made out here for including it also within 'disturbance of regular progress' for contract purposes.

DISRUPTION AND PROLONGATION

Disruption can take many forms, as the art of claimsmanship demonstrates. Three broad, basic conditions leading to it may be discerned:

(a) A change in the sequence and pattern of the intended work, without a significant change in what is to be produced eventually, perhaps due to delay in, or modification of, the information needed to carry out work. (Examples are the discovery of the ancient fort in Ch. 19 and of the power cable in Ch. 21.)

(b) The introduction of some significant element of additional work, which may be seen in the finished project, in such a way or at such a time as to cause a change, complication or delay in the sequence and pattern of the original work. It is extremely unlikely that significant omission of work will produce disruption, however else it may lead to financial recompense. (Examples are the annexes, the infusion plant and work due to the floor damage in Ch. 19.)

(c) The introduction of numerous, individually insignificant additions or omissions or other changes of mind, in ways or at times which cumulatively upset the smooth running of the project. (Examples are difficult to give in the nature of things, although numerous interruptions corresponding to the delays under 'Amendment option 1' in Example B below would relate.)

The essence of each of these conditions is that the contractor has to absorb the effects into his programme of work when elements of that work are in progress, so that he cannot plan in advance how to fit them in smoothly and in the most economical way. Even if he had adequate warning, he might still incur additional costs in performing the original work because of changed conditions, but these costs would be reflected in the rates for variations under JCT clause 13.5 or IFC clause 3.7. They would not be due to disruption, but to rearrangement.

By distinction, prolongation occurs without any change in sequence and it changes the pattern only to the extent that it lengthens the contract period. Disruption may or may not extend the overall completion date, that is lead to prolongation on its own account. Conceivably, disruption need not extend the programme period for even a sub-section of the works. It is also possible

to have subsidiary prolongation of a non-critical activity without extension of the overall programme.

The essence of prolongation is a straight shift back of the programme by enforced cessation of some or all work or, alternatively, by attenuation of activity due to some stifling effect, such as shortage of enough information to proceed at the usual speed. In its pure form it does not affect the sequence of work at all, but simply when it happens along the time line. As a break, it may be known about in advance or may crop up suddenly, the main difference being the practical one of how resources may be harboured according to the opportunity to redeploy. As attenuation, it tends to creep up gradually, otherwise a halt might be called by the contractor for economy's sake. In practice it is hardly likely to appear in its completely pure form, but when it does it must be emphasised that it can lead to payment for loss and expense only when the appropriate matters are the cause. For other reasons given as relevant events only, there can at best be extension of time only, which is usually seen as a fair apportionment of risk.

Whichever way it comes about on its own, and particularly when compounded with disruption, prolongation does have the effect of disturbing regular progress. Such progress is not to be seen simply as planned and orderly, but also as steady and even. It materially affects regular progress and costs the contractor money, which may be classed as loss and expense in suitable cases. Notably, both clauses allow an instructed 'postponement of any work' (which could be the whole) as a matter, while delayed possession of the site clearly does not cause disruption, unless it be of the ordering process or of other concurrent contracts.

There is the possibility of substantial amounts of extra work, fed in as variations instructed well in advance, extending the contract period. While these should lead to extension of time, they will not lead to disturbance as considered here, since they have appeared in an orderly manner. All their financial effects should be taken up under the valuation of variations (as is illustrated in Ch. 19), including any inflation effects in a fixed price contract.

In general, the single word 'disturbance' is used in subsequent discussion to cover both disruption and prolongation, according to the context.

SOME BASIC EXAMPLES OF DISTURBANCE

By way of simplified illustration, two examples are taken here to isolate principles from the above. They raise two points.

One point is that the contractor is under no express, contractual obligation to mitigate loss and expense, as he is required to do over delay leading to extension of time. He is, however, under a general common law duty to do so and not to allow the employer's costs to mount unnecessarily. This does not mean, say, that the architect or the quantity surveyor can sit back after the event and pare down the loss and expense amount to some theoretical minimum. It just means that the contractor is to use reasonable discretion over

the measures which he takes. In general, he is under an obligation 'regularly and diligently [to] proceed with the Works', even if this is more than he needs to do to complete by the due date. It may suggest a bias to make progress, even when this is expensive. Cases on the question of mitigation show that the 'innocent' party suffering damage has a fairly wide discretion in special circumstances.

The second point is that the architect in turn has no power to instruct the contractor positively what action to take, that is to say he cannot tell him how to organise the construction of the works when things are going wrong, any more than he can when things are going right. There is not even express permission for him to require the contractor to do what is reasonable to achieve some economy (as there is over maintaining progress when there is delay), although the contractor still has the general legal responsibility on his own initiative to mitigate his loss. All that the architect has is the drastic option of holding up work completely by postponement, if this is likely to reduce the excess expenditure.

The point of the contractor putting in an 'application' over loss and expense under the contract clauses is to warn the architect of what is happening, so that he can request any data and keep his own records. It also allows him to take such action as is open to him. This is restricted to putting right the things that are causing the loss and expense, if they are within his control, and to instructing postponement. The latter is desirable only if the benefits are seen to outweigh the disadvantages, as illustrated below.

Example A

This is given in Fig. 13.1 and shows an egg-crate structure consisting of a slab foundation, with alternate lifts of *in situ* concrete walls and slabs (they could almost as well be precast) rising from it. The obvious sequence is to put up each lift in turn for the full width of this fairly narrow structure. For some reason, the detailed information for the left-hand ground-floor lift of wall is not available in time. If the contractor proceeds with as much work as he possibly can before he stops due to this shortage, he will erect everything below the heavy line stepping up to the right. When he carries on to completion, he will have performed in all six wall lifts and five slab lifts, and all but the last slab lift will be smaller than the three of each which he would originally have performed. This introduces piecemeal working for labour and plant and, in a more complex example, would carry the risk of the gangs getting in each other's way.

It may be questioned whether the contractor would not be better advised to wait in such a simple case for the missing information at some intermediate point in his work, perhaps even before performing any walls. To put up the one second-floor wall in particular may be seen as really pushing progress at the expense of cost.

Example B

This is given in Fig. 13.2 and shows an initial network analysis for a project

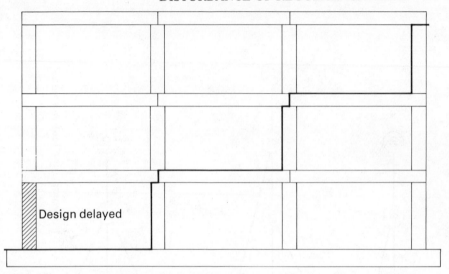

Fig. 13.1 Programme delay (Example A in text)

and two possible amendments of it, to allow for a single lapse in information. This is delay in providing the design for operation C.

The first option for the contractor is simply to wait until the information is provided at event 2A, giving a waiting or dummy operation (B). If operations E and H are on the critical path, this may create dummy operations (F) and possibly (H) to absorb delay. The extents will depend upon the float within operation F. Operations J and L are not affected in duration. The finishing event 10 is delayed, so that the project is completed late.

On this basis, operations before the dummies are not affected, while those following are simply performed late, with possible inflation and reorganisation costs. There is a general prolongation effect and the dummies represent a disturbance of regular progress by interruption.

The second option for the contractor is to attempt some reorganisation to limit delay. He might find it possible to perform parts of operations J and L (which are not on the critical path) and H (which is), before achieving events 4, 7 and 8. This creates operations J1, J2, L1 and L2, and also H1 and H2, in place of the original three, with the possibility that extra costs are incurred through smaller scale working and perhaps otherwise. The programme shows complete recovery of total time, but this may not happen. Even if it does, it gives disturbance without extension of time.

In both options, the separation of operations B and C from running in parallel will provide a further extra cost beyond prolongation costs, if they were intended to use common facilities, say batching plant or scaffolding. This is despite them not being closely interrelated at the point of application on site or in their effect on following operations, as the network logic indicates and as a distinction from the effects on operations J and L.

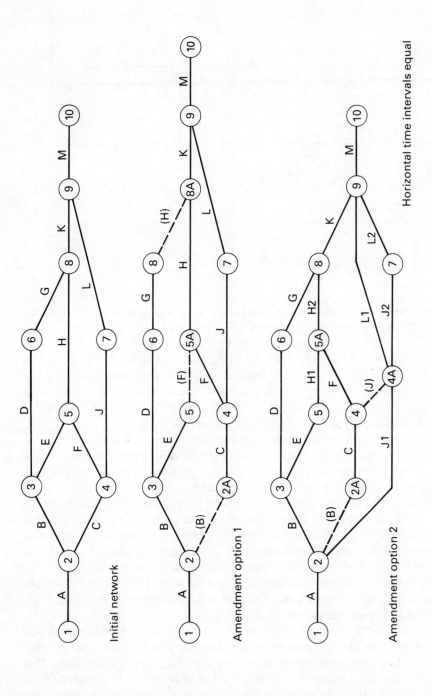

Fig. 13.2 Programme delay (Example B in text)

Initial network

Amendment option 1

Amendment option 2

Horizontal time intervals equal

The comments made under Example A about what the contractor is obliged to do are as valid here. The possibility of splitting operations highlights a little more the dilemma between mitigating the employer's extra cost and the contract responsibility to maintain progress, unless an instruction of postponement is given. On balance, the first option suggests a mitigation approach, while the second suggests maintenance of progress, within the simplified illustration provided. In practice, this conceptual division often cannot be identified with confidence. At most, the architect can suggest action by the contractor, and even here he needs to act with care to avoid running unwittingly into some excessively expensive situation. The question of the contractor's inefficiencies is discussed later in this chapter.

Some factors related to disturbance

VARIATIONS OF PHYSICAL WORK

The effect of variation instructions is to cause a replanning of work in the area concerned. If the replanning is then implemented in an orderly manner, all the financial effects are to be covered in the valuation of variations, including any undue costs of the replanning and the effects on other work associated with that varied, but which remains unvaried. Only direct disturbance costs, or the excess costs of performing work in disturbed conditions, are to be allowed as loss and expense.

The distinction is not always easy to maintain, although easier than that under 'Variations of obligations and restrictions' below. There is a special need to deal clearly with such elements as overheads, as some extra for these will be included in the valuation of additions variations themselves, which are a more likely source of disturbance than omissions. This is illustrated in the case study calculations in Chapter 20.

VARIATIONS OF OBLIGATIONS AND RESTRICTIONS

Under JCT clause 13.1.2 and IFC clause 3.6.2, the architect may instruct variations of 'any obligations and restrictions imposed . . . in the Contract Bills'. It is argued in Chapter 6 that these clauses (except in JCT amended 1987) limit his power to varying, by addition or omission, those categories of obligations and restrictions alone which are already given in the contract bills, although this is not the point at issue here.

Just as with variations of physical work, so with this variety the intention is for the immediate valuation to embrace all the financial effects, while it is provided for the related value of unvaried work to be adjusted to take account of the repercussions of the variations. This means valuation which is at the price level of the contract bills, whether by a *pro rata* method or one of fair valuation, taking care of overheads, profit and other elements in the contract sum. In particular, there may be adjustment of preliminaries items and change of allowances for working conditions as originally embodied in

measured and other prices. All of this is to take into account the effect of variations instructed early enough for the contractor to reorganise his work so that it is performed regularly and without disturbance of progress. The valuation will include for any reorganisation to this end.

It is worth repeating here the list of obligations and restrictions concerned:

(a) Access to the site or use of any specific parts of the site.
(b) Limitations of working space.
(c) Limitations of working hours.
(d) The execution or completion of the work in any specific order.

In a number of cases, the instruction of a variation of one of these items at short notice will have effects on how effectively the contractor can go about reorganising his activities, more particularly if there is an intensification of the obligation or restriction. If it is eased, he should be facing lower costs and be able to rearrange his work without disturbance, although much will depend on the length of warning given.

If there is a disturbance effect, it falls to be reimbursed as loss and expense, because it is due to a variation instruction. The distinction between the two categories, variation valuation and ascertainment of loss and expense, is important for the reasons given in Chapters 6 and 15. It will be seen, from the nature of the items listed, that segregation of the categories is easier in concept than in practice. If an important criterion of disturbance of regular progress is that work is performed out of sequence, then where is the distinction to be made in the case of item (d) above? The point is illustrated in Chapter 21, where the programme is severely modified without clear reference to obligations and restrictions.

ACCELERATION OF THE WORKS

There is no contractual provision for acceleration anywhere in either the JCT or the IFC form. Indeed only postponement and extension of time are envisaged: things either stay the same or get worse!

It therefore follows that no acceleration-related effect appears among the matters leading to loss and expense in either contract. If the employer wishes to advance the date for completion, or simply to regain lost time, he can only approach the contractor as to whether he is prepared to modify a term of the contract on some negotiated financial basis. The contractor does not have to agree to such a thing at all.

A similar position exists over any element of acceleration cost put forward by the contractor within other loss and expense items. There is no need for him to work additional overtime to what is standard on the site to catch up, while any argument that he had to work overtime for some other reason should be investigated with care. Suggestions that it was or is necessary to attract or retain labour are a regular instance. One area where some sensible margin may exist is that presented by an attempt to mitigate

a loss and so the employer's payment, but even here the contractor is well advised to secure agreement to what he proposes before he implements any policy. The choice of options given in Example B over whether to rephase work could involve some incidental overtime which might well be justified as part of an amount.

Elements of cost such as additional supervision may sometimes edge into this grey area, but are usually less clearly straight cases of acceleration expense. They should be considered equally carefully just the same.

Patterns of disturbance

While the nature of disturbance may be seen as disruption or prolongation, separately or together, it occurs in various patterns. Again, these are by no means entirely discrete single occurrences, but frequently are blurred combinations of the matters and other causes.

Distinguishing these patterns may be unnecessary, but often the key to a solution of a loss and expense amount may be in the way in which the causal matters are linked or have occurred. As is noted, this is particularly true when responsibility over causes is divided.

For many, these patterns may be so self-evident as to make their setting out rather trite. It is suggested, however, and with respect, that the ways in which the contractor's working system may be disrupted are not always considered by some who may be concerned with the evaluation of loss and expense. Someone who is aware by education and experience of the systems within which effective briefing, evaluation and design proceed, will know how such systemic activities can be nullified by random inputs from outside the system, even when actual construction proceeds later in an orderly manner. Equally, someone who understands the need for a disciplined methodology in cost control on behalf of the client within the design process and thereafter, knows the ways in which runaway decisions made in isolation from other team members can wreak havoc, even when again construction is not disturbed. The former gives an inefficient design, the latter weak cost control. But neither need mean excessive payment for what is produced.

But, just as these areas of activity differ from one another and have their own problems, so is the construction activity different from either. It is also the one which is the most inflexible in that it is no longer a straightforward case of jettisoning and substituting ideas, but of altering physical work or halting and rearranging a complex of men and machines. Following operations are due at dates which mean that deliveries of materials, etc. are already in hand. To add to the potential for confusion, this organisation on and off site consists of a whole array of firms, each with a different perception of success in the operation. They have different goals and means of making profit, they have other work in different places and their time scales of achievement vary. They are not all committed to the success of the project as a whole.

Therefore, those out of the direct field of building production need to sit back and visualise or, better, analyse closely what is going on at site.

SINGLE SELF-CONTAINED MATTERS

Examples A and B fall into this category. One mishap occurs and its effects run their course without interaction with any other problem. As the examples show, the effects may be fairly complex with ripple sub-effects, but once the original matter comes about the results are predictable within close limits. If the effects work themselves out fully and the contractor reorganises his programme in their wake, any subsequent single disturbance will also have quite separate effects.

SERIES OF SELF-CONTAINED MATTERS

This category may be distinguished as that in which two or more matters occur quite separately in time, but close enough for their effects to overlap, so that there is some compounding of them. A later matter starts off 'on the wrong foot' in that its effects are injected into an already disturbed situation. This means that the countermeasures which the contractor is taking to restore regularity to the programme are upset before they have become fully effective.

This pattern is likely to become most troublesome when the matters are individually below the contract threshold of 'materially affecting regular progress', but together build up into a significant effect. For instance, the contractor receives a relatively minor variation instruction, followed in turn by late receipt of information and by an instruction to postpone some work. They are in three distinct physical areas of the work, as well as distinct in time, but they lead to quite considerable disturbance in a fourth sector.

An insidious version of this pattern occurs when a near interminable series of such matters crops up through a project, causing major disturbance incrementally. The problem for the contractor is to know when affairs are building up to the 'material' stage, particularly when delayed effects are being produced. He needs to rely on such words as 'has been' if he is a bit late, or 'likely to be' if he is a bit early. On the whole, he is better to be early, while not running into the alternative trap of 'crying wolf' by over-reacting to every little pinprick.

In view of the practical sequence of events here, the contractor may be advised to approach the architect to agree some rationalisation of a potential maze of separate applications over, for instance, every late piece of information. It could be established that a near-constant shift into lateness of requested information is to constitute one matter for purposes of the procedures. This fits with the wording of the clauses which refers to matters as groups, such as delayed *instructions*, as well as the reference to making an application relating to 'one or more of the matters'. For any one matter or group, once established, it is then necessary to make only one application to cover any effects, past and future. When the same category of matter recurs

at widely spaced intervals, the system of separate applications should still be followed.

GROUP OR HIERARCHY OF MATTERS

Another conceptual option is for matters to occur at about the same time, so that more than just their effects overlap. Several separate matters may act together to produce a greater effect together than they would have done separately. On the principle of Murphy's law, they never manage to cancel each other out! Such matters may just be of equal status, or there may be one or more governing matters, which control the others and affect their severity.

The remarks just made about establishing some relationship among the applications are valid here also, although the opportunity to present them as one will be more apparent, assuming that the contractor retains his sanity!

TOTAL BLANKET OF MATTERS

There comes a point at which any formal categorisation breaks down. In the present context, this happens when it becomes practically impossible to separate out the effects of matters in any sure or meaningful way. A barrage of matters may simply swamp the project, with interactive effects which cannot be logged. It may be described as any combination of the foregoing classes which appears to fit, but description does not aid analysis or, ultimately, ascertainment of the loss and expense incurred.

While this case may come, every attempt must be made to keep heads above water, in the interests of progress and of retaining a basis for settlement. At some point a contract becomes subverted, so that time and money almost become at large: this needs to be avoided if possible. If it does come about, the architect *must* seek the agreement of the employer to any change of basis, however inevitable it may be.

CONJUNCTION OF QUALIFYING MATTERS AND OTHERS

Any one of the patterns described may be complicated by the presence of other, overlapping causes of loss and expense to the contractor which do not qualify for reimbursement by the employer. Essentially, these may be of two types: contractor's risk items, including those which are the 'neutral' items within the relevant events for extension of time, and items which are the contractor's own inefficiencies.

A definitive list of the latter items would need to be open at both ends, as the candidates for inclusion are legion. Fortunately, the criterion for meeting the contractor's loss and expense is that an item should appear on the list in one of the clauses. Nothing else qualifies for reimbursement of its effects as contractual loss and expense, except the effect of antiquities under JCT clause 34, which may be taken as within the present pattern, despite less detail in the clause. It is suggested that it should be similarly treated under

the IFC contract, desirably by the architect issuing instructions requiring a postponement or a variation.

This does not mean that there cannot be other issues where the employer is alleged to be liable, but if they occur they do not fall to be dealt with within the present machinery. They may be common law breaches, needing appropriate action if the employer does not acknowledge liability and instruct the architect to authorise the quantity surveyor in turn to agree and include the amount in the final account. The prime issue under this heading is the need to separate out matters proper and other causes of loss and expense, as the contractor does not stand to recoup amounts which are his proper risk and responsibility. When they occur in isolation, the position is relatively simple: they are ignored. When they overlap with matters in their timing and effects, life is more difficult.

CHAPTER 14

Ascertainment of primary loss and expense

Some basic considerations
Labour and plant
Materials
Site overheads

It is convenient to divide loss and expense into two categories: primary and secondary, as detailed in the section immediately following in this chapter. While the latter category is reserved for Chapter 15, there are a number of considerations introduced here which spill over into that chapter, so that the two should be considered together.

Some basic considerations

ELEMENTS OF COST AFFECTED BY LOSS AND EXPENSE

In discussing the concept that loss and expense are to be ascertained, it is necessary to identify the main elements which most commonly enter into their composition and which are discussed subsequently.

Primary

(a) Labour.
(b) Plant and equipment.
(c) Materials.
(d) Site overheads, such as supervision and temporary structures.

Secondary

(e) General or head office overheads.
(f) Profit relating to loss of other business.
(g) Financing and interest charges in particular situations of delayed ascertainment and payment of amounts.
(h) Extra inflation or fluctuations costs.

In principle, each amount for loss and expense should be arrived at by isolating and allocating some part of any of these which has been increased or incurred in the circumstances.

It is plain that only the first four can possibly be observed on site whatever the circumstances. The others need to be demonstrated by less direct means and are likely to involve more intricate argument over entitlement.

The first four are also the ones where the temptation to resort to the original tender levels is the most seductive, or where some practical use of them creeps in most easily without always being observed. This is because, as direct costs, they can often be calculated on some quantitative basis for loss and expense purposes, while they are also known to exist for the build-up of prices in the contract bills. They thus offer themselves more obviously for analytical comparison. This is somewhat illusory, as the division between them and general overheads and profit remains the problematic element in any analysis of prices. The issue is expanded below.

THREE STARTING-POINTS

From what is said in earlier chapters about the broad question of loss and expense, it may be seen that this concept relates to the *actual amount* by which the contractor is out of pocket, compared with where he would have been had the element of disturbance not occurred. It is the equivalent of common law damages and not a payment for extra work or expenditure, as is reimbursement for a variation. It should therefore leave him with the same total profit as he would have had, again if disturbance had not occurred. It is also distinct from allowing a *quantum meruit* to either party, as explained in Chapter 10.

The problem with ascertaining this amount is that it is not waiting 'out there' to be found in the same way that the amount of a variation may be. In that case, the contractor is paid for a measured variation on the basis of the product of quantity and price, with the former objectively present on the site and the latter in the contract bills or deduced from them at least fairly objectively. Whether the result reflects the contractor's actual expenditure is another question, but this is the accepted method within the contract system. By distinction, loss and expense occur in the cracks between the various events which should have taken place, in the hiatuses when nothing is happening, or when something is happening unevenly out of normal control. They are a form of waste and so are not fully visible and open to detection as entities. They certainly are not measurable: one cannot say 'here they are – and there, get hold of them and add them up in isolation from the productive bits'.

While the courts are charged with the task of awarding damages which reflect the loss and expense concept (even if they describe it slightly differently), there should be no illusions about them having some electronic judicial crystal ball which renders discharge of the task accurate to the point of infallibility. Judges are mere mortals too, who have to use whatever guidelines are available, as outlined in Chapter 10. At the end in a case of divided responsibility, they may still be found saying 'Sixty per cent damages are awarded to the plaintiff', with even the total open to some uncertainty.

With this stated, there are three datum levels which might be considered when ascertaining loss and expense in a building contract:

(a) The contract sum, which is analysed by the contract bills or similar documents into a particular distribution or loading of the figures, and which is adjusted by the final account to allow for variations, etc. even without any loss and expense amounts. The original distribution may have been done for ease of tendering or with an eye to cash flow or the pricing of variations (see Ch. 3). There may even have been a claims situation in mind. At any rate, this represents in its totality what the contractor hoped would be his costs plus profit, but not the detailed reality of events in terms of costs.

(b) The contractor's actual costs as they would have been, had no disturbance of progress occurred. These include any elements of extra efficiency compared with the tendered expectations, but also any elements of greater inefficiency. According to the extent of disturbance, will be how far these costs are confused within the total body of costs that have occurred, or have been changed into other costs in substitution for what would have been incurred.

(c) The contractor's actual costs as incurred, inclusive of the elements in (b) and also of loss and expense.

Each level has its problems. The first is not reality, in its parts or necessarily its total, but a hypothetical construct for commercial purposes. As such, logically it cannot enter into a precise calculation of a damages-equivalent figure: real 'out there' loss and expense. To take the difference between it and the actual costs as loss and expense would be to reduce the reimbursement formula in the contract to one of prime cost. The result simplifies into this:

$$\text{Total payment} = (a) + [(c)-(a)] = (c)$$

The second level is a reality which did not actually materialise. As such, it is for ever beyond reach. How far it differs from the third, which is the amalgam of everything actual, will depend on the impact of the disturbances that have occurred. If it were accessible via the crystal ball, then the difference between it and the third level would represent one approach to loss and expense, subject to some qualifications. One of the more important of these, discussed hereafter, is the problem of how to allocate overheads and how far they should differ between the two levels. The other is that the levels of efficiency and inefficiency may vary between the two, although it is probably fair comment in most cases that any divergence should be attributed to the disturbance itself leading to extra chaos or greater discipline. But alas, the second level is missing by definition, so that this approach is impossible in any precise form.

It appears highly unlikely that tenderers could make any reasonable allowances in their tenders for the effects of disturbance, were they told of them in advance. By 'reasonable allowances' here is meant amounts which would be comparable within the normal tolerances of estimating.

This unlikelihood exists, even allowing for the possibility of anticipating and damping down some of the consequences. This is another indication of the problem of sorting out affairs in the circumstances of actual, but (worse) unexpected disturbance.

Before following the main theme through, the question of inefficiency may be pursued a little further. In itself, it is usually viewed as something which happens on site due to indifferent or poor management, but it may better be seen as representative of a number of factors, broadly falling under the heading of inaccuracy and imperfection of operation.

Like many other matters, inefficiency is a relative affair. Hindsight will show numerous times and avenues for greater efficiency than was achieved, while any sensible tender and programme (which is the reverse of hindsight) make allowances for 'contingencies', 'float' and other titles which cover inefficiency, remedial work, over-optimism, error or whatever the causes may be termed. In any assessment which depends upon looking at what has actually happened, there is therefore a strong argument for allowing some margin for such elements. It must be assumed that the contractor, in tendering and in operating on site, will have made some allowance for the inevitable aberrations. If these then are the cost to the employer of progress unimpeded by him, it is unreasonable to extract them from the reckoning when he has impeded progress. Following this line of argument, it is suggested that some normal level of wastage should be made in calculations where appropriate, as much for time-related elements like labour and plant, as is routine for materials.

This suggestion again is one which is more easily made than implemented, as inefficiency, or for that matter efficiency, is not readily to be isolated or quantified. The step should not be made uncritically from the productivity assumed in tendering, to what occurs in conditions of disturbance, because the former is dependent upon or masked by all sorts of factors, including:

(a) Inefficiency assumed.
(b) Bonus payments against hourly rates.
(c) Keenness of tender, affecting the trade-off between basic costs and profit.
(d) Loading of areas of pricing for reasons other than strict 'scientific' estimating.
(e) Estimating errors.
(f) How certain any analysis of tendered rates may be, which is another way of stating the foregoing points as a group, but also in terms of data for performing the analysis, such as apportioning between labour, plant, materials and overheads.

With these reservations, it must be admitted that there are occasions when practitioners use some degree of analysis of what was intended in order to achieve one side of the balance in a settlement of loss and expense. This

may be ignorance of the principles, but equally well may be the need to use some base rather than none. Sometimes, this is done without it being made explicit, as is pointed out in later discussion of detailed calculations.

Any approach which uses 'adjusted average' times, etc. for operations performed in particular situations, is effectively leaning upon distilled experience derived from many projects. This may be done when loss and expense are being assessed, just as much as when tendering. In neither case is 'reality' being invoked directly, as the principles underlying ascertainment properly require. It is one step further away to use the narrower data base of the particular contract currently operating, and open to strong objections for the reasons listed above. But there are occasions when it may form a useful cross-check on what is being done by other means (see discussion of evidence in Ch. 17).

If any concession to the inevitability of using such information is made, the effect of 'inaccuracies' or 'inefficiencies' must be included or excluded on both sides of the balance. Two crude, but strictly theoretical, examples illustrate the position:

(a) Original figures from the tender are used for an element of loss and expense, while a total cost of what happened is also used. How directly one is set against the other is not an issue here. If inefficiencies are detected in the cost, these should be allowed if at a reasonable level which it may be assumed is also allowed in the tender, but deducted if excessive, even in the circumstances of disturbance of regular progress.

(b) An amount for loss and expense is calculated by taking some original figure and allowing 30 per cent of it. If the original figure includes an inefficiency allowance of 3 per cent, then the loss and expense percentage should have been abated proportionately to avoid increasing the intrinsic amount for inefficiency, unless the conditions of disturbance somehow warrant an increase. Inefficiency within loss and expense is a suspect concept.

The crudity of these examples is obvious, while the theoretical aspect arises because of the assumption that inefficiency can be readily segregated from disturbance.

What is not being argued for here, is the approach which says 'let's see what has been lost, and then dress up the results to look like a genuine ascertainment of loss and expense'. This is just the prime cost method, rejected above. It comes about when the whole contract is so subverted that it is agreed between the parties that a different basis must be introduced. This means the substitution of a new contract for the old, and so is outside the bounds of this book, which deals with matters inside a given and continuing contract. The argument here is for a limited allowance being made for normal working slacknesses, which employers pay for in the give and take of contract pricing based originally upon feedback from site.

BACKGROUND USE OF TENDER AND COST FIGURES

This is an area also taken in Chapter 17, but from a different viewpoint. Both initial and final figures have a value as regulative of the bounds of possibility over loss and expense. This is useful for the architect or the quantity surveyor, whoever happens to be ascertaining amounts. It may also help the contractor, if he is thinking of flying a kite!

Provided that the tender figures are reasonably distributed and that the keenness of the tender has been assessed, they can be used in conjunction with the final account, which is derived from them, to give a guiding framework within or around which the total costs should have been incurred. The detail will become progressively less reliable for this purpose, as it is chopped finer. The more the amount relates to the contract as a whole, because there has been widespread disturbance, the more use will the figures be, on the 'swings and roundabouts' principle. This is likely to apply to a rolled-up claim (see Ch. 12) or one where there are just one or two major and closely related parts. In any instance, it is necessary to analyse out sub-assessments for labour and plant, as the major elements subject to stress on site. These usually should be taken together, as the original intentions for using one or the other are unknown or may have been changed. The ebb and flow between the two is one of the uncertainties in dealing with loss and expense.

The approach may still be of use for assessing the feasibility of amounts relating to sections of work, provided that they can be isolated quite rigidly either on the site layout or in the construction programme, that is in space or time, but preferably both. Considerable care is needed to ensure that common facilities, etc. are allowed in a rational manner, as these may not show separately in the contract bills. Once there are site costs which run on from one period to another, between several sections of work in a straggly manner, the corresponding initial figures will become much less useful. Within such a framework for instance, it may be possible to demonstrate that a suggested drop in productivity for some part of the works represents an unduly large increase in costs in percentage terms, when set against what presumably has been achieved on the rest of the works.

This approach becomes the more valuable when used in conjunction with that of reviewing total costs actually incurred. If it is instituted by, say, the quantity surveyor, it means asking the contractor for quite an amount of cost information which would not normally be forthcoming, but which falls within the terms of what the contract clauses permit. In fact, the decision about what is needed rests with the one who is carrying out the ascertainment, subject to the requested information being reasonable. In the case of major disturbance, the contractor could be asked for all of his cost framework, to be supported later by any detail required.

This information usually gives a different distribution from that in the bills and final account. While the latter splits the works into finished products, such as buildings and external works, themselves divided into work sections or similar, the cost detail splits the costs into types of inputs, each of which may have gone into various parts of the works.

Input information comes into play in considering whether particular suggested excess costs fall within the right range. It is most valuable when discrete and identifiable parcels such as single categories of plant are involved, which are used widely over both the disturbed and the undisturbed areas of the works.

For instance, it may be seen from the analysed bill and final account information that these two areas (both taken as undisturbed) should have absorbed about one-third and two-thirds respectively of the plant category. If these figures in practice show a moderate swing, matters may be feasible, given strong disturbance and remembering that what comes off one side in a swing goes on the other, as a gearing effect. If they are reversed, whatever their intrinsic values and relationship to those extracted from the contract accounts, there is a 'factor of four' change and something catastrophic must have occurred in practice – or in drawing up the figures! At least, a broad control has been established, before too much effort has been expended by going off in the wrong direction. A slightly different illustration, based solely upon costs, is given in Chapter 17.

How valuable anything beyond the global figures will be, depends on how efficient and reliable the contractor's costing system is in presenting feedback. He certainly has no incentive to hold anything back, as far as his total expenditure is concerned – the more the merrier. Only if some element reveals the wrong thing can he wonder whether to keep it to himself: what aids loss and expense may have repercussions elsewhere! It is possible for a whole sweep of information of this type to be fabricated, but it must be observed that it is very difficult to do this convincingly in advance of events and not knowing in which direction they may take off. Even leaving something out tends to show. Commonly these records, at the micro-level of what individual workpeople and cost clerks produce, present many idiosyncrasies (as a convenient euphemism!) which attest their reality.

Again, this approach becomes less useful as the section under review becomes smaller. It tends to be least useful when the section exists alongside others being performed at the same time, so that misallocation by laxity or a philosophy not concerned with loss and expense may occur. It is also most useful when it is performed by looking retrospectively at data, so that it has probably been prepared without thought to its use in this way, or alternatively has been prepared by the contractor and the quantity surveyor acting closely together to ensure its suitability and reliability.

But, given the problems of both tender and cost data, they may be seen as cutting the cake in different directions. This is useful, provided it is kept in mind that it is not precisely the same cake, or at least not the same tier of the cake layer of price and cost which are under dissection. To modify the analogy, at least some grid lines have been ruled on the map, even if they are somewhat blurred and wavering.

It bears repeating that neither of these sets can be used to give a final and definitive amount of loss and expense, but simply to establish guidelines for closer work.

Labour and plant

Two elements of the contractor's costs are linked here because they are interchangeable within limits, on site and elsewhere. Thus, the contractor may suffer because he is forced to exchange one input for the other at greater cost in the circumstances in which he has to perform the works. More probably, this would be labour used instead of plant, because of such problems as piecemeal working or restricted access or space.

LABOUR

The distinguishing features of labour for present purposes are that it is engaged by the period of time, that it cannot be 'stored' when its use is temporarily halted and, above all, that it is human. (For convenience of shorthand reference, labour is termed 'it' here, because to the extent that it costs money it may be narrowed to a commodity.) Plant is similar on the first count, although it may actually be owned, and it can be semi-stored when not in use, while still costing money. It misses out on the last count.

Any period of engaging labour, assuming that it is not in the permanent employ of the contractor, is preceded by some effort and time to secure it. Equally, it needs time to disengage it. In the meantime, there is a period of building up the workforce, numerically and in its familiarity with the precise task or tasks on the particular site. (Again for convenience, 'site' is used to cover all workplaces.) Within 'task or tasks' is concealed the facts peculiar to the project about how far there is repetition and how intricate the work happens to be. It is the intention of building contracts cast in the standard forms that, once the contractor has assessed these elements and tendered upon them, he should be allowed to perform what he has priced without disturbance and without change of the contract sum, other than by defined occurrences, such as instructed variations and allowable market price changes.

The loss and expense provisions are included to cope with disturbance of regular progress, which upsets the contractor's rhythm of working, be it otherwise smooth or bitty, as he properly anticipated it and provided the disturbance is due to a proper 'matter' (see Ch. 9), as set out in the contract. In the case of labour, some of the most common and important items put forward as loss and expense are:

(a) Drops in productivity due to disorganisation, frustration, etc.
(b) Loss of bonuses due to inability to meet targets anticipated in the contract prices, and similarly of overtime payments.
(c) Standing time when nothing can be done.
(d) Extra activities, not covered by the original contract or by variations, etc. including reorganising activities to meet change.
(e) Familiarisation time picking up fresh aspects, including that due to engaging fresh squads after a gap.
(f) Extra supervision by leading hands and forepersons.
(g) Aggravation of costs of labour-related items, such as transport and messrooms.

It is obvious that there are potential overlaps between several of these items, leading to practical problems of accounting and calculation. At present these problems are left aside: the principles are in view rather than the practicalities of segregation – always an author's alibi for what he leaves out! Some illustration is implicit in the case study calculations in Chapter 19. The first item is the core item in many cases and introduces the greatest number of issues.

The effect of changes in labour costs, usually increases, when there is delay is ignored here as it is a distinguishable issue not needing explanation. Its calculation is treated under 'Inflation on fixed price contract' in Chapter 20.

Drops in labour productivity, smaller cases

By this effect is meant what may occur when work is proceeding continuously, if not economically, on tasks in conditions of disturbance. It is related to directly employed workpeople paid on a time basis, rather than on piece-rates. The effect on piece-rates may be deduced, if it is remembered that these are rather like overgrown bonuses (see below).

The argument has already been advanced that loss and expense cannot readily be seen 'out there' in many instances, and this is particularly true of labour, in view of its characteristics. Further, calculations are not to proceed on the basis of tender figures and actual costs alone, but are to take in the elusive middle figures of what would have been expended (see the calculations in Ch. 19), to meet the criterion of reimbursing loss and expense as the equivalent of damages. In practice, purity of approach is seldom possible and it may be noted that a combination of figures is suggested in what follows.

The most simple case, and so the least likely, is that of a straightforward prolongation affecting only tasks which also occur during the programme in conditions of normality. Provided that there is no suspension of activity, so that work proceeds fairly continuously, but with reduced vigour, the first approach here must be to look at an increase in labour costs proportionate to the increase in time.

It may be possible to draw upon evidence from extension of time granted, but this has its limits. It relates to the project as a whole, whereas the prolongation may affect only some part, which may or may not have contributed to some part of the extension of time. More precisely, an extension of time is granted in respect of delays affecting activities which are on the critical path of a network (or its equivalent) or which come on to the critical path because of those delays, and so extend the completion date. Sub-critical activities are not taken into account in granting an extension, but may feature in a loss and expense item, as happens over the ancient fort affecting the laboratory in Chapter 19. It is also the case that an extension of time is granted in advance of its full run, or usually should be, and then confirmed or adjusted after practical completion, while loss and expense are calculated as or after they are incurred, making for complications of record keeping.

Further, it does not follow that labour hours have been extended directly with the contractually granted extension of time, which is given for quite distinct reasons. While this may be a starting-point and useful regulator for calculation, it needs to be evaluated against such other evidence as may be obtainable. Such actions as spreading labour across other work, so that it is engaged more thinly on the affected work, may reduce the impact of the delay in terms of cost, if not in terms of programme time. Other activities, such as dealing with non-qualifying delays and remedial work, may need to be excluded. On balance, the extension of time approach must be seen as a maximum assessment method (as it is for overheads costs), to be trimmed down by closer analysis to reflect the realities of the situation.

If this approach is suitable, it should be seen as absorbing all such effects as occasional stopping times. No attempt should then be made to evaluate these separately in the way mentioned below. However, any major break is best taken out of the reckoning and dealt with quite distinctly. It becomes more difficult to apply the method if any task is finished during a slowed-down period or if the nominal pace would have been changed in either direction during such a period. It is then necessary to make proportionate adjustments to allow for such 'wedges' of work. It definitely requires close records of what is being performed during any period of delay, and whether all parts are affected by the delay. If they were under pressure in the unaffected programme, they may even be helped to greater economy on occasions.

The clear alternative to prolongation is a straightforward case of disruption alone, with only the same tasks involved before and during the disruption, and possibly after it has ceased. This is something of a laboratory condition, likely to be encountered only when there is a very localised dislocation. Here the aim should be to secure data on the productivity being achieved before, and perhaps after, the disruption and to compare this with what happens during it. There is a potential weakness in using data from after the disruption, unless it is the major share of the work, as there is the possibility of a special acceleration of work affecting the results.

To operate this alternative, it is necessary to obtain output rates per unit of work in both conditions and to calculate the excess in the disturbance situation, after allowing for any other variables applying to the 'same' tasks. In the case of the disturbed work, this is coming close to a daywork assessment, and the usual precautions should be taken of checking that due efficiency in deploying resources is observed. It is, however, the substitution of one set of costs for another and not for measured valuation. If it is done, it must be done for the whole period of disturbance: use of 'the first week or so', for instance, is suspect. Apart from deliberate excessive slowing of work while it is under observation, there is the possibility that work will inevitably be slower then, as the contractor is adapting his organisation to changed conditions. Disruption may also produce effects which vary from day to day all through the period.

More likely, and almost always when there is an extensive and extended disruption, the set of tasks will not be entirely the same in both conditions.

Some will start and some will stop, while others would have changed momentum even without the disruption. When a number of matters conspire to create large-scale confusion, perhaps pulsating in intensity, the practicability of 'doing neat little sums' is not there. Nevertheless, the general principles of the two approaches for prolongation alone and disruption alone should be held to, so far as possible.

Drops in labour productivity, larger cases

It is at the point of pious platitude just reached that advice tends to run a little thin and the parties are left to their combined ingenuities, although several general guidelines may be given.

The two approaches given may be combined, to delineate some limits to the amount of loss and expense over labour. When disturbance is extensive, it is most likely to include both elements and the question may be looked at from each direction in turn to see what emerges. The difficulty is that a large disturbance does not take place inside a neat and tidy box of space and time, but has ragged ends and edges, so that it starts and stops irregularly.

Another line of action is to break the disturbed area into subsidiary areas, but not just into pieces which are manageable in size while bearing no particular relation to one another. Dividing a problem into parts sometimes eases its solution, but it may also obscure the possibility that the whole happens to be larger than the sum of the parts. For this method to be fruitful, it should represent a systemic analysis of how the components affect each other. The contract programme offers an obvious starting-point here, as in the use of the network in Chapters 19 and 20. Each sub-system can then be looked at on its own, to see how it is affected by the ripple effects of preceding or parallel sub-systems and also to see what effects it creates itself. The resultant pieces can then be analysed on their own, using whatever tools are best. This method has the advantage of maintaining the relationship between the several matters of disturbance which have led up to this complex disturbance.

A further way into the problem is to look unashamedly at some form of comparison between the contractual valuation emerging from all elements other than loss and expense on the one hand, and the contractor's costs on the other. As indicated earlier in this chapter and in Chapter 17, this may show up some area of discrepancy so intense that it cannot be shrugged off as entirely due to errors in pricing or site inefficiencies or the like. If the contractor has incurred genuine loss and expense because of inadequacies from the employer's side, he may need to be given the benefit of the doubt. This is quite distinct from cases in which he is pumping up a claim to make what he can out of a situation which has fallen to be exploited.

Lastly, within the realm of ascertainment proper, allowance can be made for the impact of the other causes of labour expense which are considered under the headings following. If there are clear areas which can be taken out of the relatively vague sphere of general productivity, so well and good. While this area has been taken first because of the issues it raises, it may be the last to settle.

Beyond ascertainment, there are finally instances where the only recourse open is to employ straight judgment of the effects. This is actually present in all the other approaches already suggested, as none of these can be used uncritically, and various asides indicate this. The difference now is that there are situations in which nothing but judgment is available. This may be dressed up under all sorts of guises, but is how it often is. Affairs sometimes come back full circle to the judicial crystal ball mentioned earlier in this chapter. The result is negotiation as an alternative to seeking the judicial solution, which depends so much on case and counter-case. So does negotiation, but it also involves considerations of ultimate expediency for the parties, such as speed of settlement and the extra risks and costs in going to arbitration or court.

Loss of bonuses and overtime

A common point advanced in a loss and expense situation is that disorganisation of work has meant that it has not been possible for personnel to achieve bonus targets or have overtime available, for reasons beyond their control. As a result, it has been necessary to make enhancement payments as compensation and to avoid demoralisation causing further loss of output, but without any positive benefit accruing to the contractor and in addition to payment for extra hours worked. Some examination of this contention is needed.

When the contractor formulates a rate for an item of measured work, for example, he does so on the basis of a certain labour content. This consists of some combination of the rate per hour payable, inclusive of allowances for overtime and other such directly variable costs, and of the expected bonus payments which will be earned. This takes account of the saving in actual hours due to the incentive of the bonuses available, so arriving at a global labour cost for the unit item. An illustration of this arrangement would be:

100 hours (without incentive) × 5.00 rate	= £500
80 hours (with incentive) × 5.00 rate + bonus of £100	= £500
80 hours × 6.25 consolidated rate	= £500

In essence, the contractor prices for a given quantity of production for a given payment to labour. In doing so, he allows for the expected split of the benefits of increased productivity built into the level of bonus targets (be it money or programme time saving) and for the rate of production likely, so that faster working saves payment of the one type, wages, but increases payment of the other, bonuses. The actual levels of targets are negotiated with the labour force, gang by gang and week by week or as necessary, according to the work immediately in prospect. These levels may be intended to give the contractor some benefit in lower total payments to labour. There are, of course, also economies of supervision and other overheads to be gained by the contractor from more rapid working.

If a disturbance situation occurs, the contractor is faced with lower output,

as discussed under 'Drops in labour productivity, larger cases' above. From the above figures, it may be seen that a drop of (say) 20 per cent in productivity has the effect of increasing the contractor's costs by 25 per cent, whether he was previously paying any bonus or not – always assuming that he has set his figures at the correct level when tendering. If therefore he arranges to pay his workforce at rates per hour in lieu of bonus which compensate them for the loss of actual bonuses, he should remain with a shortfall in recovery of the same margin of 25 per cent, as his costs will be:

$$100 \text{ hours} \times 6.25 = £625$$

It is therefore important to be clear whether the hourly productivities and rates used at each stage are based upon incentives or not.

The figures assume that there is a precise lack of the extra production which bonuses are intended to achieve. If an intermediate position of some extra productivity, and so payment of bonuses, results, then his extra costs will also fall into an intermediate position. A greater drop will lead to an increased loss. Whatever the position achieved, the argument also assumes that the contractor does his sums correctly in arriving at payments in lieu of bonus and in supervising work in the possibly confused situation of disturbance. There is therefore some room for manœuvre, but it should be the case that any plea for complete reimbursement of lost bonus amounts in addition to other labour elements is unfounded.

An argument for the payment of additional bonuses to make up time when it has become possible to resume normal progress should also be treated with reserve, for several reasons. One is that extra speed should reduce total basic hours, just as less speed has increased them. Another is that there may be the possibility of engaging more people or working overtime, rather than working faster, although both of these measures have their costs. A third is that behind this argument is a hint of less efficient working which may affect quality as well as productivity, as the original working must be assumed to have been at the optimum pace. But most cogently, there is the contractual position that the contractor is not required to regain lost time, which would be an acceleration, only to lose no more than is inevitable. He therefore should not be reimbursed for extra costs which he has incurred without authority. It is difficult to separate this in all circumstances entirely from the contractor's general duty to mitigate his loss, discussed in Chapter 10, as sometimes an extra expense in one place may avoid greater expense, or loss, somewhere else. The message for the contractor is clear: seek authority, obtain agreement in principle in advance.

To the extent that overtime is worked and paid as an incentive to attract and retain labour, it falls into the same category as bonus payments. This may mean that it becomes necessary to pay enhancements to compensate for lack of opportunity to work longer hours, but either the enhancements or the non-productive time should be seen as giving a similar cost per unit of work produced. If so, the same argument applies as for bonuses.

Other elements stand in the background of these payments made directly

to labour. They include supervision, transport and insurances, which are by way of on-costs. To an extent, they may be seen as costs which offset against hourly wage payments, rather as do bonus and overtime, so that a claim for them to be reimbursed may not always be valid. But this is only to an extent, and they are discussed separately hereafter.

Standing time

There may be a complete stoppage of significant duration, as distinct from a minor hiatus during a period of reduced productivity, as already mentioned. Here the main position is clear, that the contractor is due to be reimbursed for payments made without any return, so that hourly amounts and compensation payments for incentive amounts all become eligible, without arguments over which elements offset which. A distinct set of records can usually be kept.

It will be necessary to take account of how much of a run-down period there is before cessation occurs, as it is not always a straight case of 'stop on Friday'. There may be a phasing out of work and activities to bring affairs to a tidy position without much progress. Similarly, there will usually be a phasing-in period as work recommences after the break. This means time in refamiliarising the workforce with what is to be done.

When a break is obviously going to be prolonged, there is a case for the contractor reducing the level of personnel standing unoccupied. He should therefore be expected to look for alternative work, which most likely means on another site, unless he is able to put them on relatively unsuitable (and so uneconomic) work on the same site. The alternative is that he must lay off workpeople altogether, which is reasonable only if the delay is really extended. Otherwise the costs of taking on and familiarising a fresh set of labour will outweigh the saving.

The break-even point in this latter instance is not something falling out by entering a few values in a simple formula. Worse, the decision is easier in retrospect than when things are actually still going sour. An architect's instruction to empty the site for six weeks is susceptible of advance assessment, whereas a creeping paralysis may pass the break point before it is clear and then leave too short a time for any laying-off to be of value. The various situations may be discerned in the case study chapters hereafter, although not in strict isolation, which is symptomatic of the problem.

This illustrates the difficulty in applying with any rigidity the principle applying to all loss and expense, that the contractor should mitigate his loss, and so that of the employer. The contract confers no power on the architect to direct the contractor as to how he should act during a period of disturbance. There is power to issue instructions on matters specified in the contract and so relieve the situation indirectly, if this is practicable, entirely at the architect's discretion. All that there is beyond this, by implication and on common law rules, is a right to reject elements of cost which stem from failure to mitigate. In situations where the parties are proceeding affably in the face of adversities, there is much to be said for consultation over how to proceed for everyone's benefit.

Extra activities of reorganisation, etc.

Items falling into this set are those left over when variations have been valued, so as to cover as many aspects of cost as possible, which should be the primary approach, allowing payment which includes a profit margin, among other things. Many matters of site reorganisation, for instance, fall under the variations provisions over obligations and restrictions. Where these do not fit and in other 'untidy' situations, it is necessary to resort to the loss and expense provisions, with all their stricter bounds. When such activities occur, they should be dealt with as entities, allowing records to be kept or a separate assessment to be made.

Familiarisation time

This aspect has been referred to above, as part of the resumption costs after a break. It may also occur when sequences are changed, so that certain personnel are engaged upon tasks previously assigned to others. It is therefore likely to be a feature of piecemeal working. Whether it needs to be separated from a general productivity drop, will depend upon how records are best kept.

Extra supervision

Supervision breaks into two levels: the overall supervision of the project or of major sections of it and the close supervision by leading hands and forepersons of the detailed production of quite limited parts of the work by their own specialisms. The former is taken hereafter as it is affected differently and structurally by conditions of disturbance, and as its cost is not related so directly to the total labour content of a project.

The latter is meant here, and it may be said that in many instances the increase in its cost is proportionate to that of the labour being supervised. This is because the span of control of a supervisor of this type is fixed fairly closely, so that more workpeople means more supervisors on a proportionate basis.

But often the direct supervision of detailed operations needs to be intensified, so that a structural change among the persons concerned occurs. If this happens, greater costs will arise which need to be assessed on their merits. It is difficult to argue the case for any saving of supervisory costs during disturbance, except by suggesting that there has been a failure in the duty to provide people to keep adequate control, so incurring labour costs.

Labour-related items

There are numerous costs incurred during a project, at or near the site, which are related to the cost of labour, but not necessarily in a direct, straight-line way. Two examples may be given.

Transport for labour, such as buses, tends to rise fairly directly with the numbers employed, so that the costs may be expected to rise with

labour costs. This pattern is affected particularly by the indivisibility factor, that is that buses cannot be chopped in pieces to allow for changes in the workforce. If therefore the workforce is attenuated, while the transport provision must remain constant, the cost of transport will rise more rapidly than the cost of labour itself. This is especially the case if labour is being brought in from several locations, or (as a special case of this) if a number of sub-contractors are involved. Alternatively, an intensification of labour in conditions of disturbance may lead to better use of transport, and so to no proportionate increase of cost against that of labour itself, conceivably even to a decrease. Whether there is still an intrinsic increase will depend upon the detailed relationships.

Messrooms and other facilities for labour, such as toilets, are in a different category. Usually a disturbance of regular progress will not change the basic pattern of their use, as they just stand there. It is not practicable to reschedule their availability although, if there is a significant drop in the rate of use, it may be possible to divert operating staff to other tasks or sites. Unless there is a huge increase in the workforce, more facilities are not likely to be needed, as these are somewhat elastic items. An exception could come about if delayed work led to bunching of labour demand, when put alongside later work. More commonly, these items are likely to be extended in their period of use, so falling into the same category as other site overheads considered later.

PLANT

As noted in discussing labour, plant has some characteristics partly in common with labour. These are expanded here, while others are introduced now. The labour associated with plant is to be treated with other labour, as discussed above. Because of the differences about plant, 'Special cost features at all times' below treats some general factors in plant costs which apply even in the absence of disturbance.

Special cost features at all times

Plant is also engaged by the period of time. This is strictly so when plant is hired and effectively so when it is owned, as it is realistic to account for its cost on a time basis, by taking in its special features of cost of capital and depreciation, as well as its immediate operating costs. It can, however, be set aside and so 'stored' when not in use, as labour cannot. The practical effect of not incurring some costs when plant is idle is that there are two hourly rates for plant: working and standing. This difference is more significant when plant is owned by the contractor himself.

This is because a hire firm will charge at a rate, by the day or week, which does not vary to take account of how intensive the contractor's use of the plant is going to be. An average rate of use is assumed, which any one contractor may exceed or not. When the plant is not actually working, the contractor stands to save fuel costs and labour costs, in so far as it is his

own labour, but there is no change in wear and tear costs to him. Capital charges, depreciation and maintenance are also covered in his hire payments. When the contractor owns the plant, wear and tear and so maintenance of most parts are cut down when plant is not being used, along with fuel, etc. The total effect here is to give a greater difference between running and standing costs when plant is owned, so that the status of plant is important when loss and expense are in prospect. The distinction has been observed in judicial circles in *Bernard Sunley Ltd* v. *Cunard White Star Ltd* (1940), when a reduction was made for standing time of the contractor's own plant. The case is also interesting for the refusal to cover loss of other output in the absence of reasonable proof that this had occurred.

But the status of plant is important for two other reasons. One is that the hourly rates for hired plant are generally higher than for owned plant, partly because it is hired at overall rates, but also because it is usually hired for shortish periods. The contractor's own plant, by contrast, is with him somewhere for a long time, relieved only by when he can hire it out to others. He hires plant in at relatively high rates when he does not have enough use for particular items over a matter of years to cover their initial purchase. The policy followed is also complicated by features like taxation arrangements, resale options and other matters which cannot be pursued here.

The other reason why the status distinction matters is simply because hired plant is not permanent – it can be sent back if necessary, so ending the hire charges completely. This is of course another reason why hirers charge more. The result is more flexibility, important for economy when things are going wrong on site. For his own plant, the contractor is dependent upon having another use elsewhere, if he is to save costs. For neither category of plant should the rates be as high as those for plant used in daywork. This is usually work incidental to the main work and daywork schedules recognise this by relatively high rates for small parcels of work. They also enhance the rates, which are for working hours only, to allow for a related share of standing time.

But just as there are costs associated with sending labour packing, so there are with plant. These are costs of installation, removal and transport, which tend to inhibit how much it pays to send plant away, even when there is nothing for it to do. There is no advantage to the contractor in sending his own plant away if there is no work elsewhere, unless it is just in the way of whatever work he can do.

These basic costs of plant may be summarised:

(a) Bringing to site and commissioning.
(b) Working or productive time.
(c) Standing or idle time.
(d) Dismantling and removing from site.

Some special features over loss and expense

Plant is less flexible than labour, in that it can only perform a few

tasks (perhaps only one) per item. It also occurs in units which are dearer per hour and so less divisible in terms of cost. The combination of these factors means that when plant is subject to disruption effects in particular, it is more of a problem. Against this, it does not suffer the psychological effects of disturbance, except to the extent that its operators are affected and pass it on!

Related to these factors is the substitution characteristic. If a piece of plant is rendered sub-optimal by disturbance, there are four basic options:

(a) *To carry on as best may be:* this is the only feasible choice when matters are running in a 'stop–go' phase.
(b) *To substitute another piece of plant*: this is possible when the length of the problem can be assessed fairly closely. It usually means a similar smaller piece of plant, but may mean something different in function.
(c) *To substitute labour*: this is necessary when either the amount of work or its positioning renders anything else impracticable.
(d) *To suspend work*: this applies when all else fails.

These are in some order of feasibility, but much depends on what work is involved. The nature of the work and the practicability of carrying on with it, without running completely dry, are conditioning factors. So too is cost, but this must be seen as the total cost of work and not just the cost of the plant or the immediate operation on which it is engaged. There are some large items of plant, such as concrete batching plant, where the cost of substitution is very high in relation to the gain to be experienced.

It is thus true, even more of plant than of labour, that the decisions about how to reorganise it in conditions of disturbance depend upon the whole structure of production which the contractor has set up and which is now under threat. Because they have no powers, even less can the architect or the quantity surveyor, whoever is dealing with the ascertainment, dictate what steps are to be taken, although again the contractor may consider it expedient to consult over major dispositions of plant. Apart from anything else, he may need guidance over how long the delay is going to be. Something fundamental to many site operations, such as a tower crane, can be whisked away only if the contractor is convinced of the rationality of the action.

One point coming out of this is that any attempt to question whether the contractor has done his best to mitigate the loss and expense must be based upon very sure ground. It is even harder than with labour to make statements based upon hindsight, and this is all that there may be to go on. When things have gone wrong in any major way, the contractor must be given the benefit of any doubt – a recurring theme!

Relationship of plant and labour

The immediate effect of inadequate use of plant is to incur extra costs of the plant and usually directly proportionate extra costs of labour operating it as well. Occasionally, it may be possible to use less labour in the immediate

task of keeping plant going, such as banksmen and other peripheral persons. How far this reduces expense will depend upon what those released are then able to do. Sometimes use of plant in restricted or difficult areas may actually increase attendant costs of labour.

The other side of this is that plant working at reduced output may mean that less labour can be kept going at the next stage of production. This is especially true of plant which hoists and distributes materials, although this type of excess cost may show for one or more of the primary reasons given when discussing labour earlier. It is usually easier to look at labour as demanding the output of plant, than plant as conditioning the output of labour. Any side-effects should be looked at and assessed carefully over the logic of their supposed occurrence.

As noted at (c) above, substitution of labour for plant may be expected to mean higher costs. Otherwise, it is reasonable to expect that labour would have been employed in the first instance. There are likely to be reorganisation costs and perhaps extra supervision, with again the question of what happens to specialised plant operators. This sort of activity is a likely one for introducing ripple disorganisation effects.

These are all cases in which the effects are difficult to trace or calculate. More critically, they may be cases in which double counting of costs occurs, unless care is exercised.

Materials

It is usually the case that any unanticipated costs of materials can be fully covered in valuing variations. Measurement and daywork are both related to quantities of materials, so that the actual amounts can be assessed, while pricing can take account of small consignments and factors like undue wastage due to special cutting and similar causes. An instruction to remove materials because a change in design has rendered them superfluous is classed as a variation under the JCT clauses, and so should be valued under their rules, allowing for any credit value.

Possible avenues of loss and expense are in materials deteriorating in conditions of delay or disorganisation, when there is exposure to the elements or excessive handling. As with labour, there is the question of inflation costs, if a section of work is moved back in the programme. Even here, the provision for work performed under dissimilar conditions is likely to prove more convenient, because of the measurement aspect. It should also be used to take the costs into a variation because it is the prior contractual option.

Materials stored off site for a protracted period may lead to additional storage costs or disturbance to the contractor's yard or a supplier's facilities. Unless the available contractual option of paying for such items while still off site is exercised, the contractor will face a constriction of his cash flow, which may well warrant recompense (see under 'Financing charges' in Ch. 15).

It may be argued that the contractor should not obtain materials far in

advance. Provided that he has a firm contractual indication that the items are to be supplied, by virtue of quantities or detailed drawings, it is quite reasonable for him to obtain them early and make any saving in cost that results. He is not obliged to wait the good pleasure of whoever may wish to initiate an unheralded variation and sweep firmness away, although he perhaps cannot demand that he should be given advance information which just does not materialise early of its own accord. This is an inference which may possibly be drawn from the limitations on early information in the relevant events and matters clauses. If the contractor does choose to purchase materials unduly early, he must of course be prepared for the possibility of having to fund the purchase himself for the excess period, so reducing the overall financial benefit which he secures. He also takes a risk if he orders materials from inadequate information at any time.

Site overheads

This term is used to cover elements of cost which are commonly and desirably priced in the preliminaries section of bills of quantities or other such documents. SMM 6 lists them in its Section B and SMM 7 in its Section A, where are also included a number of provisions which cannot be distinctly and separately priced. For present purposes, the more important elements for loss and expense may be grouped as follows:

(a) General supervision and administration of the project, covering staff and their related costs.
(b) Plant items which are not closely related to the quantities in individual work sections.
(c) Temporary facilities, such as accommodation, roads, fencing and services.
(d) Setting up and running down the project.

It will be seen that there is considerable room for overlap between loss and expense costs and amounts for variations here. As usual, the primary rule is that valuation within the variations framework is to be used where possible. This is discussed briefly in Chapter 6. In view of the complexity of this area of cost, the present discussion is limited as well, so that the main discussion is taken in connection with the case study in Chapter 20 to unite the various aspects.

The main overlap is that with variation valuation. Both there and in ascertaining loss and expense, any amounts are not related in any necessarily direct or pro rata way to those other costs, such as labour, which come about in the immediate production of physical work. A considerable amount of additional work there may cause little in the way of additional supervision, for instance, while a small amount of such work may require comparatively large efforts on the part of staff. The actual segregation of supervision costs between a variation and consequential loss and expense can become a task needing the wisdom of Solomon. Especially when variation of obligations and

restrictions is involved, it may be questioned whether this wisdom over the division is really needed, so long as everything is covered once and only once (see example in the case study in Ch. 21). The problem becomes essentially conceptual – as Solomon found!

Usually, temporary facilities are not drastically changed in a physical sense. If they are, the adjustment may fall within the variation orbit. Here again, obligations and restrictions can be particularly awkward. Plant, on the other hand, may often figure in loss and expense calculations. Here, the greatest care is needed over defining which items of plant are to be dealt with separately in a global way and which are to be treated within smaller parcels of calculation, as already discussed (the problem is illustrated in Ch. 20 over plant already allowed in the Ch. 19). The 'end costs' of the project, in setting up and closing down, are not so likely to figure in loss and expense calculations, although a fragmented end to work may give an exception (see the various case-study chapters).

Because these elements of cost are not related directly to the quantity of work performed, they tend to need quite distinct treatment when changed by variation or otherwise. For variation valuation, the figures in the contract bills may be unrepresentative, or even be non-existent, as mentioned in Chapter 20. As a result, calculation from first principles may be needed. This is as true of loss and expense, for reasons of legal principle, as well as practical calculation.

Two main types of assessment are common. One is the special concentration of extra expense when there is some relatively localised disturbance, especially relevant to supervision and plant. The other is the result of prolongation, sometimes, if not too accurately, termed 'extended preliminaries'. This may affect supervision and plant, and is the most likely way that temporary facilities will be affected. It is also more likely to occur when there is an extended disturbance due to multiple, interacting causes. This head of claim may be pressed when there is extension without disturbance, and should then not be met, although extra preliminaries due to extra work extending the time may be allowable (again see Ch. 20). On the other hand. it may come about when there is a prolongation at some point within the programme, not on the critical path and not leading to extension of time. Plant is especially vulnerable here.

As site overheads build up during the earlier stages of a project, run at a comparatively constant level and then tail off, the period at which any prolongation occurs is important. It may mean extending overheads at whatever level applies in the adjacent period. Alternatively, it may mean a relatively accelerated build-up or a deferred tail-off. Some possibilities are shown diagrammatically, Fig. 14.1(a) giving a build-up period and Fig. 14.1(b) a peak period, which could also represent a run-down period, if inclined to the right. The lines relate to the following levels of overheads:

'A'   the original, unaffected programme time and levels of expenditure.
'B'   the extent of prolongation.

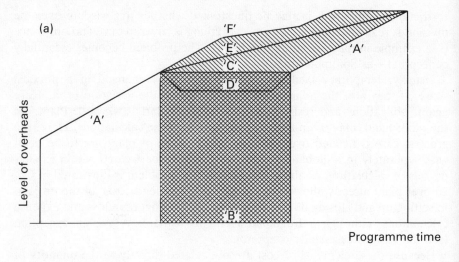

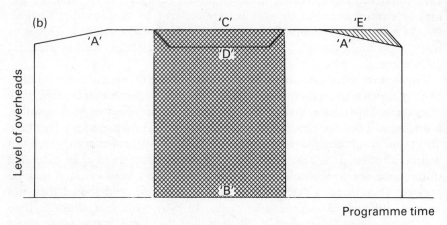

Fig. 14.1 Prolongation of site overheads (see text for explanation)

'C' simple extension of the level of expenditure at the beginning throughout the prolongation.

'D' the effect of being able to reduce the expenditure at the beginning and reinstate it before the end, both depending on some forecast of duration.

'E' extra expenditure incurred fairly evenly and deliberately during (in the first case only, it is assumed) and following prolongation, to overcome some of its effects.

'F' extra expenditure incurred during and following prolongation, but partly due to inability to avoid further build-up and partly due to extra effort to overcome effects.

The principle outlined here is similar to that given under 'Client's risk analysis' in Chapter 1 in respect of initial and ripple effects.

It is important to distinguish 'site overheads' from the more widespread overheads in the accepted sense of the expression. The latter are incurred at the level of the enterprise as a whole, and so cannot be allocated directly to the individual project, while site overheads are incurred quite specifically because the individual project is being carried out. However much they may need care in allocation, site overheads are capable of separate itemisation and evaluation. The other class is considered in Chapter 15, with quite a different approach.

Ascertainment of secondary direct loss and expense

Head office overheads
Loss of profit
Interest and financing charges

Chapter 14 considered loss and expense which, with minor exceptions, are incurred entirely at the site of the works or off site for inputs to those contract works alone. It is then possible in principle to deal with loss and expense on a contained basis, as being the sum of items related to the one contract only. Difficult questions of apportionment between various projects under the contractor's control are thus unusual. In moving from primary to what is here termed the secondary categories of loss and expense, matters are very different, in that apportionment or other indirect ascertainment becomes the norm.

By secondary categories are meant those areas of cost, etc. which are not incurred immediately on the site or in relation to discrete elements of work performed elsewhere for it, but are related to the conduct of the enterprise as a whole. The major categories are head office or general overheads, profit and financing or interest charges. While the individual project causes or contributes to them in its own measure, they are diffuse across the organisation, rather than contained within the one project. The three categories require somewhat different treatment, despite this measure of similarity.

The remarks about the nature of damages for breach of contract at the beginning of Chapter 10 should be borne in mind here. The purpose of such damages and of reimbursement of direct loss and expense under a JCT contract is to put the party suffering because of the breach back into the position financially in which he would have been, but for the breach. It is not to treat and evaluate the elements of loss and expense as extra turnover or business. Equally the elements are not to be priced at so high a level as to act as a punishment to the defaulting party. This is especially relevant to profit, as is discussed hereafter. This principle underlines the value to the contractor in most cases of being reimbursed by fully valued variations for preference, so that he secures a sure profit margin, as also discussed in Chapter 6.

The loss and expense considered here are still those which are 'direct' and

so equivalent to damages in their scope. It so happens that the type of cost considered in this chapter is largely that which accountants class as indirect, rather than direct, but this is quite a distinct way of looking at affairs. Their concern with indirect costs is broadly with costs incurred other than at the point of production. An indirect cost in that sense can always qualify as a direct expense for present contractual purposes.

The most comprehensive set of considerations arises over the overheads category, and so that is pursued first. Although 'overheads and profit' are often dealt with as a single percentage for pricing purposes, just because they are both usually available as percentages, they are not strictly linked even there. They are even less linked for present purposes. With overheads, expense is in prospect while, with profit, it is loss.

Head office overheads

IDENTIFICATION OF OVERHEADS

The term 'overheads' is used to cover expenditure relating to the business as a whole, such as staffing, premises and insurances not project specific, at least for most of the time, although they may be concentrated during tendering, main ordering and similar periods. These costs are usually allowed for when tendering by a percentage spread across prices for the contractor's own direct work, that is excluding the work of sub-contractors. Sometimes a percentage, perhaps smaller, is allowed on sub-contractors as well, so that the first percentage is then reduced. How all this has been done in the tender detail is immaterial to the question of reimbursement in the event of loss and expense, just as it is with site overheads and how they have been included in the contract sum. Originally the contractor must have assessed the cost of these items in relation to his turnover, that is historically, before arriving at the percentage or percentages which will include any adjustment for changes in levels of cost which he foresees.

The same problem arises with these costs in loss and expense as with those, such as labour, which are incurred on site: the extra amounts are not directly visible 'out there' as showing separately from the costs which would have been incurred without the disturbance occurring. The problem is 'merely' intensified by the fact that the costs cannot be related in any simple way to quantities of work performed on site.

THE PRINCIPLE OF EXTRA OVERHEAD EXPENSE

There is, however, a further aspect to the problem, perhaps almost a new problem. This is the more philosophical question about whether extra expense ever occurs at all, or at least very often. It is sometimes argued that particular events on a site just do not affect the contractor's costs at head office at all. He will maintain the same organisation, but the attention

which it gives to this project or that will switch according to what is needed at any time. When there is a small case of disturbance on a site, this is usually true. The contractor takes it in his stride, as his organisation is not so finely tuned or hypersensitive as to be thrown out by a distant ripple on the pond. The exception may occur when there is need for highly specialised attention to deal with a highly specialised disturbance. Even here, it may just mean diversion of resources and not any extra cost.

The counter-argument is that there often is extra cost, because the disturbance is significant in scale or complexity. It is just not feasible that no extra cost ever arises. On first principles, that the contractor has tendered for and planned the project on the basis of a straight run through, this argument logically must have the upper hand. The other argument appears to be based upon the difficulty of being able to detect just what the effect has been, and so declares it non-existent. The two arguments are not entirely opposed, as both tend to use such qualifications as suggest that there is some threshold below which no effect is produced because any organisation has some slack or resilience with which to deal with minor problems during progress.

The extreme form of the second argument is embodied in uncritical use of one of the formulae for calculating extra overheads (and sometimes profit), which are considered below. Formulae assume, *inter alia*, that there is a direct and inevitable link of a mathematical nature between certain quantifiable elements (usually money and time) in the contract and the cost of disturbance of regular progress. All the assumptions made are open to question, but the formulae do at least illustrate the ways in which loss and expense may occur.

It must be suspected that most contractors price work by taking their total past turnover, including loss and expense amounts, and applying their total past head office overheads to obtain a percentage for future use, with any relevant adjustment for changed conditions. In theory, they might extract all past loss and expense reimbursement from their turnover, and so arrive at somewhat higher percentages for overheads in tenders, but this is theory. The difference may be shown by a simple, if exaggerated, illustration:

(a) Total turnover, excluding overheads   £10,000,000
    Total overheads   £1,000,000
    Overheads as percentage of rest of
    turnover   10%
(b) Total turnover, excluding overheads
    and loss and expense reimbursement   £8,000,000
    Total loss and expense reimbursement   £2,000,000
    Total overheads   £1,000,000
    Overheads as percentage of reduced
    turnover   12.5%

If the former method is used, and if there have been significant loss and expense in the past (usually higher on sites than at head office, as

will be suggested below), then contractors will be adding somewhat lower percentages than would otherwise be the case in future tenders, which of course exclude loss and expense allowances. The recovery of the balance of their overhead costs will then depend upon enough loss and expense claims arising to bring in the difference. Given very bad experiences one year and very good the next, contractors could be out of pocket in the good year! They will equally be out of pocket if the ascertainments of loss and expense granted them exclude overhead allowances. While the figures shown are a slight parody of reality as it usually is, they do point up the strength of the argument for at least some reimbursement of overheads, remembering that what contractors can actually add for overheads in future tenders is conditioned by how competitive the market then is, rather than by whether they would like to recover any past under-reimbursement in loss and expense payments.

This example suggests merit in paying the contractor some reasonably assessed amount for extra overheads, and no doubt this often occurs. The attitude of the courts is not sympathetic to excessive use of such an approach, to put it mildly, as is shown hereafter. Any contractor faced with some offer in this direction, but wishing he had more, should weigh up whether to go to court or whether it might not be better to settle with his adversary!

The two discrete methods of ascertaining loss and expense in this area may be contrasted as by use of a formula or by isolation of individual items of cost. Whether they may be segregated quite so rigorously in practice is another point, as also is the approach of the courts. It is convenient to start to answer these points by looking at the formula system of calculation.

FORMULA CALCULATION OF HEAD OFFICE OVERHEADS

There are several formulae widely known within the industry, and three of these are considered here. They aim to take account in various ways of factors of delay time and of extra money payments for primary costs arising from disturbance, by making fairly broad assumptions about their effects on secondary or overhead costs. It is the broad assumption aspect which is disliked by the courts, as discussed below. By definition, a fixed formula cannot be *ascertainment* in a variable situation.

Two of the formulae also include profit in their orbit. This may be noted, but otherwise ignored at this juncture, as profit must receive separate treatment and cannot be put in with overheads. The formulae are first described critically and then compared. An example of their effect is given in relation to the case study in Chapter 20.

The Hudson formula

This is the formula included by the editor in the tenth edition of *Hudson's Building and Engineering Contracts*. It includes an allowance for profit, which is shown here, but which has a different significance from what is apparent at first sight, as is explained later. The editor himself enters his own caveat

about the profit allowance. The formula has three main sections, and is as follows:

$$\frac{\text{Head office/profit \%}}{100} \times \text{Contract sum} \times \frac{\text{Period of delay (in weeks)}}{\text{Contract period (in weeks)}}$$

The first section needs little comment. It assumes that overheads and profit are to be linked in one composite percentage. Each may have been included at different levels in various parts of the tender, for instance in respect of direct and sub-contract work, with the further distinction between domestic and nominated sub-contracts. If profit is treated separately, this point becomes less significant, but does not disappear.

For arithmetical correctness here, and assuming a single flat rate percentage, the percentage used must be that of overheads (and profit if included) as a percentage of the contract sum and not as a percentage of the balance of the contract sum, which is how it will have been calculated initially. The effect of misapplying the formula may be illustrated:

Contract sum, including overheads and profit as 10% of itself	£100,000
Overheads and profit amount therefore	£10,000
Same overheads and profit as percentage of remainder, i.e. as calculated when tendering	

$$\frac{10,000}{90,000} \times 100\% \qquad\qquad 11.11\%$$

With the latter included in the formula, the base amount for overheads and profit incorrectly becomes

$$\frac{11.11}{100} \times 100,000 \qquad\qquad £11,110$$

What this erroneous calculation has done is to allow overheads and profit on the original overheads and profit. It will then be applied compound fashion to any increase due to disturbance.

The second section needs comment because it consists of just the one item of the contract sum. This also ignores the distinction between direct and sub-contract work, mentioned above, but further the difference between the contract sum and the final account. Many elements in the account will include something for head office overheads, because they are calculated by a pro rata or similar method based upon the original level of pricing (see Ch. 6 for variations and case study in Ch. 20). Whether therefore the account is higher or lower than the contract sum, there will already be some automatic adjustment of overheads in the arithmetic of quantities and prices to be set

against that provided by the present formula used raw. The third section of the formula is based upon time change alone, so that any adjustment here will lead to some overlap of reimbursement, given a *higher* account due to the effect of variations.

This is not a simple relationship, and certainly not one of using *either* financial values *or* time periods alone. It is pursued further in the case study in Chapter 20.

The third section has the effect of reimbursing overheads at the percentage derived in strict proportion to the time overrun on the project. This is in itself a suspect concept, and one of the central areas underlying the antipathy of the courts to such formulae, as it assumes a straight-line increase of cost directly with time and without proof. But it also ignores the distinction between those delays resulting from events which are also matters leading to loss and expense payments, those resulting from 'neutral' relevant events and those which are the contractor's responsibility. The effects of these neutral events are shared between the parties, with the employer bearing the delay and the contractor the extra expense.

The consequence of this section of the formula is also that there is no reimbursement of overheads if there is no time overrun. While this is quite possible if a disturbance is not on the critical path of the project, it by no means follows rigidly.

The Emden formula

Predictably, this formula also takes its name from the book in which it appears, *Emden's Building Contracts and Practice*. It is very similar, differing only in the calculation underlying the percentage for head office and profit. Whereas the Hudson formula uses the value included in the tender, the Emden formula calculates the percentage so:

$$\frac{\text{Total overheads and profit}}{\text{Total turnover}} \times 100\%$$

This becomes the numerator in the first section of the formula. 'Total' here means the total in each case for the whole of the business for a year.

It would appear best to use the percentage resulting from the year or total contract period (as in the Eichleay formula below) in which the loss and expense occurred, according to how prolonged the disturbance is, although this may mean a delay before figures are to hand. The alternatives in order of preference are those for the immediately preceding year or those applying when the tender was made, each with some allowance for any expected change in the current period. The reason for this order is to comply as closely as possible with the criterion that the contractor's actual loss is what is being sought. To this extent, by relying on actual values rather than amounts hoped for when tendering, the present formula has some advantage over the Hudson version.

Otherwise the formula attracts the same set of comments as does its

companion above. The use of total annual figures means that it does not matter in quite the same way that percentages used in tendering may have been different for various elements of work. A less refined method is used on both sides of the calculation, so removing any particular bias. The need to ensure that there is not a calculation of compound overheads and profit remains to be watched just the same.

The Eichleay formula

The last formula to be examined draws its name from a case in the United States in which it was applied. It has been used to quite an extent across the Atlantic although, even so, there appear to be reservations over it there. It is usually set out in three stages, which it is possible to conflate into one formula, as ever:

(a) Contract billings

$$\frac{\text{Contract billings}}{\text{Total contract billings for contract period}} \times \text{Total head office overheads for contract period} = \text{Allowable overhead}$$

Here 'contract billings' means the amount of the project final account and the amount of all final accounts, or portions of them falling to be considered. This is the equivalent of annual turnover in British practice. As with the other formulae, it is necessary to compare like with like, so that all billings should either include or exclude overheads (and if appropriate, profit). As they appear above and below the line of the fraction, it does not matter which in this instance. Inclusive amounts are easier, as these form the basis of billings, or payments.

(b) Allowable overhead

$$\frac{\text{Allowable overhead}}{\text{Days of performance}} = \text{Daily contract head office overhead}$$

Here 'days of performance' are the total days spent on the project. It is arguable that their use will give an attenuated spread of overheads in particular patterns of disturbance, but the reverse is possible.

(c) Daily contract overhead × Days of compensated delay
      = Amount of recovery

The use of a rate per day or per week in the various formulae is not of the essence, and the periods could be interchanged.

Running the formula into one and using British terminology, gives the following as the recovery:

$$\text{Total overheads for contract period} \times \frac{\text{Final account}}{\text{Total accounts}} \times \frac{\text{Days of delay}}{\text{Days of performance}}$$

This rearrangement makes for simplicity in overall presentation. It also shows that the formula amounts to taking the contractor's total overheads during the relevant site work period only (in most cases), apportioning from them by other amounts payable to the single project and then apportioning from them to the period of delay. It is thus the only formula of the three to take some account of the final account, although care is needed to arrive at comparable figures throughout.

This method apportions overheads without using a percentage as such, because it uses total real amounts, but the effect is the same. It also introduces overall amounts payable, rather than just the original contract sum. This is an improvement in that it comes closer to actual amounts, but still needs care in the detailed treatment about loss and expense amounts taken in across the contractor's whole activity, as well as on the contract being adjusted. All the questions about whether the method represents reality remain. It also means more investigation of the contractor's business at large, but this is also implicit in any non-formula method which the courts regard with any measure of favour.

Limitations of formula calculations

The three formulae considered may be set down in brief form for comparison:

$$\text{Hudson:} \quad \frac{\text{HO\% tendered}}{100} \times \text{Contract sum} \times \frac{\text{Delay}}{\text{Contract period}}$$

$$\text{Emden:} \quad \frac{\text{HO\% actual}}{100} \times \text{Contract sum} \times \frac{\text{Delay}}{\text{Contract period}}$$

$$\text{Eichleay:} \quad \text{HO total for period} \times \frac{\text{Final account}}{\text{All accounts}} \times \frac{\text{Delay}}{\text{Actual period}}$$

(HO = Head Office)

Hudson differs from the other two by its reliance upon the tendered overhead percentage (the question of profit being ignored now). This is a weakness in that the calculation is based upon intentions or hopes, and not reality over loss and expense. (The caveats expressed in Hudson are mentioned under the heading of 'Profit' hereafter.) The other two agree by taking actual figures in the same way, even if the arithmetical approaches differ superficially.

Eichleay differs from the other two by taking the final sum (preferably inclusive of primary loss and expense amounts) and not initial sums, and by taking the delay in relation to the actual total period and not in relation to the initial period intended. The former difference is a definite move nearer to accuracy. The latter simply rearranges the time figures by reference to a different base time: provided calculations are done carefully, the results should not differ.

With this comparison to suggest that the formulae rank in ascending order of reflecting reality, their limitations should not be underestimated:

(a) They do not ascertain actual loss and expense, which is the primary reason why the courts are loath to use them without great caution and in the absence of proof of what they suggest. Arbitrators, and more particularly those negotiating settlements, are sometimes not quite so constrained, but do well to take note of judicial views.

(b) They need care in applying the arithmetical detail to avoid inaccurate results, as has been explained above.

(c) They do not allow for differences within the structure of the contractor's pricing, such as different weighting of overheads applied to his own and sub-contractors' work.

(d) They ignore the uneven rate at which work proceeds on site, whether sub-contracted or not, by allocating overheads evenly over time. There is a build-up to a peak and then a run-down on most projects (commonly known as the 'S' curve, see Fig. 15.1(a)), and the timing and effect of any delay due to disturbance are not reflected by calculating overheads *pro rata* to time alone.

(e) They do not allow for some disturbance effects causing higher or lower concentrations of head office costs than normal, needing special assessment. Minor disturbances may be absorbed from this point of view, although when they lead to extension of time this may be countered by the general principle that overheads should be spread according to attenuation of work.

(f) They are strongly time-related and so do not cater for disturbance without delay, which may occur when activities affected do not lie on the critical path of the programme network or its equivalent. There may still be additional head office costs in some instances.

(g) They take no account of the difference in overheads recovery which may arise due to amounts contained within payments for varied work, fluctuations, etc.

(h) They take no account of the general common law principle that the party suffering under a contract must take such measures as are possible to mitigate his loss, such as by redeployment of resources. No formula can do this, as what is possible depends on circumstances, but an adjustment must be made when appropriate.

When the first two formulae are used to deal also with loss of profit (which they link with overheads, but which is considered separately below), some of these points recur, perhaps with a different reference, and should be noted.

With these limitations noted, it remains that formulae of some sort must enter into some overheads calculations, if only because overheads are measured when accounting and allowed when tendering on a percentage basis, that is by formula. The main burden is the question of proof that the percentage and how it is applied are both reasonable. This is indicated by *Tate and Lyle* v. *Greater London Council* (1982), already referred to in

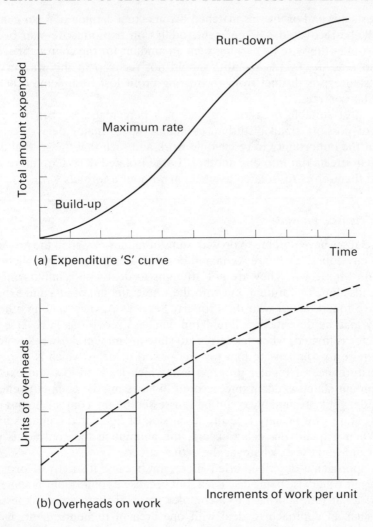

Fig. 15.1 Rates of expenditure and overheads: (a) expenditure 'S' curve;
(b) overheads on work

Chapter 10, where the judge said, 'I am satisfied that this head of damage
can properly be claimed, [but] I am not prepared to advance into an area of
pure speculation when it comes to quantum.' This was with reference to an
addition of 2.5 per cent for managerial expenses as a customary amount, but
without any supporting calculation. It is therefore clear that such overheads are
reimbursable in principle, but equally that they must be properly quantified,
even if then expressed as a percentage.

  In a Canadian case, *Ellis-Don Ltd* v. *The Parking Authority of Toronto*
(1978), the contractor demonstrated that a tender allowance of 3.87 per cent

for overheads and profit was matched by an actual earning of 4 per cent. As a result, he recovered 3.87 per cent (oddly) on unproductive staff because they 'would otherwise be earning such an amount for the contractor'. There was 'no reason why the plaintiff should not recover' in this way in these circumstances, as distinct from recovering profit lost from some other and particular contract.

The most suitable occasion for use of a percentage is when there is a series of possibly small disturbances adding up to major delay, occurring without the opportunity to reschedule work and such that the several delays and their effects run into one another. Large isolated delays are more likely to lend themselves to isolated assessment without a formula.

Brown clauses: an aside

These clauses have nothing to do with sums of money passed in the proverbial brown envelopes. They are so named because they have been publicised by a certain Mr Brown. They are not attempts to deal with reimbursement of overheads alone by formula, but with the whole amount of loss and expense, and have found favour with the Property Services Agency, among others.

They may be described as liquidated damages provisions in reverse. The contractor is invited, when tendering, to state an amount per week which he will require to compensate him for any period of delay which is associated with disturbance of regular progress and which leads to loss and expense. The amount stated is taken into account in assessing the competitiveness of the tender, but presumably could be reassessed by the courts if found to be of the nature of a penalty (see the discussion of liquidated damages in Ch. 10). When a qualifying delay occurs, the amount in the contract is paid, neither more nor less, whatever the actual effects.

This approach is described briefly here, not because it strictly belongs with the matters otherwise being discussed, but because its philosophy is somewhat similar: a flat rate approach to a complex issue. If there are weaknesses to using such an approach to deal with one area of reimbursement, namely overheads, how much greater they become when it is used for the whole sweep. The list under 'Limitations of formula calculations' above suggests a few, while others too readily abound to need enumeration here.

Any contractor who accepts such a clause to cover the reimbursement of 'any delay however caused and whatever its consequences' (or words to that effect) could well be putting his head into a noose. If the circumstances of application of the clause are spelt out with any qualifications, however, he may well be able to demonstrate that the clause does not fit the actual position, and so escape to fight his battle on more normal methods of reimbursement. Alternatively, he may need to go to the courts, whose attitude to such clauses has yet to be tested, but may be inferred from that to formulae.

With this brief reference to Brown clauses, the attitude of the present work may be adequately delineated, and it is not intended to refer to them further in any context where they might be held to fit more logically.

THE WIDER QUESTION OF OVERHEAD ASCERTAINMENT

While formulae have their limitations on practical and legal grounds, if used alone, the approach of direct and detailed ascertainment labours under the problems of practicalities.

When it is used, it requires the eliciting of individual costs, such as staff and equipment time. It may be practicable to isolate time for key personnel, such as directors, departmental heads and senior assistants, but the further enquiry moves down the hierarchy, the less easy does this become. This is because, while higher-level staff will perform tasks related to the disturbance which are unusual in nature and in keeping with the disturbance itself, other staff will often be performing comparatively routine tasks. These may be out of sequence, but may also be so mixed in with expected tasks as to render clear accounting impossible.

The practical answer may be to assess such staff, and often equipment for similar reasons, as a percentage of those staff who can be separated out. This, it will be noted, is a reversion to a formula approach at a different level within the organisation. It also becomes the only sensible way to deal with premises and similar large, indivisible items of overhead (again, see the case study detail in Ch. 20).

It follows that direct identification of head office overhead costs, when used alone in any but the most simple cases, is likely to result in an under-reimbursement of costs, rather than an over-reimbursement. There would therefore appear to be some merit in using both this approach and that of some formula, modified for any of the reasons given above, to attempt to reach the truth out of what each has to offer. This is partly the method used in the case study just mentioned.

Overheads are calculated in the normal course of events for future application as a percentage by reference to total overhead and non-overhead expenditure in the immediate past. This assumes implicitly that the curve for the percentage rate of change, expressed graphically, will be smooth in any part of its length, rather than jump vertically at points, so as to be virtually discontinuous. This, however, is a practical simplification for such purposes as accountancy and estimating. In reality, many elements of overheads present the vertical step effect, as when an extra member of staff is taken on or extra accommodation is acquired. The usual method of representing overheads smoothes out these steps, as indicated in Fig. 15.1(b), and this is quite acceptable for most purposes in any enterprise large enough for the inaccuracies not to warrant greater finesse.

It is usually stated that uncritical adoption of a formula of the type discussed will always lead to an excessive reimbursement of overheads, that is that a disturbance is bound to occur on a horizontal or slightly sloping part of the actual cost curve. While this is frequently the case, there is the possibility that it will lead to under-reimbursement if a step is caused solely by a particular disturbance. This is likely to be difficult to demonstrate conclusively, as there is seldom a single cause, unless the extra overhead is highly specialised and

can be attributed to the one project and its disturbance. From previous discussion, it is clear that there still needs to be care in using the available sources of data, as it cannot be argued that the approach should be 'formula calculation plus extra cost of jump'.

This leads into the area of contributory causes, as with extension of time, and the possibility of allocating costs between the parties. The problems of responsibility for overlapping events are mentioned in Chapter 11 and are as relevant here, as are the principles for resolution.

These slightly digressive points may be concluded with the comment that the objection to using a formula for head office overheads is not usually carried into assessment of site costs. All-in labour rates, for instance, carry allowances expressed as percentages and the underlying amounts do not necessarily increase absolutely *pro rata* to the actual hours expended. While allowance should be made, as mentioned, when dealing with labour loss and expense for the effect of changes in overtime working, etc. a formula can be a relatively crude method of doing this. However, any other approach would be impractical to use. There appears to be room for rather greater tolerance in the courts over head office matters also.

Loss of profit

It may also appear that there is room for greater tolerance over the element of profit in loss and expense calculations. The aim of this section is, however, restricted to setting out the strict position which follows from the philosophy, outlined in Chapter 10, that direct loss and expense are to be calculated as equivalent to damages at law.

ENTITLEMENT TO REIMBURSEMENT

The intention of either basis of reimbursement is to put the aggrieved party (in this case the contractor) in the position in which he would have been financially, but for the occurrence of disturbance of his regular progress. There is not scope for including extra profit on the loss and expense themselves, because this would be equivalent to allowing profit on damages. It may be argued that loss and expense, or more particularly expense, amount to additional turnover which has been forced upon the contractor under the terms of the contract, and so are rather like variations where additions (and for that matter omissions) include a profit margin. With this view, much sympathy may be felt, but it does not find legal favour. The position should be distinguished from that occurring when the contract is determined by the contractor, when he may be entitled to payment of the profit on work which he is unable to perform because of the employer's breach (see *Wraight Ltd* v. *P. H. & T. (Holdings) Ltd* (1968), discussed in Ch. 16). Even here, it is profit on what has *not* been done which is in view.

The root distinction may be made that, while the contract gives the

employer a clear mandate to introduce variations within limits via the architect (see discussion in Ch. 6 over the limits), it does not give any mandate to disturb regular progress. The basis of the contract is that the contractor is to be afforded complete and uninterrupted possession of the site and full information as and when he reasonably requires it, among other things. If the employer does not afford these things, he is in breach of contract. The provisions over ascertainment of loss and expense are present to ease matters by giving a procedure for settling which may save recourse to the courts, but without spelling out the formula for settling, as do the variations provisions.

What the contractor may be entitled to, in lieu of profit on the additional 'turnover' which he unwillingly acquires, is reimbursement of loss of profit on other work which he might have been performing with the capacity which he has had tied up against his will. Even here, it is necessary for him to be able to demonstrate a reasonable likelihood that he could have been so engaged, and not just to allege that this would have followed without question, a point established in *Bernard Sunley* v. *Cunard* (see Ch. 14).

This does not amount to showing that he has been unable to take on a further contract or so, simply because of the overrun on the present one. Except in extreme situations, this is most unlikely to occur as a single event which can be traced so inexorably within his records. What he needs to do is to show that he is running with a reasonably full order book across the contract period and beyond, so that his prime resources are adequately committed without the disturbance element now in question. His prime resources are those which condition how much work he can undertake, such as his capital, permanent organisation and workforce, provided that the elements concerned cannot reasonably and economically be supplemented to carry him over the hump period.

The point was made in *Peak Construction (Liverpool) Ltd* v. *McKinney Foundations Ltd* (1970), which dealt with a contract in which a year's suspension had occurred in conditions of uncertainty about resumption. While the plaintiffs appeared to hesitate in some respects over the basis of their case, the Court of Appeal came to the view that they were arguing for loss of opportunity to earn profit on other work which they could not take on. This was the case as presented earlier to the Official Referee. On this basis, the Court of Appeal rejected the defendants' submission that no loss of profit had been established, this being 'probably untenable' on the facts presented. However, the Court was quite strong over the sort of evidence which the Official Referee might need in a new trial:

> . . . every issue under this head should be open for the official referee [sic] to consider. It might be of some help to him not to be left only with the evidence of the plaintiffs' auditor on this point; possibly some evidence as to what the site organisation consisted of, what part of the head office is being referred to, and what they were doing at the material times, could be of help. Moreover, it is possible, I suppose, that an official referee might think it useful to have an analysis of the

yearly turnover from, say, 1962 right up to say, 1969, so that if the case is put before him on the basis that work was lost during 1966 and 1967 by reason of the plaintiffs not being free to take on any other work, he would be helped in forming an assessment of any loss of profit sustained by the plaintiffs.

Notably, this suggests a long period spanning the actual time of suspension and considerable data made available for assessment of the likely position, although not to prove cast-iron loss, which is impossible in most instances. This is not therefore a matter of absolute proof, but of showing a sensible balance of probability that the disturbance has imposed an extra load on the contractor beyond his expectations. Rather like overheads, it is a case in which the capacity of the organisation has some flexibility to cope with a single contract subject to disturbance, but where any instance can be argued as causing some theoretical effect which cannot be absorbed. If the contractor is subjected to disturbances on several contracts then, according to his scale of business, the result can be assumed to be that his general capacity is under some strain.

This overload is a situation in which a time overrun, as well as the financial overrun, may lead more easily to a loss of profit being considered. On the other hand, a plain intensification of working within the same overall period may mean little more than taking on extra labour or plant, to be absorbed within the main organisation of the project. There is no categorical answer to dealing with profit, although it is clear that allowing this element becomes the more credible, the larger the rest of the amount for loss and expense.

The Hudson formula discussed above is given by the editor of Hudson as subject to the caveat that the element of profit, as distinct from overheads, included in the standard formula ranks for inclusion only if it would be reasonably possible for it to be earned elsewhere (as *Peak* v. *McKinney* shows), in the absence of the disturbing events. This lessens the objections to that formula over profit, but not overheads, provided that the profit corresponds to the whole of the disturbance. The formula actually shows it as profit on the balance of the loss and expense themselves, so that it would need to be stated formally in the ascertainment as being rather profit lost elsewhere. However, the broader criticisms of the formula remain.

CALCULATION OF LOSS OF PROFIT

The amount of profit to be included consists of two factors: its extent and its level. Once the inclusion of profit has been established in principle and as related to all elements of disturbance, the extent may be a matter of taking the amount of loss and expense otherwise ascertained as equivalent to work displaced elsewhere which the contractor has been unable to perform. In this case, this factor of the profit calculation is the same as if profit had been allowed upon the additional 'turnover' within the contract generated by the disturbance.

It is not always suitable to work like this. There may, for example, have

been a small disturbance early in the programme which alone does not substantiate loss of profit on other work, followed much later by a significant disturbance which does. If these two are quite distinct, there would appear little justification for allowing loss of profit due to both. On the other hand, a series of individually small disturbances may add up to a combined case for loss of profit. Between these, the gradation of possibilities is considerable, with room for difference of opinion over what is allowable.

The second factor is the profit level to be applied to the first factor. Here, as indicated by the legal cases under 'Some principles of damages' in Chapter 10, the guide is the level of profit which, before the disturbance, the employer may have expected that the contractor would reasonably have earned on the alternative work forgone. Usually this is to be equated with the normal level of profit available to a comparable contractor operating in similar market conditions and with a similar range of work. Only in peculiar circumstances made known to the employer in advance of the contract will the contractor be able to claim for an unduly high rate of profit, on the principles enunciated in the *Victoria Laundry* case also outlined in Chapter 10.

At this point the distinction between allowing profit on additional turnover and allowing loss of profit on work forgone becomes important again. This is because the measure of profit allowed does not depend directly upon the profit level included in the immediate contract, which need not be demonstrated for present purposes, and whether this profit has been achieved or even exceeded, or not. It is the level of profit forgone which is relevant (see the example in Ch. 20). Given even conditions of business for the contractor, this distinction may not matter. If conditions are fluctuating within limits such as might be anticipated even by a moderately businesslike employer, then it is the general level which counts. Even if the contractor obtained the contract at cost by adding no profit margin, this in itself will not debar him from being reimbursed at a positive level. On the other hand, he may then need to demonstrate that he left off his profit margin by mistake, rather than of deliberate policy to obtain work in a slack period. Otherwise he will be needing to show that work prospects have improved since, so that his order book has cheered up!

Interest and financing charges

These two terms have a number of precise, but differing definitions, according to when they are being used and by whom. For present purposes, they are taken as having limited meanings:

(a) *Interest*: the charge on monies owed by one person to another, most particularly the amount that may be due from the employer to the contractor on outstanding sums.

(b) *Financing charges*: the cost to one person, and here the contractor in particular, of servicing his working capital or maintaining an overdraft to keep solvent.

It may be seen that one man's interest is another man's financing charges. Normal, recurring amounts are covered by contractors within their head office overheads, whether taking the form of payments against borrowing or dividends to shareholders, the latter becoming elements of profit. So far as loss and expense leading to extra amounts are concerned, the situation is rather like that existing over profit: the contractor is not entitled to charge interest, but he may possibly be able to recover financing charges broadly as charged to him, with the actual amounts in practice not too dissimilar. These mainly relate to the delay in performing work and receiving payments generally, due to disturbance and so leading to an impaired cash flow for the enterprise. They are higher to him for his own costs than for those of sub-contractors, where they may not arise for him, although the sub-contractors may have their own expenses. An illustration is given in Chapter 20.

INTEREST

It remains the general legal position that interest is not payable as damages simply because a sum legally due is paid late. This appears to go back to the ancient dislike of usury, backed perhaps more recently by fear of the possibility of a creditor not desperately needing his money and failing to press for it, while welcome interest mounts up.

The point has been maintained in *London, Chatham & Dover Railway Co.* v. *South Eastern Railway Co.* (1893). While the courts do not wholeheartedly embrace this position today, they are not completely free to avoid it without proper legislation, but have 'distinguished' it in some cases. What legislation there is, does not give complete freedom. It is also the case that interest in the courts can be awarded as simple interest only, not as compound. An arbitrator may, however, award interest on amounts still outstanding and included within a reference, by virtue of the Administration of Justice Act 1982 amending the Arbitration Act 1950, although the former Act mainly regulates interest on debts. It would appear that there may even be compound interest in calculating financing charges up to the date of an application over loss and expense under JCT clauses, although only simple interest thereafter (see *Minter* v. *Welsh Health* discussed below).

The line taken in distinguishing other cases from the *Chatham* case is to take the latter as relating to 'general damages' for delayed payment. By distinction, 'special damages' may arise when the serious possibility of loss by the other can be supposed to be in the contemplation of the defaulting party. This is the line of reasoning flowing from *Hadley* v. *Baxendale* and other cases taken in Chapter 10. In *Wadsworth* v. *Lydall* (1981), the Court of Appeal awarded special damages for interest due to late settlement of provisions in a dissolution of partnership. The House of Lords has approved this decision in *President of India* v. *La Pintada Compania Navigacion SA* (1982), a shipping case, stating that the *Chatham* decision 'did not extend to claims for special damages'.

Thus, in a straight loss and expense application, at present the contractor

has no absolute assurance that all inclusions of interest as such will be met with favour. Only special cases at arbitration and at the discretion of the arbitrator may turn out otherwise. Things are different if, but only if, the contract expressly provides for interest on overdue amounts, as the Institution of Civil Engineers contract provides over late honouring of certificates.

FINANCING CHARGES

The essential distinction with financing charges is that they are costs incurred by the contractor in operating his business, so that an excess may rank as 'expense' when due to disturbance. They may arise in two ways: the contractor may use his own capital to run his business, and so be deprived of a return which he might gain on his money invested elsewhere, or he may need to borrow by way of overdraft or otherwise, and so incur interest charges himself. As this interest is an expense to the contractor, it does not rank as interest charged directly to the employer. It is thus admissible as loss and expense in suitable circumstances. It needs to be proved reasonably (like loss of profit), and could not often be supported in a small claim, when no extra financing would really arise. This is considered in Chapter 22, where the comments on small contractors should be noted.

The old view, perhaps helpful to smaller contractors and set out by the House of Lords in *The Edison* (1933), was that financing charges must arise out of the claimant's 'impecuniosity as a separate and concurrent issue' distinct from the cause of direct loss, so that they rank as indirect. The House of Lords and other courts have tended not to follow the decision here, or at least to 'distinguish' the position in other cases, as the argument is highly suspect in the light of modern financing arrangements throughout industry. So, for instance, in *Dodd Properties (Kent) & Others Ltd* v. *The City of Canterbury & Others* (1979) allowance was made for inflation relating to an indemnity amount.

Some leading cases

In *Sunley* v. *Cunard* (see above under 'Loss of profit' and Ch. 14 under 'Plant'), the contractor was awarded, among other things, both depreciation of and interest on the cost of plant tied up in a delay, as wasted costs incurred. Somewhat more recently in this field, it is worth going back to the position obtaining under the 1963 JCT contract, as related legal cases lead into the distinctions introduced by the 1980 JCT contracts and the 1984 IFC contract.

Salient in this respect, is the Court of Appeal case of *F. G. Minter Ltd* v. *Welsh Health Technical Services Organisation* (1980). This upheld that direct loss was the equivalent of damages for breach, so following the distinction in *Saint Line Ltd* v. *Richardsons, Westgarth & Co.* (1940) between direct and indirect or consequential loss. This means that all loss flowing without intervening cause from the primary cause is direct, so that financing charges are in principle recoverable. In *Minter* v. *WHTSO* the contract under examination was JCT 1963, and in particular its clause 24(1), predecessor of the 1980

clause 26.1, and also the then clause 11(6) which dealt separately with loss and expense due to the instruction of variations. These clauses contained wording as follows:

11(6)   if the said application [over loss and expense] is made within a reasonable time of the loss or expense *having been incurred*.

24(1)   if upon written application being made . . . the Architect is of the opinion that the Contractor *has been involved in direct loss and/or expense*.

The emphasis has been added in each quotation. It highlights the critical wording which was held to mean that an application had to relate to loss and expense which were entirely past and incurred at the date of application. Minters had applied after the loss and expense had been incurred, mainly on site, but in the action sought to recover financing charges from the time of loss and expense on site up to the date of payment following the architect's certificate.

It was held that Minters could recover only the portion up to their application, as only this was past by then. It would appear from the judgment that they would have been able to recover up to the last application, had they given a series of later notices at the appropriate intervals stating that they had incurred further loss and expense by way of financing charges. The Court of Appeal definitely disagreed with the High Court's view that such later charges were indirect expense rather than direct. They thus confirmed that financing charges were in principle admissible in loss and expense claims.

In that case, the Court of Appeal rejected the defence that Minters were not claiming direct losses at all, but were making 'a naked claim for interest'. This is an instance of the courts tending to undermine the long-standing principle about interest-related damages noted above.

The JCT 1980 form has amended the critical wording by giving, in clause 26.1 (which absorbs both the earlier clauses), the words 'written application . . . that he has incurred *or is likely to incur*', the emphasis again being added. The effect of this is thought to be that one application made 'as soon as it has become . . . apparent' will suffice in principle to cover all aspects of loss and expense, including financing charges (see the next case mentioned below). It is, however, prudent for the contractor to mention this element in his application when it applies, as it is not one which will always apply and not one that may be obvious to an employer. It may also be a very large item. Otherwise, he may face a rebuttal on the grounds that the urgency of settling had not been made clear, so that charges have been mounting up at least partly avoidably.

More recently, but still in relation to the 1963 JCT wording, there is *Rees and Kirby Ltd* v. *City of Swansea* (1985). Here the Court of Appeal considered a situation in which the contractor had duly given notice of claim. This was not pressed with maximum vigour, because the Council and the contractor entered into prolonged alternative negotiations about whether to turn the fixed price contract into a fluctuating one or even to settle for an *ex gratia* payment in a

time of high inflation. This was seen by the contractor as a way of absorbing the loss and expense. Unfortunately, the negotiations broke down, leaving an extended period to be covered for financing charges. The contractor then lodged his claim for these which was rejected by the Council, so leading to the action. The judgment ranged over several points:

(a) The correct timing of the application was contested, but upheld by the court as it had been made after the loss concerned, even if delayed by the intervening negotiations. In the *Minter* case, there had been no such following application.

(b) The notice given had referred sufficiently, if in a 'most general' way, to the charges being incurred. The need to make successive applications, so that they were within a reasonable time of the suffering of loss and expense, was endorsed. This had been done. It was indicated in passing that this specific mention *might* not be necessary under the JCT 1980 form.

(c) The Council's defence that there was a cut-off in principle for any amounts to accrue at practical completion was not accepted. Charges could continue to build up until the last of the periodic applications which the contractor might make before a certificate is issued including the amount ascertained. This effectively means until agreement of the amount and would appear as relevant under the JCT 1980 contract.

(d) The Council's argument that a part of the delay during which charges accrued was not due to the disturbance was accepted. This was on the basis that the negotiations, as a collateral activity, were not caused by the disturbance and so were not a direct contribution to the expense, but only indirect by being an intervening cause. This is based on the special factors in the case and is not of general applicability.

(e) The contractor was allowed the charges at compound interest, rather than simple interest, which is normal when a court allows interest as such. In this instance, the basis was that financing charges as such are calculated on a compound basis, so that the contractor should recover on the same basis as that on which he had lost.

Rees and Kirby Ltd thus received a substantial part of what they had claimed, but not all. The special element here was the delay to which they were party, while the abortive negotiations went on. But for this delay, it would appear that they would have been entirely successful in the action as it would have been. In particular, they would have been entitled to a resumption of entitlement *after* the invalid period, provided notices had been resumed under the JCT 1963 requirements.

The question of such delays is an interesting one in view of the way that negotiations often proceed over a long period, even when they relate directly and solely to ascertaining loss and expense, and are allied to the possibility of either party unduly protracting discussions. If the contractor drags things out, the employer may be on good ground in refusing to meet the whole amount. If the employer is the tardy party, the contractor should

watch carefully that he does not lose his right to charges by default. He should keep up his notices if under a JCT 1963 contract or equivalent, and advise the employer of his continuing claim for financing charges under a 1980 form, where a notice may look ahead. This is against the background of the desirability of making it clear whenever these charges arise, that they will be included in the claim, as this last case emphasises.

Advanced warning of these charges under JCT 1980 should lead to a desire to settle early and avoid a build-up of charges. There is also a clear argument for the employer to pay amounts progressively, and perhaps on a provisional basis, in interim certificates and so reduce the level of charges accruing up to the point of settlement.

While the contractor may be able to keep his right alive up to the point of inclusion in a certificate, or virtually so, by his last notice of loss or by the date of agreement of the amount ascertained, he cannot secure any extra reimbursement of financing charges when once a certificate has been issued and payment is then not forthcoming. Amounts for loss and expense are no different from any other when certified payment is delayed, and what would be straight interest cannot usually be claimed (but see Ch. 8 for possible developments in the courts). Although it did not itself relate to financing charges, the case of *Croudace* v. *Lambeth*, considered in Chapter 12, shows that the employer cannot hide behind the absence of a certificate to put off payment, when it is missing due to his own dilatoriness.

Calculation of financing charges

Several points arise over calculation of amounts, without going into technical detail here. It has been noted that compound interest may be applicable. Whether it is actually appropriate will depend on whether it was chargeable to the contractor himself. Equally the rate of interest used should reflect the rate chargeable, not necessarily the actual rate which the contractor paid, but rather the general commercial rate obtaining in the market place during the period concerned.

This reflects the possibility that the contractor may have been charged a specially high rate due to his own circumstances and standing. As the employer cannot be held reasonably to have anticipated this as the likely level of loss, unless he had explicit warning of the fact, he cannot be expected to pay the difference (see discussion on damages at the beginning of Ch. 10). This should be distinguished from the situation when the contractor incurs charges at all because he is in, for instance, overdraft because he is 'impecunious', that is has inadequate capital. Here, he is not debarred from the appropriate normal level of recovery, as discussed above regarding *The Edison*.

Whatever happens, it is necessary for whoever is ascertaining loss and expense to check what actually is being paid by the contractor to his regular funding body, modified perhaps in the light of published general lending rates plus the usual 1 or 2 per cent applicable in the circumstances. The rates are likely to fluctuate frequently over the lengthy sort of period which warrants

the inclusion of financing charges as a head of claim. Within limits, some sensible averaging can be used to avoid what could become daily calculations. Compounding of the amounts should be applied at the intervals applicable to the contractor himself in any routine case.

Taxation and the abatement of financing charges

As a tailpiece, this element may be mentioned. In the case of *Tate & Lyle* v. *Greater London Council* (see under 'Formula calculations' above), it was decided that account should be taken, when calculating interest, of the effect of setting off the sums still due against profits for the year in question, when making returns for corporation tax. This has the effect of deferring the payment of some tax, so that money remains with the contractor or other person claiming reimbursement of financing charges and reduces the charges effectively. It appears that contractors dealing with central government departments are meeting pressure for this sort of abatement to be made in all relevant situations.

The calculation of amounts may be quite complex, owing to changes in the rate of tax, the period over which it arises to be set off against, and the particular tax status of the contractor and whether he can defer payment, quite apart from the immediate issue of financing charges as an element of loss and expense. It will be apparent that the existence of several contemporary contracts with this element further complicates affairs, over whether the abatement should be shared and precisely how. This is a case where the contractor is responsible for producing figures, as always, so that loss may be ascertained, but where the onus of proof of precise quantum perhaps lies with those acting for the employer.

It appears that the argument for such an adjustment under any form of contract and with any type of employer is sound, and this type of calculation may be expected to increase, given commercial life as it is. It is an area where some reasonable averaging of amounts should be acceptable to avoid effort reaching the near absurd in minor instances at least.

CHAPTER 16

Damage to the works and determination of employment

Damage to the works, and related insurance
Determination of contractual employment

The twin aspects taken in this chapter lead to several areas of dispute in their own right. They also link with other aspects such as extension of time and disturbance of regular progress taken in other chapters in more detail than the present topics, which are considered in context from a limited standpoint. References mentioned below should be followed up for a rounded view of the material.

Damage to the works, and related insurance

The wider subject of liability for injury to persons and property, including damage to the works, cannot be pursued here, any more than can issues of insurance be. Discussion is limited to the impact of these issues on the main thrust of the present work. In respect of the amended standard contract and sub-contract clauses referred to below, JCT Practice Note 22 contains extremely detailed comment and guidance on the extensively revised and amplified clauses introduced. There are numerous aspects which cannot even be mentioned in the present highly selective treatment.

LIABILITY OF THE CONTRACTOR TO CARRY OUT THE WORKS

Responsibility for reinstatement after damage

As standard contracts are entire contracts (see Ch. 2), the contractor is placed under an obligation to complete which is very demanding, except to the extent that the contract terms amend the basis. Fortunately for him, and in many cases in practice for the employer as well, they do this. Over the obligation to complete the works on time and at the contract price, as well as to the contract quality, there are several provisions relevant to what happens when there is damage. Without these, the contractor would be obliged to replace the works and complete them without extra payment, even in the event of total destruction during progress. Determination of the contract

would still be a fundamental breach. It appears that he would be responsible for delivering the works up on time as well, even though this might well be beyond the limits of the possible, so that he could face liquidated damages during a period of overrun.

In *Charon (Finchley) Ltd* v. *Singer Sewing Machine Co. Ltd* (1968), alteration work was almost complete when it was damaged by vandals. The cost of reinstatement fell on the contractor, despite the manner of damage. The contract was not in the JCT form.

Delay due to damage

Standard contracts allow extension of time when there is damage to the works, due to the same contingencies as are covered by the insurance provisions described below. A comparison of the old and the revised JCT insurance clauses is important here. The contracts also allow extension when there is delay due to *force majeure*, which remotely could lead to damage to the works beyond the normal scope of insurance, although it is a much wider concept – so wide as to be almost limitless. Otherwise, delay due to damage remains the contractor's responsibility in cases not covered by the insurance requirements of the contract. In these instances, he still faces liquidated damages should he miss the completion date as currently fixed.

While the contract insurance provisions help the contractor by covering reinstatement costs, including extra overheads, they do not afford him protection over the costs of disruption and delay as such and he is not entitled to any further payment from the employer over any other costs of reinstating damage. He must therefore look to his wider insurance cover for any protection against these elements, and indeed over liquidated damages.

Within the revised insurance provisions, there is a clause giving an option (subject to an appendix entry) to the *employer* to have insurance included to cover his loss of liquidated damages. This is done post-contractually and the premium becomes an addition to the contract sum.

INSURANCE PROVISIONS OF STANDARD CONTRACTS

General scope of the provisions

The publication of the 1980 JCT contracts saw a set of clauses over injury and insurance, clauses 20 to 22, which were very similar in all points of substance to those which had been in use previously. As work was proceeding on revisions to these in view of developments in the insurance world, but was not advanced enough, it was decided to publish the 1984 IFC contract with essentially the same clauses. All of these clauses, and the related clauses in sub-contracts, were amended with effect from the beginning of 1987, although significant revision is limited to clause 22. They affect several other clauses in points of drafting or even substance, but these are issues beyond present concern.

The overall pattern of the main contract clauses, old and new, giving the JCT and IFC numbering, is the same:

(a) *Clauses 20 and 6.1*: injury to persons and property and indemnity.
(b) *Clauses 21 and 6.2*: insurance in general against last injury.
(c) *Clauses 22 and 6.3*: insurance of the works in particular against loss and damage:
    (i) works insured by the contractor;
    (ii) works insured by the employer;
    (iii) works, existing structures and contents insured by the employer.

In all of the options under clauses 22 and 6.3, old or new, the requirement is for insurance of 'the full reinstatement value', an expression discussed under 'Loss and expense' below, but adequate to cover the immediate costs of putting matters right. In the new clauses, the arrangement is for the insurance to be in the joint names of the parties, and further for sub-contractors to be substantially included by a recognition or a waiver procedure (see further below). In view of the breadth of coverage of these various persons, it is necessary for local authority employers to take out the appropriate insurance under the revised clauses, whereas they do not have to insure under the old clauses.

Under the old clauses, when the first option applies, the insurance is to be in the joint names of the parties, but without mention of the interests of sub-contractors. When the second or third option applies, the insurance is not in joint names and also the employer takes the risk for the consequences of damage, whether or not insurance is required. This is a radical rearrangement of the risk normally existing under an entire contract, except over the existing elements which are the employer's property. Under the new clauses, this drastic and, in principle, unwelcome shift does not take place. All-risks remain where they would be in an unmodified entire contract position, but with insurance mandatory to support responsibilities.

Insured risks

The 1980-based main contract clauses 22 provide for insurance to cover against loss or damage by the 'Clause 22 Perils'. These are defined quite widely, but exclude a number of significant risks, especially impact, subsidence, theft and vandalism. The 1987 clauses 22 of the JCT form (and the IFC is similar) use three concepts:

(a) All risks insurance: this is defined in clause 22.2 as providing 'cover against any physical loss or damage to works executed and Site Materials', with defined exceptions relating to such elements as wear and tear, defects in design, etc. consequences of war, unidentified loss and excepted risks (see (b) below). There are further limitations for work in Northern Ireland.
(b) Excepted risks: these are defined to cover those risks due to radioactivity, sonic booms, etc. which are uninsurable, but are covered by statute. They

form part of the definition of clause 22 perils in the 1980 forms, by way of exclusion from what is covered.

(c) Specified perils: these are those risks which are covered positively by the 1980 forms as clause 22 perils. They thus exclude the categories mentioned above of impact, subsidence, theft and vandalism.

The 1980 and 1984 forms restrict themselves to the clause 22 perils for all insurance of the works. The main forms are silent over sub-contracts, it being left to the forms for them to spell out the implication that 'the Works' in the main forms includes the work of sub-contractors. The several additional perils mentioned are thus not matters for mandatory insurance by whichever party is responsible for effecting insurance, but would normally be covered as a matter of prudence.

The 1987 revisions, by the all risks provision, extend insurance to cover the additional categories of impact, etc. so far as the main contract is concerned over the works as performed, whether consisting of new construction, alterations or additions. The reference is to the more limited set of specified perils in respect of several important aspects:

(a) Insurance of existing structures and contents, when there are works of alteration or extension (which themselves are covered by the all risks level of insurance).

(b) The benefit of the joint names policy which is provided for nominated, named or domestic sub-contractors, with a further limitation in the case of domestic sub-contractors that they are not entitled to benefit from the policy at all over existing structures.

(c) Extension of time due to the delaying effect of damage, so remaining in scope as in the 1980 and 1984 versions.

(d) Determination of the contractor's employment due to a prolonged, continuous suspension of the works.

It is therefore up to the contractor or sub-contractor concerned to decide whether he should be covered against the excess of liability, which the contract itself does not require to be covered at these points. It remains the case, as a matter of normal insurance pattern, that there is cover against the negligence of whoever is at fault among them. It is now much clearer that the insurance not only provides cover for damage to the work of all these persons, but that it is so cast that the insurer does not have a right of subrogation against any of them to seek contribution, because of negligence. It is, of course, very much a matter for those on whose behalf insurance is taken out, to check that they are being properly and adequately covered. An instance relevant to the employer over design is given under 'Some further aspects of the damage to the floor' in Chapter 20.

Negligence was in issue in *Scottish Special Housing Association* v. *Wimpey Construction (UK) Ltd* (1986), where the contractor caused damage by fire to housing which he was renovating. Under clause 20(C) of the 1963 JCT conditions incorporated into the Scottish Building Contract, the contractor

was to be paid for reinstating after his own negligence and the employer sought to avoid this. The Scottish court agreed with the employer, but was overruled by the House of Lords. Insurance was by the employer, so that all concerned were covered, as though they had insured themselves.

Extension of time and determination of employment

Extension of time and determination due to damage are dealt with under the general clauses of the contracts dealing with these for a range of reasons. In any of the versions of the provisions, there is the distinction that the former has to be granted when justified by a case of damage, and without reference to whether there has been negligence by contractor or sub-contractor. In the case of determination, this can be invoked only in the absence of such negligence, and loss and damage do not apply for the contractor's benefit. The parties bear their individual loss and damage.

In the case of damage under the third option of the employer insuring new and existing, there is separate provision in all versions for an optional determination by either party when this 'is just and equitable'. There is an enlargement here: in the old clauses, this links to the clause 22 perils, but in the new it links to the more extensive 'all risks' set. It is related to damage to the works and materials, rather than to the existing structures and their contents. It would appear, though, that the primary reason for the determination provision must be the existing, rather than the new. Given damage to the new only, particularly if it is a clean-cut extension, it is no more arduous to replace the work than it is for a free-standing structure. The only extraneous consideration is that the employer may be more prejudiced in his plans, because it is the combination of the two sections which he needs, and the delay may be that more biting. This of course is one of the reasons why he should seek insurance over loss of liquidated damages initially.

But there is the possibility that when the new is damaged, so is the existing. Reinstatement may involve types of work which the present contractor is not equipped to tackle, so that either he does not wish to proceed or the employer does not wish he should. Again, the extent of reinstatement of the existing may far outweigh that of the new, so that the scope of works amounts to a variation of the contract which the contractor is not obliged to accept, and which the employer may not wish to place with him for the same reason. An extreme case would be refitting by a contractor, specialising in joinery and finishings, of the top floor of an existing framed building which is razed to the ground during progress of the refitting. Unless the existing were replaced, replacement of the new works is impossible: the contract is frustrated by the destruction of its subject-matter, the building which was to be refurbished.

It appears therefore that a determination by either party would be viewed as just and equitable only when something more was at stake than normal reinstatement. When notice of determination is given, the other party may choose to accept it by doing nothing within the time-scale stipulated. His alternative is to seek arbitration which proceeds at once, and needs to, so that

the issue may be settled. If the determination is upheld, settlement follows that discussed when the contractor determines under clause 28.

Payments for reinstatement after damage

The old clauses are less explicit over the immediate destination and routeing of insurance monies, when there is joint insurance under the first option. The new clauses specify that they are to be paid to the employer with the agreement of the contractor. In each case, they are then paid to the contractor under certificates issued alongside the routine interim certificates for the works proper. These sums represent all that the contractor is to receive for reinstatement work, so that he has a prime interest in agreeing the amounts to ensure that he is adequately covered. Indeed, he should resist any influence from the employer's side which might reduce his entitlement, although he might welcome any support that tends to increase it.

It is then the duty of the architect and the quantity surveyor to arrange how the amounts are paid out, to keep in step with the progress of reinstatement. The amounts need bear no fixed relationship to the original figures for the work which has been damaged, quite apart from the extent of removal of debris. No retention is to be held, as that already exists for the work originally executed. The employer is naturally out of pocket on site until the work catches up with its previous position, but he has the insurance monies in hand to cover this. Further amounts under the regular certificates are still payable during this period, despite the apparent duplication of payment which may be noted. The only major problem will arise if the contractor becomes insolvent during the time in which work has not caught up. The insurance funds are not intended to cover this sort of eventuality.

In the second and third options, that is when the employer insures, the monies clearly should go to him. Under the new clauses, it is still necessary, because of the joint names arrangement, for the contractor to agree to this happening. The basis of settlement is quite distinct here, as the contractor is due to be paid for the reinstatement as though it were a variation instructed by the architect. The contractor may therefore expect to receive all that is due to him as part of his contract payment. The position is the reverse of the previous, with the employer particularly concerned that the settlement of the insurance claim is adequate, as he will receive no more, whatever he actually pays the contractor. No special certificates are needed, as the amounts of variations are reflected as usual, but under JCT 80 and IFC 84 the contractor will face retention on the amounts for this very reason. Under JCT 80 (amended 87), he is relieved of having to bear retention.

In view of the uncertainties so often inherent in demolition and repair in circumstances of damage, settlement of amounts is frequently progressive, so reducing the problems outlined and leading to closer reckoning. This may well be an advantage to the insurer as well.

Should a determination occur because of a prolonged suspension after damage or, for that matter, because of any other provision in the contracts,

the benefit of the insurance monies will accrue to the employer, subject to any work which the contractor may perform. The overlap of the twin problems of damage and determination may well complicate settlement. The insurer will not expect to pay out a higher amount because of the interruption caused by the determination, and this margin must fall into the determination settlement. If the contractor has determined due to the suspension, the employer will therefore remain out of pocket, as in other instances of the contractor determining. If the contractor has taken out the insurance, the employer will need to take a much greater interest in the insurance settlement, as he (rather than the contractor) will be recovering the money in final settlement.

LOSS AND EXPENSE WHEN DAMAGE HAS OCCURRED

It is a matter of vocabulary that the clauses mentioned use the term 'loss or damage' to mean physical damage to work and materials, while the determination provisions use the term to convey broadly the equivalent of loss and expense when there is disturbance of regular progress. There is, however, the question of the interrelation of payments under the insurance arrangements and loss and expense.

Directly, JCT clause 26 and IFC clause 4.12 do not refer to the effects of damage to the works, etc. in the way that the corresponding clauses about extension of time make it a relevant event. This means that such damage is not in itself a 'matter' under the clauses, leading to possible reimbursement of loss and expense.

Whichever party insures is entitled to receive payment related to 'the full reinstatement value', even though the basis of assessment varies as has been described. This term covers performing work at current price levels and in the conditions of working associated with reinstatement, but it is not to be taken as covering associated loss by way of disruption or prolongation of other work, not itself damaged. This means that normal loss and expense are not covered by the insurance settlement. For the reasons in the next two paragraphs, it is for the contractor to ensure that he insures elsewhere or by an extension of the contract policy against this aspect.

All three of the alternative arrangements include a provision, 'The occurrence of such loss or damage shall be disregarded in computing any amounts payable to the Contractor under or by virtue of this Contract.' This must be read as embodying some such qualification as 'other than the monies payable from the insurances'. It precludes any reimbursement of the contractor by the employer for loss and expense on work beyond what is damaged. When the contractor has insured under the first alternative and this is taken with the expression 'not entitled to any payment . . . other than the monies received', the possibility of reimbursement for loss and expense is closed.

When the employer has insured under either of the other alternatives, restoration, etc. 'shall be treated as if they were a Variation . . . under

clause 13.2' (quoting from the JCT clause). This must mean 'shall be valued in themselves as if . . .'. The wording cannot readily be stretched to allow them to be regarded as variation instructions for the purpose of clause 26, in the light of the provision 'The occurrence [etc.]' quoted above, so that here again loss and expense cannot be reimbursed.

SUB-CONTRACTORS' LOSS AND DAMAGE

The philosophy of the standard contracts is that insurance is taken out under the main contract to cover sub-contractors, so avoiding a series of complex and perhaps conflicting insurances, with the danger of cross-claims, subrogation and confusion. The case of *Petrofina (UK) Ltd & Others* v. *Magnaload Ltd & Others* (1983) may be consulted for an instance when subrogation could not be pursued by the insurer, when the employer had insured all property on site in the names of all contractors and sub-contractors.

In the foregoing discussion, some of the key elements regarding sub-contractors have been mentioned. By way of summary and extension, these elements are:

(a) The term 'the Works' includes those parts performed by sub-contractors of all types.

(b) While the old clauses do not mention how sub-contractors are included, the new clauses allow for sub-contractors to be included in the policies by one of two methods. There may be a 'recognition' of the sub-contractor, individually or as part of a blanket arrangement, as a joint insured. Alternatively, there may be a waiver by the insurer of any rights of subrogation, that is to proceed against the sub-contractor to recover amounts paid out to the person actually insured.

(c) The scope of reimbursement is limited to the effects of the 'clause 22 perils' under the old clauses (as it is for the contractor) and to the 'specified perils' under the new clauses (which is narrower than for the contractor). For domestic sub-contractors, there is a further restriction when dealing with existing structures. The sub-contractor must take out such insurance as he requires to cover the rest of his potential liability.

(d) Payments for reinstatement are always valued as the expenditure of provisional sums or as variations, whatever is happening at main contract level, so that the position over loss and *expense* is as described under 'Loss and expense' above.

(e) Under the old clauses, amounts for these putative variations are added to the sub-contract sum, whereas under the new clauses they are to be recovered as a debt, that is outside the principal settlement of the sub-contract. The reference does not allow loss and expense amounts to be similarly relegated, and these fall to be included in the sub-contract settlement proper within the main final account.

As with the main contract provisions, there are numerous matters of significance with sub-contract insurance which do not fall within the

boundaries of present discussion. Again, the JCT practice note may profitably be consulted over the new provisions, while the present author's *Building Sub-Contract Forms* may be consulted over the old provisions and over other facets, affecting old and new and not covered by the practice note.

Determination of contractual employment

The area of determination overlaps with others taken in varying detail in this book, such as ownership of materials at an insolvency, sub-contracting and re-nomination or its equivalent. It is treated in this chapter only over aspects which relate strongly to the main themes of the book. The clauses mentioned may be followed up in more detail elsewhere, and should be if other aspects are at stake. Commentary on them is given, for instance, in the present author's *Building Contracts: A Practical Guide* and *Building Sub-Contract Forms*.

MAIN CONTRACT DETERMINATION

Two versions of this possibility are given in both the JCT 1980 form and the IFC 1984 form: determination by the employer and by the contractor. The subsidiary elements in each case are taken side by side by way of comparison.

Reasons for determination

These break down into determination on account of specified reasons which are the default of the other party or are neutral in character (most of these being a smaller selection of what is in the list of relevant events for extension of time), or on account of insolvency of the other party. The last does not occur in the local authorities edition, although nowadays it may be considered relevant! The reasons which are also 'events' are given in Table 9.1. JCT clause 28A (newly included in the amendment 87) and IFC clause 7.8 reasonably allow the employer to determine for *force majeure*, damage by perils and civil commotion which, under the unamended JCT clause, are restricted to the contractor.

The reasons which are not included in other clauses in the case of default by the contractor are:

(a) Wholly suspending the works without reasonable cause.
(b) Failing to proceed with the works reasonably and diligently.
(c) Failing to remove defective work, etc. as instructed.
(d) Unauthorised sub-letting.
(e) Failure to observe the fair wages resolution (something of an anachronism).
(f) Corruption (not included in the unamended JCT 80 private edition, and applies under IFC 84 only for local authorities).

Those not included in other clauses in the case of default by the employer are discussed under 'Certificates and payments' earlier in this chapter, and are:

(a) Not paying the amount properly due on a certificate.
(b) Interfering with or obstructing the issue of a certificate.

In most of these instances, there are procedures over giving notices in appropriate parts of the conditions, and these should be carefully observed to avoid dropping into unwanted problems.

Procedures and terms for determination

Each of the clauses gives procedures for settlement of affairs when once determination is a fact. The standard position is that the employment of the contractor is determined, and not that the contract is determined. This means that the contract provisions over determination remain in place and still apply, so that the parties are not left to sort affairs out from a position of complete uncertainty. Provided the procedures are followed, the key features of the clauses rest in the terms for settlement, which may be summarised.

When the employer determines, the contractor has to vacate the site without further payment until final settlement and the employer may complete the works, perhaps utilising the contractor's plant, etc. temporarily, and engaging other contractors to do the work. Settlement embraces the balancing of the various amounts which have been lost or actually expended against those which should have been expended, had the determination not occurred. This involves quite an amount of calculation of actual and notional accounts (see, for instance, the extended example in the second case study in the present author's *Quantity Surveying Practice and Administration*). A minimal framework of payments is:

(a) Original contract interim payments made and any payments in tidying up accounts, such as nominated sub-contract retention as obligatory and perhaps payments to particular sub-contractors for special reasons as optional.
(b) Temporary measures on site during the transition period.
(c) Amounts under the completion contract or contracts, and by way of extra fees.
(d) Loss and damage for delay, discussed under 'Direct loss and damage' below.
(e) Hypothetical account for what should have been incurred, this being deducted from the other elements to give the net indebtedness of one party to the other (usually in the one direction, and probably worth little to the employer if the contractor is insolvent).
(f) An account of what the contractor actually did and provided up to determination is not strictly needed here, but may be useful for collateral purposes.

When the contractor determines, again he has to vacate the site. Thereafter, the employer may or may not choose, or be able, to carry on to completion. What is provided under the clause is that accounts are to be settled, as between the employer and the contractor, without reference to what the employer may do next. This involves settling the existing contractual account, while taking in the effects of the determination itself:

(a) All work completed or in progress and materials delivered or otherwise the employer's responsibility.
(b) Loss and expense during the works as performed.
(c) Costs of removal and leaving the site tidy.
(d) Direct loss and damage, discussed under that heading below.

JCT clause 28A and IFC clause 7.8.2 prohibit the contractor from determining when one of the 'neutral' reasons applies, and he or his sub-contractors, etc. have been negligent. This is covered only for damage to the works in the amended JCT clause, although this is the only likely case. It is always necessary for a party to be sure of his grounds before determining: the case of *Burden* v. *Swansea* mentioned in Chapter 8 illustrates the danger of choosing the wrong reason. Further, a trigger-happy attitude is counter-productive, as determination is always a last resort. It is not be used 'unreasonably or vexatiously', as the clauses put it, and an arbitrator or judge is likely to take an adverse view of determination over a mere technicality of little effect.

Direct loss and damage

For present purposes, the distinctive feature is that of 'direct loss and/or damage', as clauses 27.4.4 and 28.2.2.6 of the JCT forms express it. Clauses 7.4(d) and 7.7(b) of the IFC form use the same expression. It is often held that this expression means the same in practical terms as 'direct loss and/or expense' in the corresponding clauses about disturbance of regular progress. This may be so, but all the clauses make some distinction by adding 'direct loss and/or damage' on to the lists about either the cost to the employer of finishing the works or the amounts due to the contractor for what he has done on the works and in leaving them. 'Loss and damage' are thus what is still due to the party concerned, once the equivalent of 'expense' has been calculated. By virtue of IFC clause 7.9, the contractor may not recover it when determination by either party is due to one of the 'neutral' reasons given in IFC clause 7.8.1. All loss and damage lie where they fall for the parties.

When the employer determines, the liquidated damages provisions cease to be effective, although any damages already paid or deducted need not be repaid: they help reduce the ultimate indebtedness. Instead, the employer becomes entitled for the period of delay to actual amounts which he can prove as flowing from the determination on a basis similar to that for damages at common law (see Ch. 10). The most likely areas, according to the nature of the employer and his activities, are from among:

(a) Higher costs of alternative accommodation retained or obtained while the new accommodation is not available.
(b) Associated staffing, equipment and overhead costs due to less efficient operating conditions.
(c) Loss of return on capital locked up in the uncompleted project.
(d) Loss of profit or other revenue from markets or sectors not being satisfied.
(e) Financing charges due to prolongation.

These items are listed as suggestive only, as they do vary with employers (according to whether, say, they are operating on a commercial, profitable basis or not), and there is obvious overlap between them. The first two go together as elements of higher operating costs borne elsewhere in the enterprise due to inefficiencies, arguably having started from when it was first proposed, continuing while the project is uncompleted throughout its life, but becoming a source of relevant loss only for the excess period due to the determination. The loss needs some care and analysis for its calculation, as the new premises may well be providing more accommodation, as well as better accommodation. Only the relevant part of the improvement should therefore be allowed. Even so, it is also necessary to avoid double counting against the next pair of items.

The next two are alternative ways of expressing the one phenomenon: loss of what the enterprise exists to obtain for its shareholders or other owners. Which is the more suitable expression, however similar the resulting finances, depends heavily on the type of employer, according to whether he exists to obtain a return, perhaps notional, or make an actual profit. It is subject to the propositions in the law cases in Chapter 10 about the level of loss of profit by the other party, which the defaulting party to the contract might reasonably expect with his actual knowledge to flow from breach, taking any cause leading to determination (including insolvency) as equivalent for the present argument to a breach.

The last expresses a drain on the enterprise's resources, avoiding which should result in greater return, and it may well correspond to or be absorbed in the third item. Usually, it is better for an employer to settle for one of the other heads of claim, rather than financing charges which are less cogent in these circumstances. Such charges are also subject to a greater burden of calculation, as discussed in the context of loss and expense in Chapter 15.

Whatever the items drawn into the calculation, they should all be allowed for the same period. This is to be calculated on the one hand as the original contract completion date, with any extensions which occurred during progress of the original contract and any granted during the completion contract period. These, it must be presumed, would equally have been granted to the original contractor had he continued. On the other hand, the actual overall period taken to completion should be allowed, including periods of cessation between contracts, so that the full difference may be used.

When the contractor determines, the calculation is quite distinct. Any loss

and expense incurred before the determination are included in what is really the final account for the truncated works as performed, so that prolongation costs, as well as disruption, are covered if they have occurred. There should be nothing else of substance left except loss on work not performed, which becomes an admissible head of recovery here, following *Wraight Ltd* v. *P. H. & T. Holdings Ltd* (1968). This case was brought on a contract under the JCT 1963 form, and it was held that the contractor was entitled to recover for both loss of profit and overheads on work not performed because of the determination.

This is quite a different position from that obtaining when the contractor claims for loss of profit and overheads when there is disturbance of regular progress in a continuing contract. There, the position is that set out in Chapter 15, in that he does not secure profit on the extra costs he incurs. Instead, the contractor stands to recover reasonably demonstrable profit forgone on work elsewhere which he could equally reasonably be held not to have obtained because of the disturbance, and also overheads specifically increased or reasonably attenuated by the disturbance.

Here, he stands to recover the profit on what he has not been able to carry out, irrespective of whether he has a full order book despite the determination itself, as there has been breach of contract by him being denied the opportunity to perform. However, as with loss and expense under the other arrangements, the *level* of profit is that which he was likely to achieve, given his actual efficiency and actual market conditions, rather than what was hoped for in the tender assumptions. This leaves a number of questions to be asked, over elements like sub-let work and materials purchases, beyond the relatively simple questions about site productivity. The overheads element represents the actual commitment to the project which cannot be neutralised when it fails to proceed in the expected way, because of the determination. This needs a careful assessment of the implications, following the lines set out in Chapters 15 and 20, although it is suggested that a somewhat more generous allowance may be appropriate in all the circumstances. Whereas profit is recoverable because it has been denied, overheads are recoverable because they have been incurred.

SUB-CONTRACT DETERMINATION

At this contractual level, the basic systems for determining and then settling are quite similar to those at main contract level. The main difference lies in the systems for providing another sub-contractor when this is appropriate, and these have been tackled in Chapter 7, so far as nominated and named sub-contractors are concerned. In the case of domestic sub-contractors, whether and how the contractor sub-lets is entirely in his own hands, subject to obtaining the architect's approval of any sub-contractors. Many of the various facets taken here may therefore be given together for all types of sub-contractors, with differences emphasised.

Four ways of determination

The four ways in which determination under a sub-contract may occur, giving JCT and then IFC references with any main references, are:

(a) Determination of the sub-contractor's employment by the contractor, clauses 29 and 27: the sub-contractor is at fault or insolvent.
(b) Determination of the sub-contractor's employment by the sub-contractor, clauses 30 and 28: the contractor is at fault or insolvent, or problems are being experienced at main contract level, which are affecting the sub-contract.
(c) Determination of the contractor's employment by the employer, clauses 31 and 29, and main clause 27: the contractor again is at fault or insolvent, but the employer has acted first.
(d) Determination of the contractor's employment by the contractor, clauses 31 and 29, and main clause 28: the employer is at fault or (if a private employer) insolvent, and the contractor has acted.

The last two result in automatic determination under the sub-contract.

In the first situation under a nominated sub-contract, the architect has to be involved with the contractor in allowing a determination, because there is going to be a change in the amount payable for the sub-contract by the employer through the contractor, and also because of the potential effect of re-nomination on extension of time and loss and expense matters. This involvement under clause 35.24.4 does not necessarily extend to giving direct assent to the determination or to giving an instruction to effect it, but it does mean that the architect must ensure that the contractor gives proper notice of default to the sub-contractor, with an option to give backing instruction before the contractor may determine. This leaves the contractor still with an option of whether to determine at all if, say, the sub-contractor improves performance. The clause modifies somewhat the position under *James Longley & Co. Ltd* v. *Reigate and Banstead Borough Council* (1982).

In that case, a nominated sub-contractor under the previous Green Form sub-contract had delayed considerably. The supervising officer (SO) (in that instance) was prepared to give an extension of time, but not to give the contractor permission to determine, even when the sub-contractor left the site. He said that his consent was unnecessary, but that he would renominate when determination took place. The sub-contractor went into liquidation and an early renomination was made. The contractor argued that the SO was obliged to instruct a determination when this was in the interests of the work, just as he was obliged to renominate, but it was held that this was not so. The contractor could and should determine without the SO's consent, who had no power to interfere. The employer was not liable for the costs of disturbance or for the delay.

In the first situation of determination, when there is a named sub-contract, the contractor acts on his own, but he is required to keep the architect informed of events. The amount payable is not affected in this situation,

but the other contingencies affecting the employer may apply. The reason for the difference is therefore not entirely clear.

In the second situation of determination, under a nominated sub-contract or a named sub-contract, the sub-contractor is required to give the architect notice of any default by the contractor possibly leading to determination, as the contractor is not likely to do so in the circumstances.

When there is a domestic sub-contract in the first and second situations and whatever the type of sub-contract in the other two situations, the architect is not involved in the determination process.

The reasons for a determination under each of the above patterns flow from the underlying logic of events:

(a) When the contractor determines, the defaults are those which would enable the employer to determine against the contractor, as listed above and also in Chapter 7, in discussing reappointment of sub-contractors.
(b) When the sub-contractor determines, the defaults are those which would allow the employer to determine against the contractor, these being suspension of the works or failure to proceed regularly.
(c) When there is a main contract determination, obviously the reasons already given apply.

The place of the architect in procedures has been mentioned. Otherwise affairs follow predictably from the main contract pattern, over the sub-contractor vacating the site and over obtaining any replacement sub-contractor. The terms for settlement also parallel the equivalent set in the main contract, although the parallel is somewhat distorted in places, as is noted below.

Procedures and terms for determination of nominated sub-contracts

The terms for nominated sub-contracts are the most complex. When the contractor determines, they are effectively as when the employer determines under the main contract, with one major modification. The architect remains responsible, with the quantity surveyor, for settling with the sub-contractor, and is required to issue a certificate which includes an amount for any balance of work by the sub-contractor. This is work not included in certificates up to the determination, because from then onwards nothing has been paid. The employer may deduct from the certificate, when he honours it to the contractor, any expenses in completion of the sub-contract and loss and damage which he has incurred through the determination. In turn, the contractor may deduct these amounts and any loss and damage which he has incurred himself. By comparison, under a main contract determination against the contractor, he receives no further certified amount calculated in original contract terms, but the balance of indebtedness is still calculated from the twin summations of all amounts due and actually paid. Obviously, the amount of deduction by the employer under the two systems fluctuates against the other amounts to keep the final answer the same in principle.

The present clause strictly is misworded, as it allows the employer to deduct

the whole cost of completion, rather than the excess, and is also suspect over the provisions about deductions for loss and damage. These details should be followed up in other works (see above) if entrenched positions develop, otherwise sensible interpretation should prevail.

When the sub-contractor determines, he is paid in just the same manner as is the contractor when he determines against the employer, that is for all he has done, for removing from site and for loss and damage, which includes the loss of profit on work not performed. To the extent that these amounts are in excess of what the sub-contract works would have cost, the contractor has to reimburse the employer to meet the difference. How the amounts are set against one another, and when, is not made clear in either the sub-contract clause or in main contract clause 35.24.6. Clearly, a larger payment to the sub-contractor by the employer will result in a greater element of loss.

When the contractor's employment is determined by either party to the main contract, this may be due to the 'neutral' reasons in main contract clause 28A (amended 87). In these circumstances, to keep the main and sub-contracts in step, the sub-contractor does not receive any payment covering loss and damage. This is not the position with the unamended JCT 80.

A major consideration in each of these cases will be whether the contractor who is in the middle is still solvent, as this affects the adequacy of settlement to be expected by the end party who is initially out of pocket. In the employer's case, there is also what value any employer/nominated sub-contractor agreement in force has for him. This gives him a direct line of redress over loss and expense and extension of time which he may have to grant the contractor, because of sub-contractor default.

Procedures and terms for determination of named and domestic sub-contracts

The absence of the architect from financial settlement of either type of sub-contract has been noted above, as in Chapter 7 has been his part in selecting a replacement named sub-contractor only.

The procedures for removal and completion under the two types of sub-contract are both similar to those for nominated sub-contracts. Most of the elements in settlement are the same between the sub-contracts and follow what has been said above. They allow for a difference-based settlement when the contractor has determined, so that actual total costs are set against what should have happened. These therefore take account of loss and damage in the way described above. When the sub-contractor determines, except when the 'neutral' reasons apply as in JCT 80 (amended 87) and IFC 84, the elements allow for payment for what has been done and for loss and damage, without regard for how the contractor then proceeds, if at all. They are all adduced without reference to the architect over the employer's position.

A point of significant difference is in named sub-contract clause 27.3.3. This requires the sub-contractor to pay to the contractor an amount which the contractor has undertaken to recover under main clause 3.3.6(b), when

a determination by the contractor against the sub-contractor takes place. This amount is then to be passed on to the employer. It represents the following:

(a) Loss and expense payable by the employer to the contractor because of the determination and subsequent events.
(b) Liquidated damages which the employer would have recovered from the contractor for delay on the same counts, had the contractor not been entitled to an extension of time.

This arrangement therefore provides an equivalent recompense for the employer to that which he has under the employer/nominated sub-contractor agreements. If the contractor fails to take reasonable action to recover, he becomes liable for paying the amounts concerned to the employer.

CHAPTER 17

Evidence and negotiation

Evidence
Negotiation

It is the pattern of most of this volume to be concerned with the more precise elements, legal and otherwise, of the subject of contract disputes, as these are what must be observed whenever it is considered that a rigid settlement must be obtained. Even so, there are numerous places where it is necessary to hint at, or point out explicitly, areas in which precision is not obtainable or where practitioners may have differing emphases or views about what should apply. In practice, there are also areas within which factual precision is not always easy to achieve or where there exists uncertainty over the interpretation or embodiment of facts. These areas may often be summarised as those of evidence and negotiation.

How these twin facets are to be looked at frequently depends on which person in the construction process is involved, as each has different perceptions of what has happened and different accesses to information about how it occurred and what have been the results. It must also be admitted that each has a different interest in the outcome, this being one reason why recourse to proceedings by way of arbitration or the courts is available as the last resort, which it always should be. It lies beyond the scope of this book, which is concerned with settlement within the contract machinery. It often pays to settle rather less favourably than had been hoped, to avoid the risks, costs and delays involved in proceedings.

Throughout this chapter, the pattern is more often followed of expressing matters rather ambiguously, so that they may apply from the viewpoint of employer, contractor or sub-contractor, to save undue repetition. The desired 'flavour' should be imported by the reader.

Evidence

Evidence is required for all types of dispute over construction work. As is clear from preceding chapters, it often is technical, detailed and extensive. Most disputes lie between either the employer and the contractor, or the contractor and one or more sub-contractors, although some span the complete set of persons. Often the effective difference is with the architect

or quantity surveyor. The evidence needed is not affected radically by these variant possibilities, so that reference can usually be made to main contract situations without omitting what is equally applicable in the other situations.

GATHERING EVIDENCE

In some situations, especially extension of time and disturbance of progress, the contracts are explicit in requiring the architect to deal on the basis of information provided to him or the quantity surveyor at his request by the contractor. These procedures are detailed in Chapters 11 and 12. Even so, it is regularly necessary for these recipients to gather other information of their own to supplement or confirm what is given to them. In other situations, it is up to the several participants to make their own arrangements and collect what best fits their operations.

While the contracts make explicit provisions in certain instances, those concerned with contracts should sensibly be accumulating reasonable evidence during progress, against the contingency that it may be required. As is indicated by what follows, this collection can hardly be avoided so far as some items are concerned, although proper classification and storage do ease actual use should this become necessary. It usually becomes fairly clear, fairly early when affairs are running into difficulties over major problems at least, so that warning lights should be heeded. It is often the small individual problem which may miss the net and cause trouble later.

It is inevitable that some piece of information will be missed or cannot be isolated from the mass of what is known. In these circumstances, those coming to an agreement must sort affairs out as best they can: a lack of data does not allow either party to plead that the item being claimed should be dropped.

An area where evidence is not always required is that of pricing variations. This is because the pricing is to be related to that in the contract bills in the first instance and, when that is not relevant, to 'fair and reasonable pricing', all as described in Chapter 6, and whether actual costs are higher or lower. In this situation, the actual costs incurred are frequently more hindrance than help, unless they can be suitably broken down to show the effects of working in changed conditions or whatever is involved. Only when 'valuation' is by daywork does the position change radically.

There is an attitude emanating from some contractors that it is better not to have precise evidence, as its absence makes it easier to manœuvre and gain a higher settlement. This may be so on occasions, but it can become a highly risky path to follow. This is particularly so under the current editions of contracts, where early warning of a claim to entitlement supported by evidence is required. In these cases, and indeed all others, in which a party suppresses evidence even by default, he cannot expect to gain the benefit of the doubt, but probably to suffer a reduced settlement.

There is equally an attitude emanating from some consultants that no contentious item should be considered until after completion of construction,

so that facts are to be avoided for as long as possible. This may be simple concern with getting the job finished, or it may be a hope that the problem will quietly go away if the remainder of the outcome of the project is satisfactory to the contractor. Whatever the reason, it passes the benefit of the doubt in settlement clearly across the divide to the contractor. It may also lead to additional disturbing items such as financing charges, as shown in Chapter 15.

SOURCES OF EVIDENCE

Site investigation

This source of information is perhaps so obvious as to need mentioning simply for completeness, but it is primary and one which may easily be neglected. While reports and assorted forms of feedback are valuable and may record firm data, a comparatively casual, but planned, routine stroll round the site may throw up questions or provide impressions for someone who is not concerned with the direct task of production. This sort of activity can be the springboard for mounting a claim, or supply the lead for confounding one. Many matters may come to light, such as:

(a) Labour and plant doing little or appearing to do what is fruitless, such as moving materials an extra time, leading to the question as to whether this is inefficiency on the inside or interruption from outside.
(b) Work being removed, when apparently not defective.
(c) Concentrations of effort, showing signs of inefficient working by undue use of labour when plant might be expected, or just everyone in everyone else's way.
(d) Work out of normal sequence at the stage the project in general has reached.
(e) Undue activity by supervisory staff in some quarter.

There may be quite sufficient reasons for these and many other clues which are discovered, but it is always as well to enquire. It is a matter of who is doing the enquiry which will decide how it is to be conducted: usually it is easier for the contractor's surveyor to ask than his opposite number – and usually he has a more pressing reason to ask. But the architect or quantity surveyor should not avoid finding out: this may save problems building up.

It is only too easy to become chair-bound and miss the flavour of the project as well as the details of what is happening, and so be unable to discuss matters with any authority or conviction during later negotiations. Just where oral enquiries are suitable may be left until the role of documentation has been reviewed.

Contract documents

The great advantage of what is on paper, or perhaps in the computer, is that it is on record for all to see, however accurate it may or may not be, and

however open to contrary interpretations. 'Ask for it in writing', 'confirm it' and 'confirm it back' remain permanent wisdom, and the same is true of graphic and photographic information.

The starting-point must always be the contract documents, so that a careful perusal should always precede any advance or rebuttal. This is obvious over allegations of divergence or discrepancy, but should also be applied when the apparent problem lies out in the practical operations in progress. It is especially true over reading those documents which are clearly unusual, but can follow for those which are routine, but specifically drafted. It is no excuse to say, 'Well, they don't usually say that in their specifications'.

When there is a possible doubt, it is wise to go back to what happened during the period of tendering or assessment, whether there was a substantial element of negotiation or not. While what is expressly incorporated into the contract is of prime importance, there are situations in which representations made during the preceding activities will be held to be effective. This is true of the attitude of the courts in a sufficient case (see Ch. 3), but may also become a forceful argument between those negotiating later, especially if they were also involved at the earlier stage. The position is no different from that when in court, but often a reference back to early events will give the edge in negotiation or allow the other person to concede a difficult point of bargaining without loss of face.

Post-contract documents

The main types of document likely to be of use are:

(a) Drawings, schedules and other technical data issued to amplify the contract drawings or to support instructions.
(b) Instructions issued by the architect or directions issued by the contractor.
(c) Confirmations of oral instructions or directions.
(d) Notices and other formal documents issued to comply with contract requirements.
(e) Architect's certificates, especially on matters other than payment.
(f) Interim valuations in support of architect's certificates for payment.
(g) Minutes of meetings.
(h) Wage sheets, time sheets, plant records, materials invoices and other details of costs incurred.
(i) Statements prepared for the calculation of fluctuations on the traditional basis.
(j) Programmes and method statements, whether prepared in response to a requirement in the contract documents or purely for construction purposes.
(k) Correspondence between those now involved in resolving the dispute or in creating the conditions for it.
(l) Reports on special aspects which have arisen, perhaps not in a dispute context.

(m) Diaries and other individual and private compositions, such as notes of site visits.

(n) Photographs of the site at large or of special pieces of work.

This list follows a broad pattern of setting out documents in a descending order of formal status, although this is only broad and sometimes the imputed formality is dependent on the source of the document or perhaps on whether it was ratified for some purpose (which may not be the present) by both sides to the dispute. A number of comments may be added.

When a document has been issued specifically for the contractor to act upon it, such as a drawing or instruction, its evidential value is clear, although this is modified by when it was issued in relation to other information and progress of the works, and how far it changed the preceding position or introduced a conflict. The contractor was entitled to act on it and to be reimbursed or otherwise compensated for the results. When a document is one required by the contract, such as a certificate or notice, it has a defined effect and may be read accordingly. Only an arbitrator has the power to reopen a certificate, although the persons in negotiation may well refer one back to the architect for his comment and possible agreement to amend in a particular situation.

Interim valuations and minutes of joint meetings between the contenders fall into an intermediate category. Both enjoy a measure of existing agreement or at least acceptance between the parties to give them a status. It is, however, a status achieved in quite distinct circumstances. The former group are produced as a means of calculating payments which are declared to be approximate and open to revision (see Ch. 8). They may therefore be quite misleading about, say, progress of an element of work at some past stage or may embody 'swings and roundabouts' to avoid too much elaboration. When the valuations have been prepared to serve the additional purpose of calculating fluctuations by the formula method, they will usually be more accurate, as they are final calculations in this respect. Like all figures, valuation details need care in interpretation and, subject to this may be very useful data.

Minutes are prepared to record for posterity what was discussed and agreed. The main caveat is that usually one party only produced them, even if they were then 'accepted' by the others at a following meeting. At best, they may be vague over the points later at issue: it is surprising how often a clear and accurate record does not state what is eventually needed. At worst, they may have been worded in such a way as to be bland over the contentious or misleading over the factual. The standardised recording of matters of progress on site, information flows, errors and warnings of problems helps considerably, but a close examination of unagreed minutes, perhaps additionally by someone not directly involved, is vital. They should have been prepared and circulated hard upon the date of meeting, to make this realistic. Like valuations, their present service is to give additional reminders of and tracks into formal sources of data; by themselves, they cannot be taken as embodying the architect's instructions or other documents which are issued separately.

Wage sheets, etc. and fluctuations statements have also been prepared for other purposes, but differ from the sources just mentioned in that many of them have been prepared for reasons needing financial accuracy. They should also have been prepared without a view to misrepresenting facts in the interests of later disputes. This is always possible and in the extreme circumstance should be watched. It is usually unlikely for at least two reasons, the first being the sheer complexity of mounting a large-scale, convincing deception, free from obvious discrepancies. The second reason is the normal incidence of human error, which tends to unbalance any tampering with reality. Such things as cost allocation sheets, prepared by a mass of rather disinterested employees, are often difficult to interpret and reconcile in any detail at the best of times, without a conspiracy being mounted to distort them in a particular direction.

This last point indicates the dangers which may exist in taking even the most innocent of information and giving it credence beyond what its origin warrants. The charge-hand who is keen to be off to the hostelry or to obscure odd happenings on site, may well present the claims sleuth with an utter absurdity if scientific analysis is attempted. This is one reason why 'ascertainment' requires judgment and not just a Geiger counter. The bald calculations set out in the case study chapters could conceal any amount of reassessment of crude data.

Programmes and method statements are usually open to discretion in their use for the reasons given already, particularly that they were prepared for working purposes which may diverge from the exercise of investigation. They may have been made over-optimistic for production reasons, they need not have been followed in detail, even apart from any element of delay or disruption. Again, they may omit the very facts which are crucial or subtly misrepresent them. All of this is quite apart from any intentional drafting to create an exaggerated effect when a disturbance does occur. Programmes receive treatment in Chapter 4. They are not contract documents in the normal course of events, but are still very useful evidence, treated properly.

Correspondence, reports and diaries are again usually the product of individuals, probably of those now on one side or other of the dispute. They must be assessed against the background of their production and the motives of those producing them. An external report may be utterly unbiased, a letter may have been written to set up grounds for the very contention now being advanced. Diaries are open to the same problems. Often they are intended to be fairly private documents and this may enhance their value, especially if they provide evidence in a direction contrary to what was to be expected. In this case they may never be produced! There are limits to what may be demanded, and what is produced voluntarily should be viewed in that light.

Photographs are valuable and probably under-used, although this is changing. The camera of course is not exempt from lying, but it does give an added dimension. Regular sequences of shots build up a time effect, as a single picture cannot. All photographs need to have substantiated dating to be useful and acceptable.

Interviews

When visits have been made and documents perused, it is frequently necessary to amplify or clarify what has been found by recourse to those involved. At this stage, the question of whose side of the actual or threatening dispute they are upon becomes important, as affecting their evidential value. In general, the contractor's enquirers are limited to questioning their own colleagues, whereas the architect or quantity surveyor has a wider opportunity by virtue of his position under the contract. This does not necessarily produce greater objectivity, if he has already been deeply committed to a point of view by earlier events. This is a weakness of the contract assumptions which is noted in earlier chapters.

More broadly, when conducting enquiries, it is necessary to consider the standpoint of the interviewee. This person may be constrained to defend a line of action taken which is intrinsically weak, even without the disturbing effects which are being assessed. He may do this without regard to, or despite, the position in negotiations of the interviewer. As a result, there may be a playing up or down of particular elements of the case to provide an excuse or a smoke-screen. It is always helpful to interview several people over the same set of 'facts', just as much as in road accidents! Whatever emerges, the results should be noted and shared so far as practicable with the opposite negotiator, who may even be afforded the opportunity of conducting his own interview. This can be very salutary for all concerned, including the second interviewer!

The immediate source of information should be the person suffering the apparent loss of time or money, usually the contractor or a sub-contractor. There is usually no problem in obtaining a response here – indeed, it is commonly anticipated! He is under an obligation contractually to provide some information and may offer far more than is needed.

For whoever is responding to these persons, there is a choice of others to interview. The architect may wish to interview the quantity surveyor or the latter, if dealing, will need to see the architect. As just indicated, there can be a problem here, more often with interviewing the architect, who has been deeply involved in the management of the project procurement overall and who is subject to the possibility of prejudging issues accordingly. Nevertheless, it must be done with skill, care and thoroughness. The option of proceedings is always round the corner and can always be mentioned to any reluctant interviewee.

Consultants are an extension of the architect for present purposes, although they cannot undertake any enquiries in support of a settlement, except informally on behalf of the architect. They are given no contractual authority to decide or act, as the contracts do not name them in any way. Nothing added in their specifications changes this position. Their statements are still very useful, especially as they may throw light on matters affecting sub-contractors, in ways which the architect or contractor may not be able or willing to do.

The employer himself may be able to contribute information, although he again seldom has an active part to play contractually. He too may have sufficient interest in the outcome to be less than impartial, but if needs be should be assured of the facts of proceedings. A project manager appointed by the employer is another person not recognised by the contracts, but who takes an important part in activities at points where the disputes aspect can be prominent. He is less likely to be affected by his prior involvement in providing details, but should be interviewed just as searchingly for all that.

Lastly, but not least out of those directly involved, the clerk of works may be mentioned. While he lacks authority under the contracts and exists, if at all, solely as an inspector, he is very well placed to provide comments. He is often full time and so constantly on site and sees the project through in detail, while having dealings with all the other members of the team. His diaries, if conscientiously kept, may be the fullest available. Even so, he should be questioned as carefully as anyone else.

Outside those directly and regularly concerned with the project, there is the contractor's head office. It is most likely that evidence obtained will fall into the oral category, once the formal analyses and financial statements have been obtained. This is because these statements etc. are usually of such a blanket nature that they need explanation for an outsider to glean much from them.

Any evidence of this oral type can never take the place of more formal and objective information, but it may provide just the crack in the cliff face which is needed.

Various sources

A nose for the assorted categories of information useful in special circumstances is needed, particularly when the larger, perhaps ill-defined claim is under consideration. A few of these may be listed, to illustrate the variety of what may be drawn upon:

(a) Ordering times required for materials, plant or even labour, as the result of variations or delays imposed at short notice.
(b) Shortages of inputs caused by regional or national circumstances, and not by the disturbance or other factors emanating from the employer's side of the project.
(c) Inefficiencies in execution by consultants, the contractor or sub-contractors, which have rebounded upon others in such ways as to exacerbate effects. These then may or may not result in extra payments from another person.
(d) Weather conditions, which may explain what has happened and negate the claim. On the other hand, they may explain it, by indicating how work was affected by being pushed into adverse conditions.
(e) Other 'neutral' matters, as in principle weather is, which may come into play in such a way as to be causal or consequential. If causal, they precede the direct cause of disturbance or whatever is in question and

combine with it. If consequential, they follow it and amplify the effect, without necessarily provoking it. (See the discussion of 'Consequential damage' in Ch. 10.)

Like some other points suggested above, this group is rather more a matter of instinctive development than simple listing, so that the few examples given should be regarded only as examples.

USE OF EVIDENCE

Whatever is collected, the person reviewing it is faced with the task of using it. A great deal will be discarded, as in any research. The temptation to use everything should be resisted, especially in preparing a claim. It can arise out of regard for the effort expended, for those who contributed it and averred its usefulness and for the principle that the more one throws in, the stronger the case. Often, it is just the reverse.

The logic of the situation should always be kept to the fore. This covers the basic legal position and what is specific in the contract, as well as any arguments advanced by anyone, including the investigator. It may thus be necessary to ask whether figures in the contract documents or supplied collaterally, such as prices or programme durations, are valid in the calculations being performed, either absolutely or as a means of regulating the use of other data. This position is argued out in several earlier chapters, where what is relevant in principle to particular cases is discussed, so that items out of those set out in the present chapter may be deduced.

Broad areas of loss

In the nature of the case, however, there are frequently times when the precise detail required is not available, a situation also considered in Chapter 14. This is quite likely to occur when the matter under scrutiny is a wide-ranging or umbrella type of dispute, such as a financial claim over loss of productivity. This may span a substantial period of the contract and much or all of the work performed during that period, or it may embrace the whole contract period and scope, although this should be very unusual. It may become impracticable in the former instance to segregate with assurance the relevant costs from all the costs for that period or even other periods, and very close attention should always be given to the reasoning for figures produced to assert a drop here. It may be impossible in either instance to draw up comparative costs for what the work would have cost without the disturbance element, because no similar work has been done that way. The use when possible of this approach is argued in Chapter 14. But now, it is necessary to establish figures from some broader base.

This should not be a simple comparison of tendered figures and actual costs (discounted in Ch. 14), although what is done may sometimes come close to this, by starting with an analysis of both sets of figures to establish general feasibility. Assuming a contention for some drop in productivity of

labour and plant as a whole for some period, which is seen as probable in all the circumstances, this might mean:

(a) Taking the tendered figures and assessing them to see whether they represent a fair level for the work. It may be necessary to consider whether there has been 'front-loading' or any other distortion of pricing which would give this, and how the preliminaries amounts have been allocated. Adjustment should be made, including removing all preliminaries amounts.

(b) Without or even with internal adjustments, which cannot change the overall total of what has been tendered, making a further adjustment to allow for the apparent deviation of the tender from what might have been expected as economic at the time.

(c) Within these figures, with any adjustment, to attempt to isolate the net provision for the elements which it is contended are subject to loss of productivity. Refinement to allow for fluctuations adjustments and any allowances elsewhere in the final account, such as different pricing for the same elements as varied, may be made.

(d) Taking the costs incurred and allocating these to correspond to what has been calculated under (a) to (c).

It is obvious that this process so far is subject to making a whole range of assumptions and to considerable theoretical criticism over its inaccuracy and basis. With the data obtained, there comes the problem of interpretation. The amount claimed may well have been derived from quite distinct reasoning, applied to an equally distinct set of starting figures. Almost certainly it will be different from the crude difference between the figures derived above, even if essentially the same line of reasoning has been applied to precisely the same set of figures.

The best which can be done is to 'form an opinion'. This it may be noted, is what the architect has to do over practical completion and extension of time, even if in the latter instance he then has to 'estimate' or otherwise produce figures based on his judgment. An opinion is not to be excluded from 'ascertainment', when this is what is being done. The opinion may be formed by looking at either or, more likely, both ends of the data. It may be considered on the basis of the figures, judged by experience, that the possible drop in productivity cannot amount to more or less than particular percentages of the initial or actual figures. The resulting ranges may overlap, suggesting a working limit to what should be allowed. They may not, giving more problems in reaching a probability area. An example in this category would be:

Tendered figure inclusions	£200,000
Percentage excess 10–15%	£20,000–30,000
Costs as incurred	£280,000
Percentage allocated 12–17%	£33,600–47,600
Difference between tender and cost	£80,000

Here, the higher percentage allocations from the higher costs cause the problem of the ranges not overlapping and the reasoning may be reviewed as suspect at some point. The actual amounts obtained by adding or subtracting the top of range figures to or from their base figures are close, being £230,000 and £233,000. These are not significant in achieving a reconciliation, but serve to indicate that there is a gap not explained in what has been obtained in the data figures of £200,000 and £280,000. To give just some possibilities, there may be some excess loss due to inefficiency on site, there may be some undiscovered disturbance or there may be an error in the original or adjusted bills of quantities.

These illustrative figures are deliberately wide apart to emphasise the points made, but are not utterly unknown. They indicate the uncertainties of using such theoretically unacceptably derived data, but also underline the need to look critically at other more acceptably derived data for the calculations described in earlier chapters, where marginal differences may lead to significant errors in ascertainment. It is only too easy to make false assumptions in using information obtained from disparate sources, such as cost returns, site observations and 'standard' figures from outside the immediate contract.

It is seldom, if ever, that all sections of the workforce or their plant will suffer the same percentage drop in productivity, so that the above example should allow of some refinement of calculation and result. But the problem element remains.

Single areas of cost subject to overall loss

Another way in which a broad effect may occur is when a single element of cost is subjected to loss of efficiency throughout, say the element of hoisting. This is really a special case of what has already been illustrated, there being a restriction to a single category of input affected. In the instance given, it is to be expected that labour would be affected as well, but this is ignored for present purposes.

Here there is little value in seeking the inclusion for hoisting in the tender, as the amount may be spread and lost inside the estimating calculations, and is in any case subject to heavy oscillations in practice, due to changes in method and the actual progress of work. Hoisting is something of a handmaid to much of what goes on. There is a value in knowing the total cost of hoisting as actually incurred. Given that this is £57,000 (and noting the comments about plant costs in Ch. 14), it becomes difficult to sustain a loss of £36,000, which suggests that the undisturbed cost would have been only £21,000. An increase of over 170 per cent means that something catastrophic has happened, which can hardly have been missed by the most casual observer. Something more modest is probably to be sought.

This approach does not establish an amount, but it does help to contain

the situation. From this point of view, a knowledge of broad costs can be useful, even though not sufficient to provide answers.

Variations

While variations have come into the reckoning already as fitting into the category of instructions to the contractor from the architect, they have particular significance in evidence for at least two reasons. One is that they are usually numerous and affect directly the works being produced and therefore the contractor's and sub-contractors' production activities, which are central to present concerns. The second is that they are paid for in their own right by adjustments of the contract sum, upwards or downwards. It is pointed out in Chapter 6 that the contract provisions for reimbursing variations allow for nearly all attendant circumstances to be taken into the valuation, as well as the direct contents of the work as varied from the original contract inclusion. The exception is disturbance of regular progress, as this is a result of variations, rather than part of their content.

Variations are common, but also vary greatly in their scale and effect on progress. Sometimes, a quite small variation can have an effect out of all proportion to its physical scale and the value of additions and omissions which it produces. This is where the timing of a variation becomes important, so that it is crucial to check this against the stage of progress when it was issued, making due allowance for lead times for ordering materials or building up labour and plant levels. It is extremely difficult for anyone outside the direct production process to identify all the effects from a heap of cold documents after the event, so that the evidence of those directly involved becomes necessary, as always subjected to scrutiny and such corroboration as is available. It is the interaction of a string of small variations which can be damaging, and this does not show in a list of instructions issued.

The contractor's surveyor himself, should he be preparing a claim or other statement, needs to obtain precise information from those on site before he indulges in too much work, even though the underlying variations can usually be dealt with clearly enough. In the case of *Minter* v. *Welsh Health* (1980) discussed in Chapter 15, mistakes and delay over fixing brackets for windows led to consequences out of all proportion to the cost of the brackets.

A special case of the variation is that to obligations and restrictions which affect work on site in ways which do not show in the finished construction. This is important as variation of these aspects tends to overlap with elements of disturbance. It is possible to miss something here unless care is taken, or to allow something twice. The cardinal rule remains to allow as much as possible in the valuation of the variation itself, as this is what the contracts intend and also allows for price adjustment inclusive of profit, rather than ascertainment on a loss and expense basis with profit uncertain (see Chs 6 and 14).

Even work priced as variations by daywork needs care. While the direct cost should be fully covered by this method, an unduly large element of daywork in an account may signal disruption which is not being recompensed.

Timeliness

The intention of the current contracts is to expedite settlement of matters of extension of time and loss and expense, so avoiding uncertainty and the accrual of financing charges. The search for evidence should therefore go on steadily and, when found, it should be assessed and used as warnings or by incorporation as soon as practicable. There is still a 'wait and see attitude' which does not help. All else apart, memories fade and accurate assessment becomes more difficult. This may not be the advantage it is sometimes thought to be. There is much to be said for those dealing for each party setting up a mutual system for recording events which even may lead to later evaluation. This is not only efficient, but it also breeds confidence that the other is dealing in a straightforward way and helps subsequent negotiation. If necessary, agreements reached can be contingent on later developments.

Negotiation

Volumes have been written on the practice of successful negotiation, be it termed an art, a science or just a result of experience. It is not presumed in the present short compass to do more than set out a few points by way of review. Treatment is limited to the context of post-contract negotiation, when the parties are committed and cannot withdraw without considerable cost, as also there is if they continue.

In principle, it might be deduced from most of what has gone before that settlement of contract disputes is really a case of following the rules and totting it all up. It is hoped that this is not the impression created, as life is not like that. The case studies in particular should dispel any such illusions. The following headings indicate a few guidelines during the actual process of agreement.

FLEXIBILITY

It may sound like a counsel of compromise to suggest flexibility in negotiating, and so it may be on occasions. There are though times when what is at stake is by no means so clear as cold principles would suggest. Examples may be found by a close reading of the case study chapters and the use of a little imagination. Another is in the discussion of umbrella disturbance costs earlier in the present chapter. But with this said, flexibility has a wider applicability.

It relates here to the attitude of being prepared to listen to and understand the point of view of others. Construction is based upon a number of long-established routines and segregated specialisms, and the managerial and other professional aspects are no exception, to say the least. It is therefore very easy for the participants, in gaining experience initially in a single discipline for the most part, also to gain an unbalanced view of the whole enterprise. Successful negotiation is not about beating the other fellow into

the ground, but about achieving a result which is fair to all concerned. This is not, of course, the same as achieving what everyone might have wished.

An important aspect of flexibility then is that of not being blinkered, whether as a designer who sees the construction as flowing automatically from naturally unambiguous information provided whenever is convenient to the design office, or as a site manager who sees the designer as someone to be goaded for his lapses, or as a quantity surveyor who sees affairs as represented by his analytical and rather theoretical concepts set out in the frigidity of a cost plan or bill of quantities. Flexibility therefore comes about when the limitations of upbringing and standpoint in working are recognised and there is respect for the integrity of another's work, so that the wrong entrenchment is avoided.

Even more painfully, it may mean giving up self-preservation when threatened by the direction which investigations are taking. Negotiation is not just about the final settlement, but also about defining one's own position in a complex pattern of events. It may also mean admitting ignorance of what the other fellow is about and learning on the way through. Seldom is the right conclusion reached without letting down the guard of invincibility and omniscience.

ENVIRONMENT

While negotiation is often seen as the confrontation of two or more individuals who have a specific arena and tasks, it may also be seen as part of a wider structure of relationships and actions. As a minimum, those directly negotiating are usually operating on behalf of others: the ones whose money or other resources are at stake. It is therefore useful for a participant to keep in mind what it is that his opposite number is concerned about in coming to an agreement. If the other is constrained by having to go on until a certain level of result is achieved, and if this is beyond what is within the first person's remit, then there is not that measure of consensus about what is being done, which must be present for two persons to interact usefully. It becomes necessary for one or both to go back to whomever they represent to see whether any change of brief is possible, so that continuance has any point.

This situation may come about for several reasons. It may lie in the formal constitution of a party to the contract, probably the employer who is governed by standing orders or similar matters, unchangeable so far as he is concerned. The singular is adhered to, as throughout this book, despite the corporate nature of such an employer. Here, the person who 'is' the employer for the negotiator may have no way of breaking a deadlock other than going to some committee. Where they go may not be his concern.

A deadlock not quite so formalised, but equally compelling, may be caused by a ceiling on funds with which to settle. The budget allocated may not permit movement further or, worse, the party represented may face

insolvency if pushed over the line. In any such case, the negotiator can do no more than explore where the other side will settle, and even to do this may be to reveal more of one's hand than is desirable at the stage reached. A provisional offer to settle at what the negotiator considers a satisfactory level, subject to authority, can sometimes ease matters if the authority is forthcoming, indeed it may be a useful counter to play. But if it turns out that authority will not or cannot be given, it can lead to an impossible position for the one putting it forward. He must stop forthwith.

Another way in which the environment can play a part, is if it affects the negotiator in what he is immediately doing. He may find that he is effectively negotiating with more than one person at the same time. This is a problem of fielding a team of people, say architect, quantity surveyor and a consultant, who have not resolved internally just where they are going. It is better to break off for a while and resolve the tension and hope that, on resumption, the other side does not make too much of what they have inferred from the break.

A variation on this theme is the situation in which the negotiator is acting because of compulsion to conciliate or impress another present, that is an act is being presented which draws off force from the actual work of negotiating. To an extent in all groups, individuals are conveying all manner of signals, so that risks of conflicts of interest or even loyalty must be guarded against. A related form of problem exists if the negotiation is also being conducted with someone who is not present. A common version of this pattern is that of the contractor dealing with either the employer's representatives or a sub-contractor, while knowing that he has to close with the other in due course. Either he must play for time, and this may be non-existent or the attempt counter-productive, or he must decide to settle on the current front in a way which he can stand, whatever happens when he faces about.

Even more complex, is the situation of negotiating with an absent principal. It can be that the person in the field, as quasi-agent, is at odds with his principal over some aspect. He may consider that he is being pushed too hard, he may occasionally believe he could do better than he is being asked to achieve and resents the overruling of his personal standards or pride. The temptation in either extreme is to seek a settlement which meets the letter of what has been asked for, but also gives something extra which it is hoped will bridge the point of difference without causing a rift. This may be gratifying if it comes off, but court disaster if it does not.

AUTHORITY

From the last section, there comes directly the question of authority in negotiations. It is critical that a person acting must have defined authority, which may range from 'settle your own way and at any cost' through a series of gradations to 'do not settle anything, but report back'. No one should act without his brief being clear. So far as the architect and quantity surveyor are

concerned when they act in the capacities given them under the contracts, the position is defined for them and the employer. Strictly, they are not acting as agents of the employer to negotiate for him, but to implement various terms of the particular contract. In this position, they are to act impartially between the parties. They do not have to and should not seek authority for their acts within this framework. If they do, there is the danger that they may lay themselves open to charges of bias.

That these persons appear to be acting in the polar position from the contractor on some occasions is because of some of the functions given them. The architect has, for instance, to inspect work and any adverse judgment is bound to be against the contractor. The quantity surveyor has to settle measurements and prices, and this may mean assuming an adversarial stance while sifting the contractor's arguments over something unusual, until assured of where the final position should be. These factors are the result of authority given by a contract, to which they are not parties, and accepted by the parties.

While each negotiator should have clear authority, and especially know its limits, it is also highly desirable that those engaged opposite each other in a single phase or segment of negotiation should have matching authority. It is frustrating to the one to have authority to settle when the other has to report back over comparative trivialities, even though it may give the former some edge. Equally, it is near-humiliating to the other to be in such a position of psychological inferiority, unless it has been set up that way to allow agreement to be reached gradually, uncertainly so far as the other side is concerned, and apparently grudgingly. It *can* be unnerving to the opposition to have to deal through one person with someone else who is always one step removed and inaccessible. For all straightforward activity, straightforward dealing is to be preferred, and if necessary sought by rearranging the pattern of negotiations.

So far as the more individual aspects of authority go, these are a mix of what has been outlined and of personality and conduct. The negotiator has to define his own authority out of the circumstances of discussion or even dispute. He must show that he is firm but reasonable, and that he is open but has his own undisclosed thoughts. He should make it clear when he is holding and when he is conceding, to avoid the 'cloak and dagger' atmosphere. Above all, he should be fair to the subject-matter and to the integrity of the other person. If several people are involved, he should avoid playing them off against one another so as to belittle anyone. On the other hand, while tension has its place, a properly employed sense of humour is invaluable.

METHODOLOGY

There is no one way to negotiate, and much depends on the matter under discussion and the personal approaches of the negotiators. It may also depend on how much preliminary work has been done to establish the factual basis. In the case of much construction-related negotiation, there is

no absolute demarcation between the stages and often the same persons deal with both. This means that the exercise of finding and sifting facts can have a negotiating air about it. Earlier in this book, the principles affecting settlement have been prominent, so that the processes of analysis and synthesis leading up to settlement have not been stressed. They usually contain elements of marking out the areas of discussion which will occupy the end-phase. The investigators need to be watching for clues all through.

While this is true, the discussions should proceed as informally as possible among the activities of aggregating data and the following segregation and classification. It is desirable to agree as much as may be during these stages, so that decisions are not unduly deferred. This allows the general drift to be identified and warnings to be given to those for whom the investigators are acting, even before there may be formal negotiation. The question of agreement can be a thorny one: the feeling may arise that one person can be lured unawares into a net, only to find that later findings give the earlier agreements unexpected significance. An instance is the agreement of prices for measured work of apparently minor importance, when later it turns out that considerably more work of the general type exists. To use the prices agreed in the one situation as applying to the other would give quite the wrong answer, but it seems that all has been committed.

There are at least two comments to be made. One is that if the work is quite distinct in extent, and perhaps in situation as well, then the first set of prices need not be held to, any more than need a set in the contract bills. The principles covered in Chapter 6 are as applicable here. The second is that any agreement made during the progress of settlement should be subject to the possibility of review. This does not mean reneging frivolously on all manner of details all the way through, but accepting that a broader view of the situation may justify some revision. All settlement agreements should therefore be subject to this sort of proviso, even though it is not explicit. Initial claim documents should be read in this light, a point recurring in Chapter 23. Sometimes a statement that agreement is contingent on specific, foreseen, but unquantified eventualities may be needed.

The distinction should be drawn here between such an agreement and that over the infusion plant in Chapter 19, where the agreement was by way of a supplementary contract. Even had it not been entered into quite so formally, the effect should have been the same: it was concluded as an inducement to proceed with work. But an agreement over work already past is in a different category, when it forms part of an ongoing negotiation of an account. In the circumstances of extension of time, a similar arrangement is made express in the contract provisions, where the architect has a power of review. There is also an implication that the contractor may be bringing forward fresh evidence.

Two final points may be made in this generalised discussion. The aim of negotiation should be to clarify and not to confuse issues. Sooner or later, there has to come a time of weighing all the matters together; it can only be eased by understanding on the way. Then, the avoidance of predetermined

attitudes, already implied in this chapter, is important in easing progress. False assumptions of superiority clog progress, even when the assumptions are embodied in platitudes.

But this is the point at which an author is in danger of falling into the trap himself – and should end his chapter.

Case studies

CHAPTER 18

Introduction to the case studies

The following chapters give case studies of three projects to illustrate some of the principles discussed in earlier chapters, followed by a short discussion of some principles for drawing up an omnibus claim document. If such case studies are to be kept within reasonable length, they are bound to suffer from weaknesses, even if hopefully they have the strength of putting flesh upon theoretical discussion.

One weakness is that they can illustrate only in outline, because of their brevity and the constraints of being part of an inanimate book, without the complex interactions of life. Many of the ramifications of earlier chapters are thus left unexplored, although sometimes new avenues are uncovered. As a result, the chosen project has to be delineated in a rather dehydrated form, with many of the realistic details shrivelled up or missing altogether. This leaves a great deal to the imagination of the reader, but also isolates critical features more readily. It is just this isolation which can prove difficult in real life, when there is much detail and perhaps a few red herrings as well.

Further, the projects have to be made artificial in some respects, again to keep treatment within bounds. What may really be a mass of calculations or narrative becomes much more akin to a formula into which just a few figures may be dropped. In the process, the formula distorts reality in places. All of this reads like an apologia, as it is!

More positively, the case studies may be seen as imaginary constructs which embody the essence of elements from various actual projects, chosen for their problematic nature, as well as a number of quite fictitious elements. The attempt has been made to follow through to their inevitable conclusions the elements woven in like this, subject to them illustrating some useful point. This means that in places the elements written into the scenario have turned out to have unexpected consequences in later development, but that these have been accepted and faced, rather than that the 'plot' has been rewritten to avoid them.

A frequent approach to this type of exercise is to set out a full claim document, or whatever is in question, presented from the contractor's point of view. This is then subjected to analysis from the employer's side, with the result that the time or money claimed is substantially reduced. This can give the impression that the contractually naïve (or worse) contractor has been beaten, and rightly so it seems, but it also gives an unbalanced view of where right may lie, while having the virtue of setting alternative concepts down together for comparison. In that many claim documents do originate

from the contractor in finished form, this approach is obviously useful and often to be commended.

However, with the introduction of the JCT 1980 and IFC contracts, the potential for progressive presentation and agreement should be greater. This is much more in keeping with the spirit of ascertainment by the architect or the quantity surveyor on the basis of data provided by the contractor, rather than the big bang at the far end of the contractual universe. The distinctive pattern followed in the present studies is therefore to describe progressive discussion and perhaps agreement, at least of the direct elements of cost or time, while leaving it unclear just how soon this agreement was reached. This means that there is less emphasis on setting up a contractor's Aunt Sally for demolition, although it is still possible to construct one from the implications of the more consensus models laid out. A contractor looking for 'throw-away' points to include in claims can still find them! An indication of the 'full claim' approach is given in Chapter 23.

This methodology is related to a stronger narrative form than is common, to show how situations develop and, by inference, can be at least partly controlled. It emphasises the value of progressive information while memories are fresh and of taking mitigating action by both parties. The 'full claim at the end' method is limited in what it allows here, because all is fossilised in the records. The present method even allows the parties to change their minds on the way along.

The case studies proceed with different levels of detail. Thus the first, related to a quite large scheme of new work, goes into most detail through two chapters about the procedures and calculations when once problems are arising. The other cases deal with smaller schemes of new and alteration work, and give no calculative detail in support of the narrative, which covers most of the relevant differences without resorting to repetition of essentially similar detail from the first study. While these two studies provide self-contained discussion and explanation, the reader more concerned with the type of work set out in them should therefore still read the other study first, or at least go back to it for detailed amplification of what is his primary interest.

Even within the first study, the method and level of detail in calculations vary quite inconsistently and without apology, while precise procedures over notices, etc. are ignored. The aim is not to set out model approaches into which anyone may drop actual events or figures in place of those given. It is rather to highlight the key principles at least once, but not with slavish repetition, and to use whatever method of calculation best fits this aim, often one which could not be used in the given form in practice. Precise and fully detailed calculations can best be derived from working experience or from standard texts on estimating practice. No attempt is made to relate prices given to any particular period of time, as this can so easily become dated. In short, let the reader beware over the detail. It is the principles which are critical. For this reason, reference back to earlier and more digressive chapters is vital to fill out the significance of the illustrative material presented here.

CHAPTER 19

Major case study: Laboratory Project, Part 1

Particulars of the works
Main events and their results in outline
Extra payments in the early stages
Extra payments in the later stages
Some principles over primary loss and expense emerging from the case study

This case study concerns the execution of quite large works by a regional contractor. The works covered new construction on a green field site, across the public road from another site of the employer. The problems stemmed primarily from a number of late decisions by the employer while work was under way, 'assisted' by some unexpected characteristics of such an innocent site. The main events are described briefly together below, before being explored separately.

Particulars of the works

CONTRACT DETAILS

The contract form was the JCT private edition 1980 with quantities. It was on a fixed price basis, apart from statutory fluctuations. The sectional completion supplement was used.

SCOPE OF THE WORKS

The general layout of the contract works, with the major modifications introduced during progress, is shown in Fig. 19.1. An analysis of the contract bills is given in Table 19.1, but may be consulted here to give a feel for the scale of the works. The main portions of the original works were:

(a) A three storey *in situ* concrete-framed laboratory, containing also the administration offices for the site (which was one of several operated by the same group).
(b) A single storey steel-framed process shop, of mostly open-plan layout, with some office space and toilets.

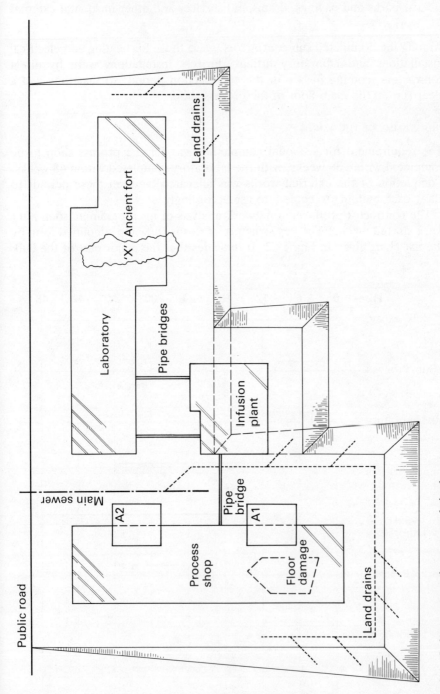

Fig. 19.1 Laboratory project, general site layout

(c) Extensive bulk excavations to cope with a sloping site, site roads,
car parks and pavings, drains and services and other incidental external
works.

Among the nominated sub-contractors, were those for heating and electrical
installations and laboratory fittings. Process installations were by direct
contractors, coming in late in the construction period, so that they had a
clear run on the main floor of the process shop.

PROGRAMME OF THE WORKS

The requirement for sectional completion was for the process shop to be
completed within 36 weeks, with the laboratory completed within 48 weeks.
Completion of the external works was allocated between these periods to
allow each building to come into use accordingly.

The contractor produced a network analysis of his programme soon after
work started on site. The key structure of this is shown in simplified form by
the bar chart given in Fig. 19.2. It indicates that the major part of the bulk

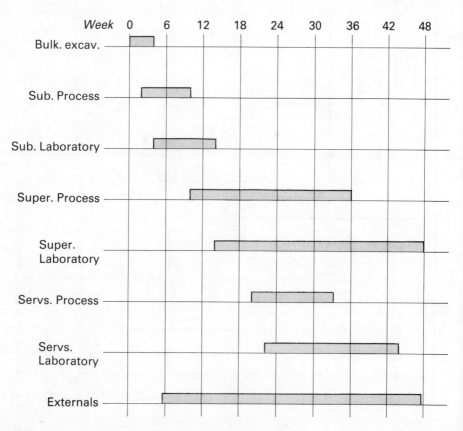

Fig. 19.2 Laboratory project, summarised programme

excavations were to be performed at once, as the process shop (required first) was at the more deeply cut end of the site. The two buildings would then be staggered in their demands for comparable work, to permit gangs to move between them. Site works would be phased in detail to suit.

The programme was somewhat optimistic in places and generous in others. It reserved very little by way of float time for the project as a whole. The network at various stages is shown in Figs 19.3–19.7 at the end of this chapter. It follows conventional notation, but modifies this in later stages by recording the achieved, rather than the intended.

Main events and their results in outline

GROUNDWORKS AND ANNEXES INITIALLY

In view of the programme, the bulk excavations started at the deep end of the site and were complete there, with foundation excavations started, when the architect issued an instruction postponing work on the foundations for the south side of the process shop, pending re-design. The contractor confirmed that he would hold all further foundation work to the shop, as he considered work would be uneconomical carried out piecemeal. He stated that special protection of the exposed formation would definitely be needed, as this was already showing signs of wetness and threatening deterioration. He indicated that he might be incurring further extra expense and delay, due to compression of the relative programmes for the two buildings.

As surface excavation moved along the site of the laboratory, the walls of an ancient fort were discovered, straddling the building at 'X' in Fig. 19.1. The contractor stated that he intended to cease work altogether at this, but the architect informed him that he must make such progress as he could, to comply with the contract. He then continued excavation from the south extreme of the site, up to the area affected by the fort, duly adjudged an antiquity and engulfed with archaeologists. The contractor received further instructions to provide assistance to the investigators to speed up their work.

Four weeks after the postponement instruction on the process shop, revised drawings were issued, showing two large staff annexes 'A1' and 'A2' and some reduction in staff accommodation within the main area. Advanced drawings had been made available to the steelwork sub-contractor for fabrication, but further delay beyond the four weeks was inevitable. Foundation work therefore proceeded, leaving out work to take steelwork bases later.

For the laboratory, foundation work was performed from both ends, involving extra setting out, slower working and a number of errors, until the investigation was completed and the remains of the fort removed. Throughout, the contractor was informally coaxed by the architect to take measures to reduce delay, rather than just stop. He also lost track of giving adequate notices over problems when once the fort had been discovered.

When the superstructures of both buildings were completing and internal work was in hand, the employer changed his plans for some cycles of his own processes on the site. The architect therefore instructed the introduction of an infusion plant as shown in Fig. 19.1.

The contractor considered challenging this on the grounds that it constituted a variation of the contract (see Ch. 6 under 'Variations and variation of the contract') by extending its scope substantially and at a late stage when comparable work was not being performed. In view of the programme and cost effects, he might well have succeeded, if needs be at arbitration which could have taken place at once. Instead, he settled for taking on the extra work, but protected himself by seeking both extension of time and loss and expense for the original works, as well as suitable rates for the extra building and its external works performed out of sequence in a restricted area.

Involved in this change of mind were pipe bridges to each of the original buildings from the power house, interfering with the actions of plant used in the main external works. Changes in the nature of services and delay in providing fresh drawings and specifications affected the work of nominated sub-contractors and of the contractor inside the existing buildings, by then at the stage of finishings.

A LATE MISHAP

All of these additions and changes had been absorbed and were under way and machines and equipment were being installed in the process shop, when the site itself again took a hand. An area of the main floor and some associated pits adjoining Annex 'A1' started to lift and crack severely. This was traced to water pressure due to a spring, now constricted by the construction work. It was necessary to interfere with work on the site roads and other finishings and lay a system of land drains, as shown in Fig. 19.1, to remove the immediate problem and to guard against it cropping up elsewhere. Only when some of this work was advanced could remedial work inside the process shop be taken far.

After this, it may be noted that work moved to completion without incident!

Extra payments in the early stages

These arose in several ways. There were separate disturbances to each building during performance of sub-structure work, followed by the interaction or 'knock-on' effect of the two as work moved into the superstructure phase. These affected the original programme in Figs 19.3 and 19.4, and moved matters to what is shown in Figs 19.5 and 19.6.

POSTPONEMENT FOR THE PROCESS SHOP ANNEXES

The instruction over this came only two weeks into the contract period, as bulk excavations at the north of the site were almost complete and

foundations were being taken out at the deeper end. This represented event 1 on the network and the initial phase of loss and expense for the contractor extended into the bases (activity 1/3) and foundation walls (activity 3/5). It also affected the nominated steelwork sub-contractor (activities 3/5 and 5/6).

The contractor's extra expense

Work stopped in the area, apart from bringing up foundation construction in already open excavations (which were then filled back) where no changes were indicated, and propping excavation sides elsewhere. When foundations were constructed, it was necessary to leave out work to accommodate steelwork, which was held up completely. Protective hardcore to a minimum thickness was laid over much of the exposed formation.

The contractor's initial claim was twofold:

(a) that all extra work and work delayed and likely to be carried out with disturbance should be paid for as daywork; and
(b) that the total amount for preliminaries should be adjusted *pro rata* to the extension of time granted.

The architect referred the whole question of payment to the quantity surveyor, while granting an extension of time of four weeks on an interim basis, as the time he expected he would spend in producing enough information to allow the annexes to be incorporated into the site work.

The quantity surveyor disagreed over the rather sweeping payment suggestions made, on the grounds that to substitute daywork so radically would mean that the contractor was being paid the difference between his tendered prices and his costs, rather than his loss and expense (see discussion in Ch. 14). He would also be receiving profit on the difference, not a loss and expense principle. In passing, he pointed out to the contractor that his preliminaries pricing appeared low in parts (as had been raised during examination of the tender). If therefore the measured prices included an element of preliminaries cost, the contractor could be losing to that extent.

So far as preliminaries adjustment was concerned, he explained that an extension of time did not entitle the contractor to a pro rata increase, even though the work affected was on the critical path of the network. The preliminaries included allowances for items not directly related to time, or even not related to it at all, such as the provisions for beginning and ending the project. Again, what was included in the contract bills was not the measure of ascertainment, whether high or low, this had to be actual loss and expense. By this time, the problem of the ancient fort in the laboratory area had appeared, so that the prolongation question was obviously going to be more complex and needed looking at as a whole. This is taken in Chapter 20.

The outline of the agreement reached after some while was therefore to pay:

(a) Costs as recorded for transferring some labour and plant to the laboratory

site to install bases there, until work became available on the process shop site, and then returning it. These would have been quite small in any case, but became almost academic when that site gave trouble.

Total £470.00, based on site observations

(b) Fifty per cent of the measured cost of the protective hardcore, on the basis that rather more hardcore would have been required for the steel erection at a later date anyway and as the base for the main floor. All that was happening was that the bed was being provided somewhat earlier and would need some extra topping up to restore levels, before actual thickening. The significance of the condition of the sub-soil was lost on everyone at this stage.

Total 5,540 m² at £1.75 per m², inclusive of using less economical plant at the time required = £9,695

(c) Standing time of plant not able to be redeployed elsewhere on the site. The principal item here was the main batching plant for site-produced concrete. This eventually stood idle for five weeks continuously (it was being erected late in the period of bulk excavation and for a week following), and intermittently for a total of a further three weeks during the time of piecemeal working. It was possible to transfer some of its attendant operators elsewhere, but not all. Some minor plant was also affected.

Total 8 weeks at £540.00 per week = £4,320

(d) Extra setting out for the annexes at the cost of the engineer already full time on site was included, pending review over the effect on site staff generally when the several disturbance matters were clarified. It was established that the net addition due to variations would not itself cover this excess setting out.

Total 3 days at £120.00 = £360.00

(e) Extra cost of executing foundation walls in short sections piecemeal between the gaps left for steelwork to avoid excessive delay, an element of mitigation at the contractor's discretion. (This is an instance of how a trade-off should be looked for, without the optimum solution necessarily being clear in advance.) Three figures were discussed:

Allowed productivity in bill rates	= 2.10 hr/m²
Achieved productivity on similar work in unaffected sections of foundations	= 1.90 hr/m²
Achieved productivity in the affected sections	= 2.60 hr/m²

The latter two figures were relevant, not what had been assumed for tendering purposes (see Ch. 14). In this instance, they gave a higher

reimbursement than using the tender figure, and so ascertained the actual loss the contractor was suffering and preserved his higher than anticipated profit. The result could have been the other way round.

Craftsman at £5.50 and 50% labourer at £4.50 $=$£7.75 per hour
Total 320(2.60 – 1.90) × £7.75 $\qquad$ $=$£1,736

(f) Extra cost of filling in foundation walls between these sections and around steelwork when erected. This was assessed on similar principles to (e), but on a cost per occurrence, taking account of such features as double handling of materials to the scattered points of use.

Each occurrence involved an average of 4 m^2, with 40 per cent productivity at the point of work, that is, an excess expense of 1.5 times, and additional handling expense up to the point.

Total 37 × 4 × 1.90 × 1.5 × £7.75 $=$ £3,269
37 × £8.50 $=$ £ 315

$\overline{}$

£3,584

(g) Additional attendance on the steelwork sub-contractor, mainly involving special areas of hardstanding for him to manœuvre his mobile crane.

Total 22 × £30.00 (average) = £660

These items gave a total for the contractor of £20,825. It may be questioned whether some of these items should be treated as variations, rather than loss and expense, in so far as a measured basis is used. None of them is due to a change in design, etc. as defined by clause 13, producing a difference in the finished works, but all are due to a disturbance by postponement of regular progress. Even the walls come within this criterion, as they are not *varied* work performed in dissimilar conditions from what was envisaged in the contract bills. The changed annexes themselves (the cause of the upset) fall to be valued by the variation rules. Had they been introduced later and out of sequence, they might have qualified for enhanced rate treatment, as happened with the infusion plant.

The sub-contractor's extra expense

A separate ascertainment was performed for the steelwork sub-contractor (activities 3/5 and 3/6), in view of his nominated status. This covered extra expense at his works, rather than at site, where the provision of extra hardstandings eased matters and where the erected walls did not interfere

with movement. The items, again described in outline, were:

(a) Fabricated steelwork not used, less scrap value.

Total 15 tonnes at £750.00 = £11,250

(b) Altering fabricated steelwork on a time basis.

Total for labour and equipment = £3,120

(c) Storing steelwork, before and after fabrication, while the architect's design and that of the sub-contractor were being revised.

Total 6 weeks at £350.00 = £2,100

(d) Design time in redesigning work, allowed as the excess not covered by the inclusive rates in the sub-contract bills.

Total 12 days at £100.00 = £1,200

These items gave a total for the sub-contractor of £17,670. No prolongation costs fell to the sub-contractor, other than those of storage, in the circumstances prevailing off site. The whole incident was too short for him to substantiate any secondary loss and expense (see Ch. 15), which possibility remained open for the contractor on his work.

In the sub-contractor's case, it is more cogent to argue that some of the items were by way of variations, so that all but (c) were technically included in the account accordingly. These amounts were all included in the total set against the prime cost sum. The contractor then obtained his profit margin on the part given as loss and expense, quite correctly under the wording of clause 30.6.2.9. This contrasts with his own part of the loss and expense and with what happens when there is a domestic sub-contractor (as there was among some of the amounts already discussed).

EFFECT OF THE ANCIENT FORT

The employer could hardly be blamed for this happening, and probably not even his own ancestors were involved! Excavation moved to the laboratory in activity 1/2 and uncovered the fort. It was the contractor's responsibility under clause 34.1 to do all he could not to disturb in any way what he had found and to notify the architect of the discovery.

The architect instructed the contractor to work round the fort and to allow archaeologists to take records, as a preliminary to removing the remains for safe keeping. These were comparatively diffuse and so not to be preserved where they were, but well worth taking away. The contractor wanted to suspend work altogether, no doubt daunted by this second catastrophe (from his point of view) within the early weeks on site. The architect reminded him of his obligation under clause 25.3.4.1 to use 'his best endeavours to prevent delay'. Work therefore continued on what was most of the sub-structure, and the central portion was filled in later. The present consideration takes matters up to event 9 of the network.

The response of the contractor was not too precise at this stage. This second delay to an extent helped to bring the two buildings back towards the phasing intended by the programme (see at event 9) – a slightly perverse benefit! He did not give proper notices about disturbance of regular progress, but told the architect when this was queried that he was under clause 34, which said nothing about notices (or properly 'applications'), as did clause 26. Even so, it is helpful to all concerned if some similar pattern of actions is established. In the end, the architect instructed the quantity surveyor to ascertain the loss and expense which undoubtedly were taking place, and which he was looking at meanwhile.

The contractor put forward a claim for several items:

(a) Extra payment for attendance on the archaeologists, who ranked effectively as direct contractors under clause 29.

(b) Extra setting-out costs, due to the position of the fort.

(c) Extra excavation and filling incurred by the problems of levels on the two sides of the fort not marrying up.

(d) An overall drop in productivity in the central third of the sub-structure for all trades up to floor level, and especially in the basement, which was close to the fort area.

(e) Daywork for carrying out all work in joining the building when the fort was removed.

(f) Extension of time for the delay occasioned to the sub-structure, with the position reserved beyond that, in view of what was happening to the process shop.

The last of these may be cleared first, as it related to time and not payment, which is immediately being discussed. It was pointed out that none of the activities were upon the original critical path and any question of extension would have to be set against whether their late performance affected the superstructure, which was critical.

The other questions were decided as follows:

(a) Payment for attendance as instructed could only be dealt with as daywork. It thus effectively became a variation by its method of valuation, even though there is nothing express in the contract allowing the architect to instruct the contractor to provide attendance, only to allow third parties to work on the site. The alternative is for the contractor to work directly for them and become, for those purposes, a third party himself. This might lead to numbers of legal problems if any injury occurred.

(b) As the fort was entirely below ground, in the nature of things, and largely below reduced level excavation, the claim for additional setting out costs was rejected, apart from engineer's time in setting out central detail as a filler operation, when the fort had gone.

Total 1 day at £120.00 = £120

(c) The same view was taken initially of the claim for extra reduced levels excavation carried out in error, leading to extra disposal and filling.

After extended discussion, it was agreed that there had been difficulties in maintaining progress, over which the architect had pressed quite strenuously to counterbalance the other delay which the employer had pitched in so suddenly. The claim was therefore met 'without prejudice', as is sometimes politic in a situation of mixed pressures.

Total 40 m³ of excavation, removal and filling at £27.00 = £1,080

(d) The productivity drop was held to have been stated too broadly across the types of work concerned, which would be affected differently, while proper evidence of actual drops had not been given. The situation was unclear, even though there was an instinctive feeling that there had been drops. As the contractor had not given notice of what he now alleged had happened, he had weakened his own position, but not necessarily precluded a right to payment, remembering that this was clause 34. A straight comparison with the actual cost of similar unaffected work was difficult, as there were differences between work in the several areas and as, when it was similar, it had not been performed in separate parcels, but by the same gangs continually moving about between the areas. This pattern was not itself due to the disturbance. The result was that the quantity surveyor had to exercise judgement (based upon the bill rates and an assessment of how they compared generally with productivity) in consultation with the architect, the clerk of works and the contractor – a common state of affairs. An outline of the settlement was as follows.

(i) Bases (actually performed ahead of those for the process shop), little effect after delay, labour content 30 per cent, allow 10 per cent of this content for one-quarter:

$$50,500 \times 30\% \times 10\% \times \tfrac{1}{4} = £379$$

(ii) Walls, more effect, labour content 45 per cent, allow 15 per cent of this content for one-third:

$$76,100 \times 45\% \times 15\% \times \tfrac{1}{3} = £1,712$$

(iii) Basement, affected by delay leading to standing time, assessed as six tradesmen and four labourers for one week:

$$
\begin{aligned}
6 \times 40 \times £5.50 &= £1,320 \\
4 \times 40 \times £4.50 &= £\ \ 720 \\
\hline
&\ \ £2,040
\end{aligned}
$$

(iv) Plant (minor items) drops in production and standing time associated with these labour losses (not shown in detail), £344.

Total for this head of claim = £4,475

(e) The recorded daywork was examined against the measured values for the work concerned. The comparison showed an excess of labour and plant costs (again related to bill rates and an assessment of likely productivity)

calculated at 17 per cent. This was considered reasonable and was used as the basis of ascertainment.

Total £1,335

The problem of how to 'ascertain' when no comparable data for undisturbed work are available, is a constantly recurring one. Despite all that may be maintained on the subject, there comes a point at which judgment has to be exercised, as it is in calculating a difficult 'star rate'.

In this instance, work on the walls (activity 9/11) was due to wait for the gangs to become available from the process shop, itself delayed. A wait had been allowed in the original network, while the activity was not critical anyway. The amended network shows that, in fact, labour moved across to the laboratory during a waiting time on the process shop, and then back again to allow the progress achieved to happen. This may again have led to some of the drop in productivity, but overall was beneficial in reducing the cost of delay for both parties. The effect of this reappears when looking at the next stage of the works.

The loss and expense total of items (b) to (e) was therefore £7,010, assuming payment for the erroneous excavation to be for loss and expense.

EARLY SUPERSTRUCTURE WORK FOR BOTH BUILDINGS

This section concerns the knock-on or ripple effect of what had already happened on activities which were not put out of rhythm by the immediate disturbances, but which suffered because their own interrelations were changed.

The main effects up to events 6, 7 and 11 have been described and evaluated. The broad position thus far is shown in Fig. 19.5, which gives a revision of the first part of the network to allow for what happened, so that only times achieved are entered. For some preceding and subsequent events, two times are shown: achieved times and (in brackets) times which might have been justified under the contract. The achieved times take account of what the contractor did by way of mitigation, broadly saving programme time and overheads and adding to direct site expenditure.

The extra time incurred owing to the increased work content in the process shop annexes has also been included, largely in elements A and G (activities 7/10 and 15/20). The effect was to move much of the more complex office and toilet accommodation out into the projections, leaving more clear floor space in the main run of the building, so that most of the net additional construction (as distinct from disturbance) was quite simple work. This aspect is returned to when extension of time is discussed later. The work itself was valued under clause 13 and need not be discussed here.

With the commencement of superstructure work, the contractor faced the consequences of the earlier disruption working their way through. It had been intended in the original programme that the same gangs should work first on the process shop and then transfer to the laboratory. This allowed for a

one-week pause on the laboratory between the two elements A, whereupon the laboratory also came on to the critical path, related to its own completion date. This saved gang confusion and switching. There were several gangs in most elements and sometimes the same gang in several elements, but this aspect has been omitted to simplify the example.

As affairs had turned out, the contractor now faced a six-week pause at this point, if he maintained the same diagram logic. While a contractor under the JCT contract is not obliged to go to extra and irrecoverable expense to regain lost time, neither may he simply hold woodenly to what he planned when things go awry. Often, as here, it does not pay him either. When there are loss and expense in prospect, he has the mitigation issue at stake as well.

The pause was enough to raise the possibility of rescheduling a whole string of elements to put the laboratory ahead, but this would have thrown the whole sectional completion sequence into difficulty later. What happened was that the gangs were shifted to and fro between elements A to C on the buildings, at the expense of productivity, but to reinstate the basic sequence as soon as practicable. This was agreed to be a reasonable course of action, so that the loss and expense were reimbursed. It is an example of the sort of area where the policy should be examined carefully, rather than just whether a particular amount of loss and expense was actually incurred, before an agreement is reached.

It is still the case that benefit of the doubt for lack of the advantage of hindsight should often be allowed. As usual over the contractor's programme and methods, the architect cannot instruct or insist, but consultation (or implication of others?) at an awkward stage can save disagreement later.

The result is shown on the network in Fig. 19.5, where the original logic is retained for ease of reference, except over the steelwork, and where elements A, B and C are shown linked to their counterparts in the laboratory by two-way arrows (activities 7/10, 10/12 and 12/14). For the laboratory, the times which would have resulted but for the reorganisation are given in brackets. The effects of these would then have rippled through the rest of the network. Element A of the process shop is lengthened only because of its increased work content, while element B and those following become just sub-critical.

The contractor argued for 15 per cent drop in productivity for labour and all plant involved on both buildings in these elements. This was purely impressionistic, as might be said were some of the allowances made earlier, but would not stand up to any rigorous comparison with the appropriate contents of measured rates, which were taken as a first datum level to see whether the percentage had any possible validity before detailed work went ahead. Work then reverted to an analysis of what had happened, followed by a comparison of productivity on the two buildings. Agreement was as follows:

(a) The crane and hoist and all attendant labour used for the laboratory
    superstructure were both tied up for 10 weeks instead of 8 (longer than

claimed in percentage terms). No such effect occurred on the process shop, other than that due to the extra work content and covered by variation valuation, which could allow for any adjustment for plant caused by quantity variation (although in this instance no adjustment resulted).

Crane at £330.00 per week × 2		=	£660
Hoist at £80.00 per week × 2		=	£160
Driver at £5.50 per hour × 40 × 2		=	£440
Attendants at £5.00 per hour × 40 × 2	=		£400
		Total =	£1,660

(b) Moving equipment to and fro between and sometimes within buildings and setting up to accommodate shorter runs of activity. These were assessed by reference to those involved directly and those who observed what happened (such as the clerk of works), and covered labour, transport and lack of productivity of the equipment itself.

Total 24 moves, varying but averaging 6 persons for 3 hours, several types of transport and 'standing' time for moved equipment of 5 hours:

£5.00 × 6 × 3	=	£90
£5.00 × 3	=	£15
£18.00 × 5	=	£90

giving

£195.00 × 24	=	£4,680

(c) Dislocation of gangs producing work, including refamiliarisation time.

Total 24 breaks, averaging 8 persons per gang:

£5.50 × 6 × 5	=	£165
£4.50 × 2 × 5	=	£45

giving

£210.00 × 24	=	£5,040

(d) Drop in productivity in the laboratory. This was an arguable concept, when once the foregoing items had been taken into account. Comparison with the process shop during periods when switching had been overcome was rather inconclusive, as there was a restricted amount of really similar work. When evidence was available, it suggested quite a marginal drop. This was agreed, on a conciliatory basis, at 2 per cent of the labour expenditure of £91,300.

Total £1,830

(e) Additional overtime. To keep the pace up with that of the process shop, overtime at 10 per cent of the normal week was worked.

Labour expenditure £91,300, exclusive of foregoing amounts. Overtime was 1/11 of the total time and attracted a 25 per cent higher rate, less

standing payments for overheads on labour, transport, importation, etc., a net increase of 13 per cent per hour. For 100 hours basic, therefore, 10 net hours' overtime were worked at an added cost of 1.3 hours' non-productive time. This constituted 1.17 per cent of the labour bill (1.3 out of 111.3 hours).

Total £1,070

The relative smallness of this item may be noted. It was not a 'compensation' to the workforce, an aspect discussed in Chapter 14.

These items gave a total for the contractor of £14,280. This is nearly 10 per cent on the unadjusted labour content for both buildings, rather than 15 per cent as originally put forward, but includes items not put forward explicitly by the contractor.

A REVIEW OF THE POSITION REACHED

The foregoing has brought the question of the early disturbances to both buildings to a tidy level. It is useful to review the section on 'Client's risk analysis' in Chapter 1, to consider how far the employer might have avoided disturbance and whether this would have been a net advantage. Ascertainment of amounts would in practice probably have taken quite a time beyond the construction programme to achieve. It must be emphasised that the figures used are very rounded and given for illustrative purposes only. In some instances, more detail is given than in others to make a point, but in all cases there would be more detail based on normal estimating practices. The total loss and expense amounts come to £59,788, of which £14,280 are ripple effects from the two sub-structure disruptions, occurring in the superstructures.

What has not been done so far is to deal with the effect of prolongation on site overheads, or to look at secondary loss and expense. This would be premature for two reasons: the overall progress of the project might not warrant any such reimbursement but, if it does, it is likely to become more complex, rather than remain unchanged.

Equally, the matter of extension of time is also hanging. In week 20 the architect upgraded his original four weeks' extension for the whole project to six weeks for the process shop and kept it at four weeks for the laboratory. This was towards the end of elements A for each building. The actual position at the ends of the two elements C was one week later for the process shop and one week earlier for the laboratory. This is acceptably close to reality, as the architect has the power to review the extensions granted up to 12 weeks after practical completion and there may be other causes leading to the differences, some qualifying and others not.

SOME ALTERNATIVE POSSIBILITIES

Before passing to the later stages of the project, some further options may

be taken briefly. These are treated as alternatives, to avoid making the main line example too complex.

Sub-contracts

When being urged to keep up progress, the contractor might have considered introducing a second gang to double his workforce on an element. If he had sub-let this element, he might find himself in the position that the firm concerned could not provide the extra labour, so that he had to seek a second firm or drop behind on site. This latter he would be entitled to do, if he had explored all reasonable ways to maintain progress in the face of his problems. According to the precise circumstances, he would not necessarily be obliged to bring on this extra resource. Presumably, the first sub-contractor was the most satisfactory over price, quality and so on, available when sub-tenders were sought. It is quite possible, although needing to be demonstrated, that any further firm is not so satisfactory, especially over price.

Given such a situation, the contractor has several points to consider:

(a) Obtaining consent to sub-letting as usual, unless the firm appears on the list of domestic sub-contractors given in the contract bills.

(b) The difference in price he now faces. In obtaining consent to sub-let, he is advised to obtain agreement at least in principle to reimbursement of the extra expense he has to meet. Usually in a domestic arrangement, the price is entirely at the contractor's risk, whether he has to choose from a list or wishes to sub-let at his own initiative, and whether his choice drops out or not (see Ch. 7).

(c) The primary reimbursable difference is that between the two sub-contract prices, measured or otherwise, without adjustment for profit or attendance. As ever, it is the contractor's net loss and expense which are in view.

(d) There could be a difference due to the efficiency of performance of the second firm being lower than that of the first, perhaps over the level of defects or other delay factors. Usually, this is entirely the responsibility of the contractor, however the sub-letting comes about. Here, it comes into play as part of an endeavour to remedy a situation which is not the contractor's fault. If he is forced to look at a firm which he suspects is going to be less satisfactory for himself, he should protect his position in advance by warning the architect and obtaining his endorsement. Actual reimbursement will still be subject to the test of fact.

(e) In the situation of work split between two buildings and being performed in parallel, rather than in series, the contractor may incur extra supervision or co-ordination with his own direct activities.

The other option which is very likely to arise, is that of a domestic sub-contractor's loss and expense, without any question of a change of sub-contractor. Here, the sub-contractor's position is governed by the form of sub-contract applying, and there is no obligation for the standard form

DOM/1 to be used with a JCT form, desirable though this is. If it is used, it gives the sub-contractor rights to reimbursement on the same lines as those in the main contract. If this happens, the contractor alone has to negotiate with the sub-contractor and come to a settlement, and the architect and the quantity surveyor are not involved directly.

However, they are due to settle with the contractor on the basis of his direct and net loss and expense. When there is a domestic sub-contractor involved, this should mean that what he receives from the contractor is what the contractor receives from the employer. The difference in price or prices between main and sub-contract is not relevant. This does not mean that the contractor can agree anything in scope, if not cost level, with the sub-contractor and then simply pass it up to the employer to pay. In view of this, there is often a need for the architect or the quantity surveyor to become involved in a monitoring way in sub-contract loss and expense settlements, or at least to reopen their basis on occasions. As earlier discussion in the present case study has shown, it may be necessary to use judgment to a degree in ascertaining loss and expense, when what is agreed at main contract level may differ in principle from what is agreed at sub-contract level.

None of these points apply directly to nominated sub-contracts, where the architect and the quantity surveyor are brought in via the obligatory sub-contract form. This is illustrated by the instance of the steelwork sub-contractor earlier in the present case study, whose amounts were settled direct and on which the contractor received profit.

The other situation is that in which either type of sub-contractor, domestic or nominated (or for that matter 'named' under the IFC contract), is involved in a 'three-cornered' dispute – that is one in which it appears that some part of his loss and expense falls to be met by the employer ultimately, and some part by the contractor alone. Here, it is inevitable that the employer's consultants will be brought in to clarify the position and draw the lines. Their part is then to settle what concerns the employer for payment – and keep out of the rest! This is illustrated in outline by what happens over steelwork in the case study in Chapter 21, but in practice it is inevitably complicated.

Absence of the ancient fort

While the fort caused extra expense in its own right, it did take the pressure off the utter distortion of the construction programme. If it had been absent, the contractor would have been faced with retardation of the process shop programme, while that for the laboratory was still pressing ahead. In these circumstances, he would have had to rearrange his whole programme to put the laboratory ahead, if the system of work gangs passing from one building to the other was to have been maintained (an alternative being for twin gangs to have been employed, as mentioned above).

In this situation, the types of loss and expense which would have emerged would have included:

(a) Costs of reorganisation, such as those of supervisory staff engaged in

preparing the new programme and seeing the gangs into their amended work stations.

(b) For the earlier gangs, the costs of removing equipment and plant from one building to the other, according to what had been set up already.

(c) Standing or waiting time associated with the last operation.

Against these features, the contractor would have had the possibility of switching his main concrete batching plant to the laboratory, rather than having it stand mostly idle as actually happened. The possibility of apparently retrieving the situation by putting the process shop back in front would not have been present, except at considerable expense and actual delay. None of this would have affected extension of time, as it actually needed to be granted, the laboratory being sub-critical at this stage.

Extra payments in the later stages

INTRODUCTION OF THE INFUSION PLANT

The programme settled down after the ripple effects of the sub-structure disturbances had worked through the project, that is by about week 25. This illustrates the possibility of a contractor regaining momentum after a disruption, given peace and quiet for long enough, and the broad philosophy of fading effects set out under 'Client's risk analysis' in Chapter 1. For simplicity, the common occurrence of a mass of minor delays due to late instructions by the architect has been omitted. On this unique contract, this factor must have been a great consolation to the contractor – not to mention the architect! If it had occurred, the result would have been dealt with by calculations (known as 'ascertainment') similar to those outlined earlier in this case study.

The introduction of the quite major requirement of the infusion plant on site in week 32 posed several questions:

(a) It was seen as a variation of the contract itself, by changing the scope of works in a major way. The contractor could therefore have declined to take on the extra work, whatever terms he might have been offered as an inducement. Strictly, the fact that it was proposed to introduce it so late did not affect the basic objection, as he could have declined the day after signing the contract. However, the timing did make matters worse in practical terms, while it was also likely to extend the total construction period in a more significant manner than envisaged by clause 25, so changing another fundamental term of the contract: that of time.

(b) Given this possibility, the employer could have been placed in a very difficult position, as the new facility had become a vital feature of his operations for technical reasons which are not relevant to this narrative. This is the sort of thing which any employer should try to avoid or limit by forethought (again see 'Client's risk analysis' in Ch. 1). If he cannot, he has the choice of paying the sitting contractor, perhaps over the odds,

or of introducing another contractor. The latter is contingent upon the stage of the current works and the configuration of the site permitting it. In itself, it varies the present contract by changing the site availability, but could be done as a species of non-fundamental breach. Clearly, neither of these solutions is at all favourable in the present instance.

(c) If the contractor had not co-operated, the employer could have done nothing, unless he had been prepared to breach the contract by termination and bring in another contractor to perform all the works. This would have been very expensive (see generally in Chs 10 and 16) and have extended the time for the existing works. It would probably have taken longer than finishing off and then constructing the extra plant.

(d) As the contractor decided to accept the extra work, he was entitled to suitable preliminaries costs and to measurement of what he did, both being priced at rates to take account of the circumstances in which he was working. He was also entitled to a suitable time for the work in its own right.

(e) With this done, there was the disturbance factor for the existing works, given that the new plant itself was to be treated as a very large variation instruction. There were two possibilities: to include the extra expense in the figure for the new plant, or to cope with it as it occurred under clause 26. The former had its virtues by being clear-cut in settlement, but had all the problems associated with prior estimation of any disturbance element (that it would have meant ignoring the 'loss and expense' principle would not have been critical in the circumstances of negotiation at the time).

(f) It was therefore decided to follow the second course on loss and expense, especially as there were some doubts at the time of agreement over the precise programme of the new building, and so over its impact on the original works still going ahead.

(g) A supplementary agreement was entered into setting out the points covered above, and all other details to give contractual completeness.

None of the detailed negotiations over the infusion plant itself need to be described here, although the agreed figures for preliminaries and extension of time are of interest later.

LOSS AND EXPENSE FLOWING FROM THE INFUSION PLANT

The installations provided in the new plant had an impact on the services in each building, because they linked to them and also changed them in a number of ways. These services were all critical activities, affected by the alteration of installed work and delays over redesign in elements (b) (activity 20/24 of the process shop) and (f) (activity 33/34 of the laboratory), with further redesign causing delay in following elements. The likelihood of time and cost both being involved was clearly high.

But some of the effects of the extra work are a clear example of how there can be loss and expense without necessarily extension of time, a situation which may be reversed. There were some relatively minor effects on the

building elements running alongside the services inside the buildings, which were sub-critical, and quite marked effects on the roads and other such work proceeding as a non-critical activity in the rear parts of the site.

There was some debate over the fact that these areas had been started quite early within the time span allocated. The employer complained that, had they been programmed later, there would not have been a disturbance effect. The contractor's reply was that, had he left the work until late, he might have hit unforeseen snags, while late introduction of delaying variations could have jeopardised completion on time. Further, this was a fixed price contract, so that he had every incentive to work ahead of inflation. Rightly, he won the day, as he was simply proceeding 'regularly and diligently'. (See and compare *Greater London Council* v. *Cleveland Bridge* in Ch. 4.)

The key items in the settlement were:

(a) Alterations to the building elements were all dealt with by daywork covering removal and some of the reinstatement, while larger sections of work were measured and priced pro rata to what was done originally. As this work went ahead continuously with that before and after, no loss and expense due to standing time occurred and the variation reimbursement covered everything else.

(b) In the case of the services (all by nominated sub-contractors), runs of pipework and cabling were extensively affected by the introduction of different specifications to suit the output from the new plant. Removals were dealt with by daywork and replacement by measured items priced pro rata to the bill items. This pricing did not take account of the piecemeal working inherent in the switching of systems and the waiting that beset the work, as design ran alongside the site work and as some plant and equipment were delayed by ordering times. Installation of items of plant and equipment within the existing buildings was also changed, but this was paid for adequately by daywork for removals and items pro rata to those in the bills for the replacements. An example of the numerous calculations for various types of pipes and cables (inclusive of fittings, etc.) will suffice:

Allowed productivity in bill rate	$= 0.35$ hr/m
Allowed productivity in new rate	$= 0.45$ hr/m
Achieved productivity for original work	$= 0.40$ hr/m
Achieved productivity for revised work	$= 0.65$ hr/m
Calculated productivity for revised work in undisturbed conditions, $0.40 \times 45 \div 35$	$= 0.51$ hr/m
Drop in productivity $0.65 - 0.51$	$= 0.14$ hr/m
Cost for 100 m, $100 \times 0.14 \times £5.50$	$= £77$

This approach was necessary in the absence of comparable undisturbed work and to allow for the generally lower than budgeted productivity.

Total loss and expense in services:

Process shop	=	£4,890
Laboratory	=	£3,260

The high amount of measured work and daywork helped to keep the loss and expense down here, indicating the narrow border often existing between the elements.

(c) Attendance by the contractor on the sub-contractors was out of proportion to the contract allowances. This consisted of a number of strands, all of which had to be ascertained by reference to what had happened up to the beginning of the disturbance and by the exercise of judgment over the allocation of what happened thereafter, including when work had reverted to a more normal rhythm. The main strands were:

Supervisory staff co-ordinating main and sub-contract work.
Attendant labour moving materials and equipment as needed.
Skilled labour performing alterations to permanent work, and
  not covered by the main variation valuation.
Scaffolding, staging, hoists, chutes and similar facilities, both
  in extra provision and in adaptation.
Temporary services and supplies (the former partly provided
  by the sub-contractors, but paid for by the contractor).

Special attendance items were also affected, but could be isolated more readily.

Total loss and expense in attendance:

$$\text{Process shop} \quad = \quad £6,550$$
$$\text{Laboratory} \quad = \quad £4,310$$

(d) Waiting time was incurred by labour and plant performing the roads, etc. while additional drains and services were laid for the infusion plant and while two pipe bridges were erected across them to serve the existing buildings. Some alteration to the road layout was needed near the new building, but this was covered by daywork. The pipe bridges also caused some hindrance to the taller items of plant when roadworks resumed under them, so leading to some work in small areas.

Total:

(i) waiting time of labour and plant:

$$45 \text{ hours at } £35.00 = £1,575$$

(ii) work in small areas, production should have cost £9,130, actual cost was:

$$£11,780 = \text{loss of } £2,650$$

(e) Cleaning costs arose because of the removal of spoil across the partly completed areas of surfacings, needing also filling in of lifted material. These were covered entirely by daywork.

As before, these items exclude the costs of prolongation. The net result was a delay of three weeks in the process shop and four weeks in the laboratory, with a total for loss and expense of £23,235.

DAMAGE TO THE PROCESS SHOP FLOOR

While the work just accounted for produced a total delay of three weeks in the process shop, its effects took much longer to work their way through, so that the affected elements in fact proceeded alongside those following. This was also true of the laboratory, but this falls out of the picture for the present.

When all the elements from events 20 and 21 onwards were going on together (except the final decorating and clearing up in element U), the final blow was struck at progress by the site itself. This came in the form of the rupture of areas of the main shop floor and associated pits and ducts adjoining Annex A1, that is the one further into the site and so lower in relation to the original ground levels. The cause turned out to be a spring, itself outside the site, but feeding considerable quantities of water under the process shop. The floor was redesigned as a variation, with other effects covered as loss and expense, in the absence of a successful insurance claim (see under 'Some further aspects of damage to the floor' below). The financial results were several, in this order, but subject to some overlapping:

(a) The clearance of the affected area and the suspension of work in and around it at lower levels in the building. Installation of services in the roof space was able to continue with some re-scheduling:

> Clearance work on daywork (not valued here)
> Standing time for labour and equipment of the contractor
> and several sub-contractors   = £12,240
> Extra supervision of services work by sub-contractors   = £1,280
> Extra attendance by the contractor on services work   = £1,100
>   Total loss and expense   = £14,620

(b) A special site investigation to check the exact problem and its extent. This led to the suspension of external works on the north side of the shop in expectation of additional work there as a result:

> Site investigation (not included in this final account)
> Total loss and expense: standing time of labour and plant
> (reduced by transfers to other areas of the site)   = £3,780

(c) An extensive system of land drains at the feet of the banks all round the site was installed, causing disturbance of executed work in more areas than where work had initially been stopped:

> Removal of already executed work was paid for as daywork (not valued here), while the drainage system was measured and priced at special rates
> Total loss and expense: further piecemeal working and standing time while the drains were being installed   = £4,510

(d) Repair and modifications to the damaged parts of the process shop,

when once the land drainage system was sufficiently advanced to prevent further damage:

All of this work was paid for by daywork.

(e) Resumption of other work held up by the incident:

This was welcomed with relief, but no extra expense was incurred by way of champagne!

These items gave a total loss and expense amount for the floor damage of £22,910. The financial effects of this story have been listed without much detail, as the principles are those which have been used already. The time effect was to place completion as follows:

(a) Process shop in week 58, owing to the effects of the floor damage on top of the introduction of the infusion plant already discussed, rather than week 45 as the revised network in Fig. 19.6, with the addition of three weeks to give week 48.

(b) The external works finished in week 62.

(c) The laboratory held to week 55, that is in accordance with the revised network plus four weeks.

(d) The infusion plant almost held to its own time of finishing in week 57, by finishing in week 59.

These effects are shown in the final network in Fig. 19.7.

SOME FURTHER ASPECTS OF THE DAMAGE TO THE FLOOR

The financial effects have also been listed without comment, so far, on where liability for the lateness of the incident might lie. This question was put when it was realised that the early need to protect the formation while the annexes were being designed should have raised signals in someone's mind. There were several possibilities canvassed:

(a) Whether the pre-contract site investigation was deficient in scope or execution. If it was the former, who had supplied an inadequate brief?

(b) Whether the architect or consulting engineer should have noticed the significance of the early problem and taken action then.

(c) Whether the contractor had failed to exercise a duty to warn over a matter within his province as a competent and skilled contractor (see cases in Ch. 5).

(d) Whether the employer had so pressed everyone in those early days to minimise the delay which he had introduced by his own change of mind, that none of them had had sufficient opportunity to notice what was in evidence in the formation.

(e) Whether in fact the formation had been bad enough for the correct conclusions to be drawn.

(f) Whether the contract insurances could be called upon to meet the costs.

These options, and there might be more, pass the blame around among all the main characters in the story or give it to none. The whole matter is

far too complex to portray in a chapter devoted to other issues, or in many ways adequately within a book and away from the actual site, but should be noted as an example of what leads up to allocation of responsibility in a disputed instance. Only in possibility (c) would the contractor have to bear the cost. It is assumed that this one did not apply, so that he was reimbursed for his loss and expense and other amounts and did not face a substantial counter-charge, including liquidated damages.

The insurance option is complex, the contractor having insured the works. Under the original JCT 80, there is no question of the insurer paying under clause 22 as such. Under the 1987 revisions, he is liable for all risks, but excluding *inter alia* 'any work . . . lost or damaged as a result of its own defect in design'. The floor was clearly inadequate for the stresses; whether it was defective in design depended on the view taken of (a), (b), (d) and (e) above. The insurer could probably have avoided liability upon any of them being found to favour him. He in fact did so, leaving reimbursement of the contractor to follow the variations method – as it would have done had clause 22B or clause 22C (for an extension) applied.

Had a counter-charge arisen against the contractor, there could have been excess costs to be met by the employer and incurred by direct contractors, working in the process shop on plant installations when the disturbance occurred. These were already running late, but the responsibility was the employer's, so that no argument could arise that the contractor had caused them to slip into the present disturbance. Unless a contractor is made expressly responsible by a sectional completion arrangement for meeting particular dates or otherwise directly facilitating the work of such persons, it is difficult to see where his contractual responsibility to the employer would lie, other than in the matters covered by the indemnity provisions. These relate to 'the carrying out of the Works' and are unlikely to be construed as relating to a duty to warn situation. If the contractor had *negligently* failed to warn, an action in tort might have lain.

Clause 29 simply provides that 'the Contractor shall permit the execution of such work' and that the employer is responsible for these persons, who are not sub-contractors. It appears likely that the employer would have to rely on any liability of the contractor for liquidated damages to recoup his expenses due to delay to and disturbance of these persons, just as he would over direct contractors due to move in on completion of the building contract.

The narrative has carefully kept matters just far enough apart to avoid the problem of overlapping causes of loss and expense, so that individual matters can be taken as such. A re-reading of the account, with some compression of what has been given, will begin to introduce extra complications, which could not be properly dealt with in an example. The situation is beginning to be there by implication in the process shop in the overlap of the work due to the infusion plant and the consequences of the floor being damaged, but is so minor in context that it may be ignored when all the loss and expense are reimbursable anyway. Affairs would have been different if even part responsibility for the floor damage had been taken by the contractor.

Some principles over primary loss and expense emerging from the case study

All the items of loss and expense have been given as they have occurred, and happen to total as follows:

Annexes, contractor's work	£20,825
Annexes, sub-contractor's work	£17,670
Ancient fort	£ 7,010
Early superstructure	£14,280
Infusion plant effects	£23,235
Floor damage and drains	£22,910
	£105,930

The total is relatively unimportant, as the point is to demonstrate the principles and practicalities involved. The more important of these may be summarised as:

(a) In situations of complete or nearly complete cessation, it is usually easy to arrive at the costs of suspension, waiting or standing time.

(b) When there is comparable work (what SMM 6 calls 'similar work') performed, it is may be possible to compare productivity of disturbed work with undisturbed. This is easier to say than to achieve, unless observations can be set up in advance and provided they can be adequately controlled to secure reliability. Often, it may be suspected that this approach is held to have occurred as a means of covering the use of adjusted prime cost and judgment (perhaps the same thing?) to arrive at an answer.

(c) When work is not comparable, what is included in the variation account and what in the loss and expense element is not always easy to divide. The narrative as given is not beyond criticism, and various competent practitioners could well arrive at different allocations. In general, it is as well to include as much as possible in the variation or remeasurement account, both to secure a more certain profit and overheads margin and because the point of clause 26 is to cover what 'would not be reimbursed by a payment under any other provision'.

(d) When several sets of disturbance overlap, it can become very difficult to segregate their effects. This does not matter greatly when all the responsibility lies with the one party, as the contract does not require each cause to be accounted for separately when this is impracticable (see Ch. 12). It does matter when there is divided responsibility, as it becomes more difficult to apportion the financial effects.

(e) When numerous sets of small disturbances occur, they often merge into a constant climate of disturbance, as when information is constantly late in reaching the contractor. Here the problem is not that of segregating effects, as these are individually too small to warrant or even permit it, but that of identifying the total effect when this is the sum of many almost insignificant effects. Ascertainment becomes something

of a guess, hopefully educated. It may rely on past experience, if only of what has been acceptable before. This reads cynically, but probably there is a tendency to settle for something near to this reality in many cases.

(f) There is no direct correlation between the timing of a disturbance within the total programme or the scale of, for instance, extra work introduced on the one hand, and the level of loss and expense on the other. (Compare loss and expense due to the annexes including ripple effects, totalling £52,775, with the net addition of work of £67,890, excluding preliminaries.) This tells against 'rule of thumb' settlements – and 'Brown' clauses. The discussion under 'Client's risk analysis' in Chapter 1 is, however, still relevant.

(g) Situations do arise in which the decision as to who has to bear the cost or the loss and expense should precede the actual ascertainment decision. Examples are those where there is negligence by the contractor or when a three-way dispute involves a sub-contractor as well.

These points may also be borne in mind when reading Chapter 20, which they partly anticipate.

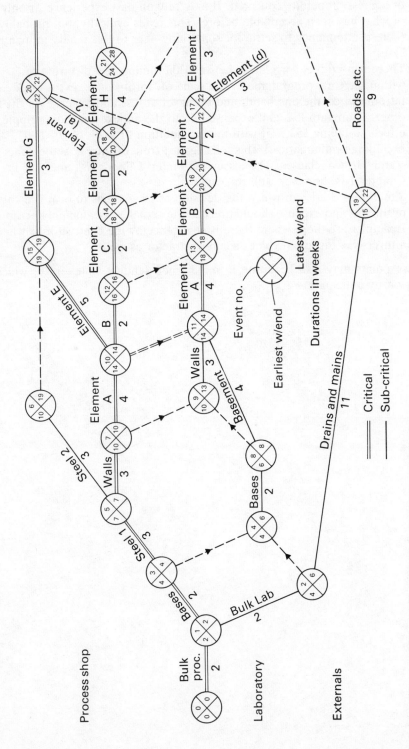

Fig. 19.3 Laboratory project, original programme, Part 1

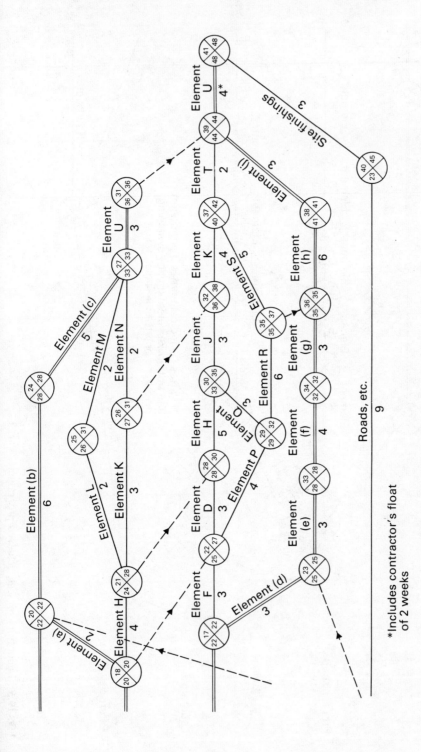

Fig. 19.4   Laboratory project, original programme, Part 2

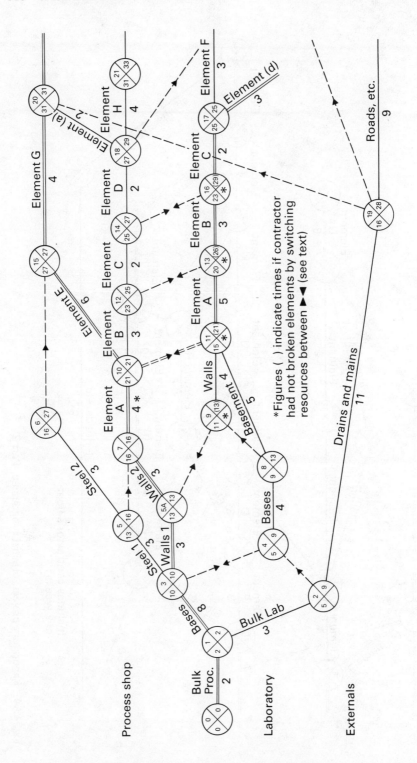

Fig. 19.5   Laboratory project, achieved programme, Part 1

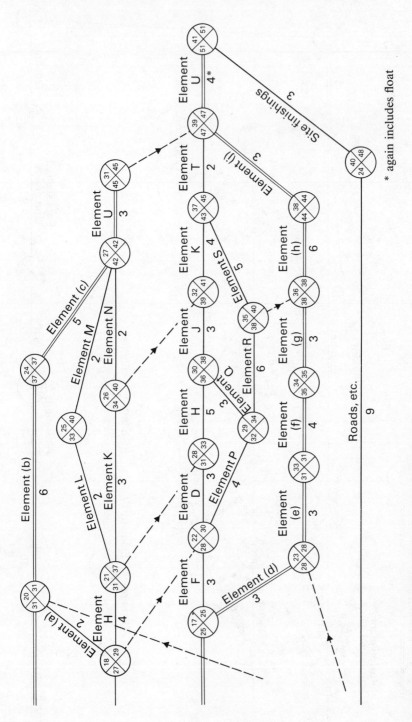

Fig. 19.6 Laboratory project, revised programme, Part 2

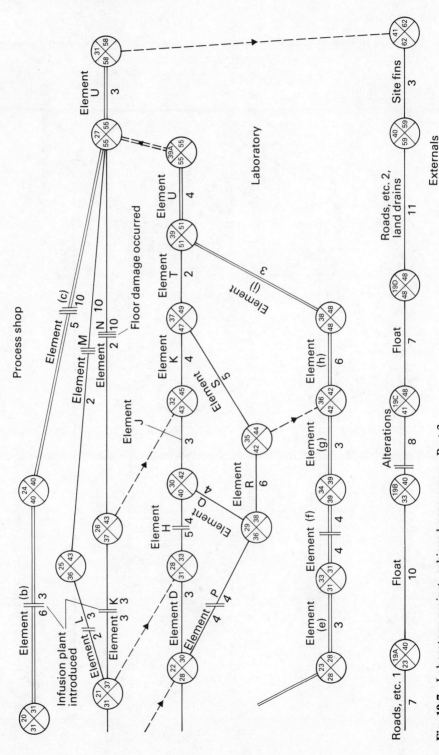

Fig. 19.7 Laboratory project, achieved programme, Part 2

Table 19.1   Laboratory project, analysis of contract bills

Preliminaries			External works		
Setting up site	20,500		Bulk excavations	91,400	
Supervision	78,000		Drains and mains	176,800	
Major plant	90,500		Roads, car parks	109,200	
Accommodation	58,500		Site finishings	29,700	407,100
Sundry items	30,200				
Final clearance	7,400	285,100			

Process shop			Laboratory		
Bulk excavation (in externals)			Bulk excavation (in externals)		
Sub-structure			Sub-structure		
Bases	116,400		Bases	50,500	
Walls	159,300	275,700	Walls	76,100	
			Basement	92,200	218,800
Superstructure			Superstructure		
Steel 1	53,200		Element A	120,400	
Steel 2	· 29,700		Element A	48,300	
Element A	74,600		Element C	45,900	
Element B	36,400		Element F	68,600	
Element C	34,200		Element D	75,900	
Element D	38,700		Element H	117,600R	
Element E	83,700		Element J	74,000	
Element G	54,800		Element K	89,700	
Element H	74,500		Element P	83,800	
Element K	40,600		Element Q	69,600	
Element L	31,200		Element R	135,900	
Element M	36,400		Element S	114,100	
Element N	33,300		Element T	50,100	
Element U	28,400	649,700	Element U	71,200	1,165,100
Services			Services		
Element a	55,700		Element d	76,500	
Element b	201,400		Element e	91,200	
Element c	118,400	375,500	Element f	127,600	
			Element h	178,000	473,300
Fittings			Fittings		
None			Element g	293,300	
			Element j	243,100	536,400
		£1,300,900			£2,393,600

Summary		
Preliminaries	285,100	
Process shop	1,300,900	
Laboratory	2,393,600	
External works	407,100	
	4,386,700	
Insurances, etc.	64,800	
Contingencies	300,000	
Total	£4,751,500	

CHAPTER 20

Major case study: Laboratory Project, Part 2

Extension of time
Preliminaries adjustment due to scope of work
Loss and expense on site overheads
Inflation on fixed price contract
General drop in productivity of labour
Loss and expense on head office overheads
Some final comments

With the individual loss and expense amounts dealt with for each phase of progress, there remained the amounts for supervision and other site overheads and prolongation and, distinctly, extension of time. These, and items in the 'secondary' category (see Ch. 15), interlocked in various ways in the final settlement and are taken in the following order:

(a) Extension of time.
(b) Preliminaries adjustment, due to the increased scope of the works.
(c) Loss and expense items:
   (i) site overheads;
   (ii) inflation on this fixed price contract;
   (iii) general drop in productivity;
   (iv) head office overheads;
   (v) profit and financing charges.

Each of these had either cropped up during progress or was raised by the contractor during settlement. Reference may be made throughout the reading of this chapter to Table 19.1 for original contract values.

Extension of time

The various delays to progress which were connected with loss and expense by sharing the same cause (not that the one automatically justified extension of time, or *vice versa*) have been mentioned during the sequential narrative

and the cumulative effect stated. The delays on the critical path were as follows:

	Process shop	Laboratory	Externals
Original time	36 weeks	48 weeks	48 weeks
Annexes	6 weeks	1 week	—
Fort	—	—	—
Superstructures	3 weeks	2 weeks	—
Infusion plant	3 weeks	4 weeks	3 weeks
Floor damage	10 weeks	—	11 weeks
Totals:	58 weeks	55 weeks	62 weeks

In addition, there were four weeks of sub-critical delays to the laboratory, due to the fort. The infusion plant itself was two weeks behind the agreed date at week 59.

Most of these times have been explained in relation to the events which occurred. Here and there, the contractor asked for more time or for time in relation to sub-critical activities. The value of the network was that it showed these features up quite clearly. When there is not a network, it is necessary to go through calculations which are equivalent to at least partly setting one up.

The sequence of events given has ignored any question of overlap of causes of delay. These are broadly of two types:

(a) Other causes given as relevant events in clause 25, some of which may lead only to extension of time and others of which may (in appropriate cases, but not automatically) lead also or instead to payment for loss and expense. The fort was an instance of loss and expense without extension of time, as that part of the laboratory programme was sub-critical. If a right to extension does arise, it is calculated by the overall duration of the two delays and not by the sum of their individual durations. The latter would obviously exaggerate the effect.

(b) Other causes which are always the contractor's responsibility, such as normal adverse weather or failure to obtain materials in time, when no shortage exists. In these cases, the contractor is entitled only to such part, if any, of the delay due to the relevant event as stretches beyond that due to the other cause.

One or two of the times were adjusted by the architect during his periodic reviews. The contractor did argue for longer extensions in places to give him a little more leeway than the one week of float built into elements U for each building. Properly, he should have been granted extensions which were abated by these float periods, as clause 25.3.1.2 refers to delay 'beyond the Completion Date'. This is a frequent cause of debate, as the contractor thereby loses the buffer which he has included to cover possible slips on his part, which is a perfectly reasonable precaution. It occurs in exaggerated form

when the contractor allows for finishing well ahead of the contract date (see discussion in Ch. 4). It is suggested that a fair approach to this problem is to allow extensions in the earlier stages which preserve the contractor's float to cover his own needs, but to tail it off towards the end as it becomes less necessary.

In this project, the contractor used up his float to ease the problems of tight working in the confusion which had set in, and no one objected. Calculation of extension of time within a one-week margin becomes quite debatable in circumstances of the nature of those suffered here. The origin of the circumstances would also have weighed in any doubtful area against the employer in an appeal to arbitration or proceedings.

The only times needing further comment are those due to the floor damage in the process shop. Within the shop itself, affairs were at a highly complex stage of working towards finality when the damage came to light. There was work involving services by sub-contractors, the contractor's own finishings and extensive direct work for the employer. On top of the delay while the remedy was being sought and during which no remedial work could be started, there followed a period when all concerned were likely to get in one another's way, with no one in convincing overall charge of the programme. There was little option but to accept whatever finishing time was achieved, in the absence of gross mismanagement, and this was done.

The other aspect of this lay in the external works, which finished after the buildings and not with them. As often happens, the sectional completion requirements had not been terribly explicit over the precise areas to be completed with each building. This could well have undermined any putative argument about areas which were needed to go with the process shop, and so any claim that full liquidated damages should apply for that building until all was handed over. While the external works were definitely non-critical in the original programme and had been progressing quite well, the incidence of the land drains on top of the work caused by the infusion plant threw them well out. Any argument for some proportion of liquidated damages for the external works alone was very likely to fail and was not pursued. *Bramall & Ogden* v. *Sheffield* described in Chapter 10 is illustrative of the results of lack of precision here.

The usefulness of a network analysis for establishing controlling extensions of time can be seen, even from the limited evidence of a book exercise. In its absence, something equivalent should be set up to isolate critical from sub-critical and non-critical activities, so that the genuine areas of delay can be seen. It needs to be remembered that only delays affecting the end date are relevant, although sub-critical activities can easily be made critical by other delays.

Preliminaries adjustment due to scope of work

This is a straightforward matter, arising from normal estimating principles

and mentioned in clause 13.5.3.3 as a matter for variation valuation 'where appropriate'. The procedure is discussed in Chapter 6. Although not a question of loss and expense, it needs to be cleared here because loss and expense matters hinge on it.

REASONS FOR ADJUSTMENT

In this contract, several issues had emerged to suggest an adjustment of preliminaries. Everything relating to loss and expense due to extra supervision or prolongation had to be ignored for clause 13 purposes and, conversely, clause 13 matters had to be excluded for loss and expense ascertainment. This is not mere pedantry, but relates to the differing methods of calculation and their results.

There had been a lifting of the value of measured and cognate work, main and sub-contract, for these reasons:

(a) Extra work in the annexes of the process shop, totalling £67,890.
(b) Introduction of the infusion plant with its own variations, totalling £346,700, excluding preliminaries.
(c) Remedial and additional work in the process shop, owing to the spring, totalling £38,600.
(d) Land drains and related work in the external areas of the site, totalling £43,230.
(e) A general incremental edging up of the value of other work by a series of architect's instructions, totalling £145,820.

The total value of all this work was thus £642,240, or £295,540 without the infusion plant.

The contractor had negotiated for the infusion plant on the basis that he would set up a distinct subsidiary site organisation to cope with it in the short time available, which also fell within the closing stages of the original works, when the emphasis for organisation was changing. His agreed additional preliminaries, set beside those in the original contract sum were:

	Original	Additional
Setting up site	20,500	1,200
Supervision	78,000	6,700
Major plant	90,500	8,400
Accommodation	58,500	3,400
Sundry items	30,200	6,900
Final clearance	7,400	1,000
	£285,100	£27,600

These additional figures were high when the work content of the two parts were compared. They reflected the fact of a much smaller 'contract within

a contract', but also the strong bargaining position of the contractor in the circumstances.

It was necessary to establish what would have happened, had all the other extra work been instructed in a regular way, so as not to disturb regular progress.

The contractor's first proposal was that there should be a straight adjustment of all the original preliminaries amounts in proportion to the adjusted amounts for measured and other work, other than the amount for setting up site, when the extra work had not been instructed, but including final clearance when it had. This would have given an increase of some £20,000 and ignored economies of scale (otherwise the effect of marginal costing) and also took no account of the change in contract duration or of features such as those illustrated by the 'S' curve of Fig. 15.1(a). It was established in ensuing discussion that major plant and accommodation had not been increased on site, but had been used more intensively, extendedly or efficiently, according to the various circumstances. Some 60 per cent of the amounts for sundry items had been similarly affected, but the rest not at all. Final clearance had been a little more piecemeal than expected, because of the staggered finish to the works.

Apart from the effects of disturbance of regular progress, there would have been an extension of time of two weeks for the annexes and general extra work, this applying to each building. There would also have been an extension of three weeks for the extra work inside the process shop to remedy the floor, had this been instructed and introduced evenly. The land drains themselves would had added four weeks on a similar basis to the external works. As the results of the floor damage did *not* occur in this steady manner, it is open to debate whether *any* of the extra preliminaries should be excluded from the loss and expense amounts, so affecting the levels of them. Practitioners differ over items such as these, but it is submitted that the present pattern is the more correct. The resulting completions would have been:

Process shop	Week 41
Laboratory	Week 50
External works	Week 52

These were all due to additional work, valued as variations, and not to 'neutral' causes such as weather. They therefore constituted elements in the valuation of extra preliminaries, in accordance with clause 13.5.3.3. That there was no separate original completion date for the external works may be ignored in the present context. Equally, it was decided not to argue over whether the contractor might have finished one week early all round, by maintaining his initial float (see above) and assuming no variations at all, that is by weeks 35 and 47.

The calculation of additional preliminaries, affecting only the original

amounts, without the infusion plant, was eventually as given under the following headings.

SUPERVISION

The extra work in the annexes had had little effect, remembering that additional setting out had been covered so far as loss and expense (but see later under 'Site overheads'). It was also not possible to isolate individual costs for the other extra work, other than the land drains. It was, however, agreed that some extra due to general co-ordination on site and paperwork was inevitable, while there was a prolongation, quite apart from the disturbance element. This would have been less on sub-contract work than on the contractor's direct work, but the proportion of these was about the same between the original and the additional work. Some element of supervision value (about one-third plus all forepersons, from pre-contract discussions) was agreed to be in the measured rates, and so already reflected in the variations net addition.

Original work, without preliminaries = £4,101,600

The staffing covered in the various figures was:
Contract manager (visiting).
Agent and two sub-agents/engineers.
Site surveyor.
Bonus, costing, wages and administration.
These were to be available according to the build-up and run down of the project. To maintain simplicity, the identities of these persons is ignored and they are allocated for illustrative purposes in the following manner (see also the histograms in Fig. 20.1) out of the amount of £78,000 in the preliminaries, while not affecting the principles of adjustment:
  Split between buildings (including share of external works):

Process shop   25% = £19,500
Laboratory   60% = £46,800
Common to both 15% = £11,700

The intensity of use of the various categories is reduced to 'units' throughout the original programme:

Process shop:
Weeks 1–5 at 1 unit   = 5 units
Weeks 6–10 at 2 units   = 10 units
Weeks 11–20 at 3 units = 30 units
Weeks 21–36 at 2 units = 32 units
£19,500 ÷ 77 units   = £253.25 per unit

Laboratory:
Weeks 1–5 at 1 unit   = 5 units
Weeks 6–10 at 2 units   = 10 units
Weeks 11–22 at 3 units = 36 units
Weeks 23–48 at 2 units = 52 units
£46,800 ÷ 103 units   = £454.40 per unit

Common to both:
Weeks 1–48 at 1 unit = 48 units
£11,700 ÷ 48 units   = £243.75

From these figures, increased 'allowances' were made, based on the timing of the qualifying extensions (see the delay times given under 'Loss and expense on site overheads' below). These all assumed regular working and attendance as at other times, so that no mitigation factor was introduced:

Process shop:
1 week at 3 units and 4 weeks at 2 units = £253.25 × 11 = £2,786

Laboratory:
1 week at 3 units and 1 week at 2 units = £454.40 × 5 = £2,272

Common to both:
2 weeks at 1 unit = £243.75 × 2   = £488

There was also special supervision because of the floor repair work and land drains (had both been performed regularly, but in their 'special conditions', as clause 13.5.1.2 has it), in each case two extra staff for part of the time:

£(100 + 70) × 30 days   = £5,100
Total additional allowance = £10,646

The straight expression of the supervision amount as a percentage of measured and other work would have given £4,970. The higher amount (exclusive of the last element for repair, etc.) is due to the time element, abated by the effect of economies of scale. The contractor would have lost out on his original proposal.

MAJOR PLANT

The original allowance of £90,500 was split:

Transportation, setting up and removal
(not in general items)   = £4,350
Hire charges or equivalent   = £33,650
Operating labour, etc.   = £52,500

For even greater simplicity than was used for supervision, plant is taken as being entirely available during the first two-thirds of the programme for each building: again, it would actually be calculated in considerably more

detail. Plant costs were higher during the earlier stages of each building and slightly higher in proportion for the laboratory, owing to its concrete frame and multi-storey nature. Half of the variations came in the finishings stage of each building, when less use of major plant occurred, so that only one week's extension was relevant. The exception was the work to the process shop floor, which needed a variety of plant, but most of this was brought in specially because of the timing and covered by daywork. The agreement was based on the following in principle, but worked out in more detail:

Hire and operating total = £86,150

Allocation to process shop, nearly one-third:

$$£28,720 - 2,200 = £26,520$$

Allocation to laboratory, just over two-thirds:

$$£57,430 + 2,200 = £59,630$$

Allow for process shop, 1 week extra on 24:

$$£26,520 \div 24 = £1,110$$

Allow for laboratory, 1 week extra on 32:

$$£59,630 \div 32 = £1,860$$

Extra major plant allowance for floor repair in process shop:

$$3 \text{ weeks at } £420 = £1,260$$

Total major plant extra = £4,230

ACCOMMODATION

This was allowed for the whole period of 48 weeks originally, on the basis that it was not reasonable to remove sections early, when the laboratory was more complex and larger. Setting up and clearing amounts in this case were in the respective general site items. It was agreed that the two weeks' overall extension was relevant and that the extra extension to the process shop caused no extra cost. The accommodation was not needed later during completion of the external works, when the employer made a room available in the process shop and when disturbance applied anyway. A simple proportioning therefore covered the elements of hire, maintenance and heating and lighting:
Allow for whole project, 2 weeks extra on 48:

$$£58,500 \div 24 = £2,440$$

SUNDRY ITEMS AND FINAL CLEARANCE

The sundry items were affected in assorted ways, and for some 60 per cent of

their value as noted above. Without giving detail to repeat principles already illustrated, the result was:

Original sundry items = £30,200

Allow 60 per cent for 2 weeks extra on 48:

$$£30,200 \times 60\% \div 24 = £760$$

The slight spreading of final clearance was compensated for by an addition of £354, based (and this could be questioned) on costs produced.

A REVIEW

These various extra preliminaries amounts totalled £18,430, less than proportionate to the increase in work executed, when allowance has been made for the special features included. It must be emphasised that they take no account of loss and expense, all of which follows, apart from small elements of supervision included earlier.

Two passing comments may be added. First, *all* the calculations ignore the sum for contingencies, not just because it is not part of preliminaries (in which section of the contract bills it is sometimes misleadingly placed), but because the contractor cannot allow any preliminaries in relation to it, as he is quite unaware of whether it will be used and, if so, how. This singles it out from other provisional sums, which usually state their scope, so that preliminaries can be allowed in addition (See 'Subsidiary provisions over valuation' in Ch. 6).

Secondly, if the contractor had allowed most of his preliminaries in his rates, he would have obtained an excessive extra, if the rates had been applied to the increased quantities without question and in particular in the absence of any programme extension. This gives point to the reference in clause 13.5.1.2 to instructions which 'significantly change the quantity', and also to 'allowance . . . made for any addition to or reduction of preliminary items' in clause 13.5.3.3. A reduction of preliminary amounts, even when these have been priced as 'nil', may be the best way of reflecting this position, effectively reversing what has been done above.

With the extended digression under this 'Preliminaries' heading to prepare the way, the discussion returns to loss and expense.

Loss and expense on site overheads

RELATIONSHIP TO PRELIMINARIES ADJUSTMENT

Ascertainment here has to proceed from the base established of adjusted preliminaries related to the works as varied, but with the works performed in a regular manner and with costs taken into account, rather than estimated figures in the preliminaries. In principle, it deals with both disruption and prolongation. In this project, it is the latter which predominates, because its

sheer extent swallows up the effects of disruption itself. Staff generally will have plenty of spare time to deal with extra activity!

It is immediately evident that the statement just given introduces a conceptual problem which has been ignored so far in this case study for ease of working, but which can conveniently be highlighted now. This is that, because the contractor's original intentions have been considerably modified, there is now an additional set of figures of consequence to add to those relevant:

(a) Expenditure which would have been incurred with the works completed unaffected by variations, etc. or disturbance.
(b) Expenditure which would have been incurred with variations, etc. taken into the reckoning.
(c) Expenditure as actually incurred.

The second of these figures is not the same as that resulting from the adjustment of preliminaries just performed, although related to it, any more than the first is the figure included in the contract bills. To calculate it, means a hypothetical exercise (as so many are) arriving at a revision of the contractor's programmed plant use and costs. The third figure can then be used in conjunction with it to reach the amount of loss and expense, although this needs analysis and adjustment to ascertain which part of the actual cost is caused by the disturbance factor: it is not the simple difference. When one theoretically calculated figure is used to ascertain another which involves a number of conjectures, as this must, the result begins to look rather suspect.

Some possible ways round this problem are:

(a) To calculate all extra costs as part of the loss and expense and not include any in the preliminaries adjustment. This is not what the contract requires (consider a contract with preliminaries adjustment and no loss and expense), and gives a different result in any case.
(b) To do the reverse. This is open to the same objections.
(c) To calculate a global allowance in a suitable form for all extra elements and then to divide this for preliminaries and loss and expense. The figures can then be adjusted to reflect the correct levels of pricing. This may well be the point of departure for many calculations, by supplying a controlling framework.
(d) To perform the two calculations in parallel, so that both relate to the original programmed intention. This avoids the multi-layer approach of the first method. It does mean that all loss and expense are related to the contract works, without variations, and this may be unrealistic in concept.

In the present case and for illustrative purposes, all calculations follow the last method, ignoring the effect of disturbance on variations. This avoids tracing the value of variations through a labyrinth of figures for very little purpose. There were, however, enough general variations (for instance, those not due to the damage to the floor) in this case to be affected by disturbance

of regular progress to a significant degree, so that in practice some of that work would need to be examined.

The extent of delay covered in relation to variation instructions, including all work which also led to disturbance, was as follows:

	Process shop	Laboratory	Externals
Original time	36 weeks	48 weeks	48 weeks
Annexes	1 week	—	—
Superstructures	1 week	2 weeks	—
Floor damage	3 weeks	—	4 weeks
Totals:	41 weeks	50 weeks	52 week
Further delays:	17 weeks	5 weeks	10 weeks

The infusion plant had, of course, started later than the rest, but also lost two weeks because the floor damage affected work around the plant. The detailed allocation of the total of each delay is shown under 'Extension of time' above.

The great distinction here is that the contractor has to show actual loss and expense, rather than secure an adjustment of preliminaries, even though this in itself is far from a straight pro rata. This can be quite difficult for him, as some expenses creep up gradually. He really has to show that he employed extra personnel and incurred related expenditure, specifically because of disturbance of regular progress. In this case, the contractor again asked for a pro rata adjustment, as he had done over his preliminaries – in fact he originally lumped the two together. With the preliminaries out of the way, progress was made on the other element. It became evident quite early in negotiations that the question of prolongation was sufficiently large to outweigh any suggestion that extra staff had been introduced.

It was convenient to examine the problem under the items given in the preliminaries, as these had been priced to highlight a fairly logical split, even if the amounts were a little uneven, with some parts included in the prices for measured work. This meant looking at both the original works and the added infusion plant.

SUPERVISION

The approach here was to calculate the cost of staff, and then allow the additional time spent due to prolongation beyond what had already been covered in the adjustment of preliminaries, because varied work necessitated extra time.

To aid illustration, these cost figures are shown as though they were adjustments of what was allowed in the preliminaries – a method *not* to be used as such in reality. In practice, the actual costs inclusive of direct on-costs should be used. The present method allows a comparison to be made with the preliminaries to show differences in values and scope.

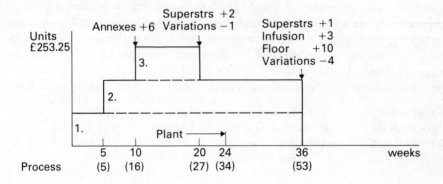

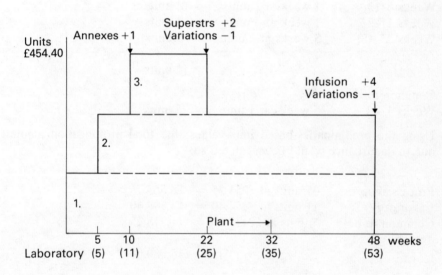

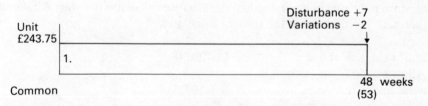

Fig. 20.1   Laboratory project, site overheads histogram

The reference is therefore to the set of figures used above in the preliminaries calculations, and also to Fig. 20.1 for the periods now involved. This assumes for simplicity that the originally estimated periods and levels were appropriate in reality. This they may well not be, and the actual figures without disturbance should always form the basis from which loss and expense are ascertained. The various elements of prolongation as they occurred affected original periods when there were differing levels of staffing 'units' as have been defined. The prolongation of the original periods is:

Process shop:

Weeks 6–10,	6 weeks at 2 units	= 12 units
Weeks 11–20,	1 week at 3 units	= 3 units
Weeks 21–36,	10 weeks at 2 units	= 20 units
		35 units

Laboratory:

Weeks 6–10,	1 week at 2 units	= 2 units
Weeks 11–22,	1 week at 3 units	= 3 units
Weeks 23–48,	3 weeks at 2 units	= 6 units
		11 units

Common to both:

| Weeks 1–48, | 5 weeks at 1 unit | = 5 units |

Using the preliminaries-based unit values, the total prolongation amount due to disturbance would be calculated so:

Process shop	35 units at £253.25	=	£8,863.75
Laboratory	11 units at £454.40	=	£4,998.40
Common to both	5 units at £243.75	=	£1,218.75
		say	£15,080.00

It has been noted when dealing with preliminaries that about one-third of the values anticipated for the staff listed there were included in measured rates, as were all forepersons. None of these have been covered for loss and expense purposes in the individual disturbance calculations so far. All should therefore be included in the present calculations.

Staff values as above	£15,080.00
Allow say 50% for portion in measured rates	£ 7,540.00
Allow forepersons as in measured rates	£ 5,100.00
	£27,720.00

Less head office and profit
amounts, adjusted up or down
for actual levels paid, say 20%   5,540.00

                                      _____

                                      £22,180.00

This gives the direct total for prolongation, and this is considerably different
in result from any direct proportioning such as the contractor suggested. An
extension of the 48-week project period by 5 weeks (the overall effect on the
main completion, ignoring extension of time as granted) gives only £8,125
when applied to the contract amount of £78,000. The calculation of the sum of
£15,080 above shows the fallacy of such an approach, which ignores the effect
in either direction of subsidiary prolongations within the total programme (a
cognate fallacy may be seen in a crude formula approach to calculating head
office overheads, as shown hereafter and mentioned in Ch. 15). The other
weaknesses show in the next calculation above, leading to £22,180.

It bears repeating that ascertainment should be done as such by building
up from actual costs as they would have been and then were, but the foregoing
isolates the potential traps in what is being done more clearly.

It remains under this heading to make some qualifications to the flat
rate calculation performed. It ignores the further programme extension of
four weeks due for the external works alone. At this stage, only a skeleton
supervisory staff was needed, partly on a visiting basis, so that the allowable
cost became:

                4 weeks at £420.00 = £1,680.00

The earlier amounts agreed for loss and expense included some elements
of a supervisory nature. When the overall ascertainment of prolongation
occurred, it became clear that some of the earlier amounts were duplicated
therein, as staff were able to perform the extra work while waiting to carry
on with their routine tasks. For tidiness of presentation in the final account,
these items were deleted from the earlier sections:

Extra setting out for the annexes   360.00
Extra setting out due to the fort   120.00
Part of extra supervision co-ordinating
services work in both buildings after
introduction of the infusion plant   740.00

                                               _____

                                               £1,220.00

The earlier supervision under the last item had occurred during the weeks
preceding the disturbance caused by the process shop floor breaking up, and
so required the introduction of additional staff from outside the project to
cope with the temporary workload. When the floor delayed matters, regular
staff had enough time to cope, once the first crisis was over and they were
waiting for fresh instructions from the architect.

There was also the question of whether the contractor had been able to

make any saving in cost by redeploying staff, or even whether he should have been able to do so when he did not. The staff working on the laboratory had not been hindered for any single long period which would have justified their physical redeployment. Those engaged in common work between the buildings, such as wages and administration, were similarly placed as there was always some relevant work to occupy them. If anything, they had had to work harder during the closing stages, when the process shop had dragged on, but no extra staff or overtime payments had resulted. They had just not had the rather easier time which they had expected! The contractor was unable to demonstrate that he would otherwise have brought in extra work from other sites for them to perform during their slack period. If he had been able to do so, he would have had a valid claim for displacement.

There was one more subtle argument lying in the background. The supplementary agreement for the introduction of the infusion plant had included its own amounts for preliminaries, but had excluded any element of loss and expense on the rest of the works so that, for instance, extra amounts for labour and plant have already been considered here. The amounts for preliminaries for the plant had been pitched fairly high, in view of the contractor's strong bargaining position. But was it not the case that, as a result of the introduction of the plant, an element in the loss and expense was an adjusted overall expenditure for supervision on the rest of the scheme? This was argued to be a net reduction, needless to say from the employer's side, on the basis that the common elements of wages, etc. in the supervisory staff were not increased, so that there was a 'negative loss and expense'. This argument could be extended to other elements of supervision, and to accommodation, etc. yet to be considered in this chapter.

Two points may be made about this argument. Firstly, it is one thing to exclude from an agreement the effects on other sections of the physical work, as these do not overlap in cost terms with the new portion introduced, but quite another to exclude the effects on clearly overlapping site overheads. It must be held that the amount for preliminaries in the infusion plant agreement was based on a 'net extra' cost basis, that is it took into account any spreading of supervision without extra staff. The saving was to be seen against the provisions of clause 13 and not clause 26.

Secondly, clause 26 of the JCT form deals with positive loss and expense incurred and does not recognise any abatement due to savings made elsewhere in the project's execution or on another, as distinct from balancing extra expenditure in an area of cost against savings in the same area in the same period. It is at least possible, even if not probable, that a contractor in mitigating his loss by transferring resources elsewhere could also be enhancing his efficiency there by bringing in resources which he would otherwise have to do without. This is a somewhat different point from that raised on the present project, but there is still no right to secure an abatement of the amount ascertained.

In this instance, the contractor agreed not to pursue his claim strongly for extra expense on the infusion plant due to delay caused by the land

drain work. He settled for a 'nominal allowance' of £100. Perhaps he was conscience-stricken about his previous deal!

MAJOR PLANT

It is possible to deal here with this element rather on the lines followed under the adjustment of preliminaries, and so more briefly than site overheads, as the guiding principles are similar. While the total allowed in the contract preliminaries, exclusive of setting up and removal, was £86,150, the actual net costs incurred for the contract period were less (the contract period only is used for the reasons given at the beginning of this site overheads section). These were less because of the exclusion of head office overheads and profit and also the variation up and down of payments made for plant and attendant labour. The actual figures for the original programme were:

	Hire	Operating	Time used
Process shop	11,260	13,150	24 weeks
Laboratory	20,310	31,690	32 weeks
	£31,570	£44,840	

As with the preliminaries, regular use over the time is assumed here in presentation and proportionate extension of use for the total periods indicated in Fig. 20.1. This would need checking in practice, as usual. The results with any adjustment were:

Process shop, hire	£11,260 for 24 weeks
	£15,950 for 34 weeks
	£1,420 reduction for partial removal
	£3,270 net extra cost

Laboratory, hire	£20,310 for 32 weeks
	£22,210 for 35 weeks
	No reduction possible
	£1,900 extra cost

Process shop, operating	£13,150 for 24 weeks
	£18,630 for 34 weeks
	£1,770 reduction for partial redeployment
	£3,710 net extra cost

Laboratory, operating	£31,690 for 32 weeks
	£34,660 for 35 weeks
	No reduction possible
	£2,970 extra cost

These figures gave a total extra cost of £11,850. When ascertaining the loss and expense due to postponement of work when introducing the process shop annexes, an amount of £4,320 had been included for plant standing idle during that period. This was now extracted from the earlier figures when the principle

of an overall ascertainment was agreed (as happened with supervision), to keep all overhead costs in one place.

It may be seen that suspension of hire or redeployment of operatives became possible when the longer delays occurred on the process shop, but was not reasonable with the shorter delays for the laboratory.

ACCOMMODATION

Here no reduction was possible by way of removing items for short periods, for obvious reasons. The basic calculation for ascertainment was therefore to take the actual net cost for the original contract period and extend it:

Amount in preliminaries	£58,500
Actual original net cost	£49,400
Extension for 5 weeks	
beyond 48 weeks	£5,150
Reduction for less	
attendance when reduced	
occupancy	£470
Net extra cost	£4,680

Nothing was needed for the further period of the external works, because of the provision of enough accommodation by the employer, which included cleaning, etc. without charge.

SUNDRY ITEMS

These fell out rather as they did for preliminaries adjustment, so that similar calculations suffice:

Amount in preliminaries	£30,200
Actual original net cost	£27,100
Proportion affected 60%	£16,260
Extension for 5 weeks	
beyond 48 weeks	£1,690

TOTAL FOR SITE OVERHEADS

The foregoing figures may be brought together as follows:

Supervision prolongation	£22,180
Supervision, external	
works	£1,680
Major plant	£11,850
Accommodation	£4,680
Sundry items	£1,690
	———
	£42,080

Inflation on fixed price contract

When delay occurs, there is a reasonable presupposition that the contractor will incur greater costs, which are not reimbursed in the absence of a sufficiently embracing fluctuations clause. This was the case in the project considered. The sensible approach to this question to give an adequately close answer is to use some form of indexation. If this is not done, the alternative is to perform calculations based upon inspection of time sheets and invoices in detail as happens when fluctuations are calculated under the cost-related JCT clauses 38 and 39 or their equivalents. Admittedly, it is cost which is in question to arrive at loss and expense, but it would be asking too much to extend this rigorously to the ascertainment of the comparatively small differential between what the contractor should have incurred and what he actually did incur. No court is likely to expect quite this amount of detail.

According to what is covered by the contract fluctuations clause, this may be done by some adaptation of the standard figures provided for the operation of JCT clause 40 and its relatives. The principle involved may be illustrated by making some exclusions from and simplifications to the total operation which would actually take place:

(a) Only the process shop is considered, without its associated external works.
(b) Only the contractor's own workforce and that of domestic sub-contractors are considered, it being assumed that the steelwork and the services alone were by nominated sub-contractors.
(c) Only the original contract work involved is considered, so that variations, etc. are excluded.
(d) Preliminaries are ignored.
(e) The indexation figures are represented by percentage changes to keep them 'timeless' and are given in four-week steps, rather than monthly.
(f) One indexation percentage is given to cover all categories of work as usually defined. The various work elements shown in the programme would themselves consist of several categories in a number of instances.
(g) It is assumed that the works started in step with an indexation period.
(h) The same percentages are used for what must be deemed to have been included in the contractor's rates to allow for inflation and what needed to be allowed for the time shift which occurred. This is marginally inaccurate mathematically, as the first value is entirely within the total rate, while the second is partly within and partly additional.

The necessary ascertainment calculations are set out in Table 20.1. The 'original' figures are derived from the contractor's programme and the contract bills and the 'achieved' figures from the actual programme and the bills. The application of the same percentages to the differing values performed lead to totals in each case, giving a simple difference, which is the loss and expense figure.

The exclusion of nominated sub-contractors is not just a concession

Table 20.1   Laboratory project, extra inflation due to delay (process shop only)

Weeks	Index (%)	Original				Achieved			
		Elements (%)		Amounts	Totals	Inflation	Elements (%)		Amounts	Totals	Inflation
1–4	100	Bases	100	116,400	116,400	—	—		—	—	—
5–8	100.4	Walls	30	47,790	47,790	190	Bases	50	58,200	58,200	230
9–12	100.8	Walls	70	111,510			Bases	50	58,200		
		A	50	37,300	148,810	1,190	Walls	35	55,760	113,960	910
13–16	101.2	A	50	37,300			Walls	65	103,540	103,540	1,240
		B	100	36,400	73,700	880					
17–20	101.7	C	100	34,200			A	80	59,680	59,680	1,010
		D	100	38,700							
		G	40	21,920	94,820	1,610					
21–24	102.1	E	50	41,850			A	20	14,920		
		G	60	32,880			B	100	36,400		
		H	100	74,500	149,230	3,130	C	50	17,100		
							E	50	41,850	110,270	2,320
25–28	102.5	E	50	41,850			C	50	17,100		
		K	100	40,600			D	100	38,700		
		L	100	31,200	113,650	2,840	E	50	41,850		
							G	40	21,920		
							H	25	18,620	138,190	3,450
29–32	103.2	M	100	36,400			G	60	32,880		
		N	100	33,300	69,700	2,230	H	75	55,880		
							K	30	12,180		
							L	50	15,600	116,540	3,730
33–36	103.4	U	100	28,400	28,400	970	K	70	28,420		
							L	50	15,600	44,020	1,500
37–40	103.7						M	50	18,200		
							N	30	9,990	28,190	1,040
41–44	104.2						N	10	3,330	3,330	140
45–48	104.8						M	10	3,640	3,640	180
49-52	105.2						M	10	3,640		
							N	10	3,330	6,970	360
53–56	105.5						M	30	10,920		
							N	50	16,650	27,570	1,520
57–60	105.9						U	100	28,400	28,400	680
					842,500	842,500	13,040			842,500	842,500	18,310

Less anticipated amount: 13,040

Extra inflation: 5,270

to simplicity. Their tenders are usually obtained at some time different from that of the contractor. When this time is later, it is possible for the tenders to be based upon the programme then current, so that any delay inflation which already exists can be allowed in the sub-contract sums. If the question of loss and expense due to inflation arises for these persons, it will be calculated similarly to the present example, but with distinct indexation levels.

Domestic sub-contractors are different, in that the contractor has to give firm prices for their work when he himself tenders. He is held to these prices whatever the levels he actually has to accept and whenever he accepts them, subject to the considerations over lists of permitted persons mentioned in Chapter 7. Within the simplifications of the example, they are therefore subject to the same indexation as the contractor himself, so far as what the contractor recovers. He may well pay different amounts (probably less) because of the timing of later sub-tenders, although also in reality what happens will depend on the character of their work and so on the appropriate figures.

Within the original programme there were some elements which were sub-critical (even more, were the external works under consideration here, the elements were non-critical), but all of these are shown as happening at the earliest time possible, thus preserving the contractor's float and minimising his inflation exposure. This is reasonable practice, but gives the maximum shift to the achieved time, and so the maximum inflation differential. Equally, none of the achieved times is queried as to whether it represents an unduly retarded execution – usually a very difficult thing to do in circumstances of disturbance. Both assumptions should be examined in practice before calculations proceed.

The achieved programme takes account of all extensions of time granted, which include those arising out of variations and not having a relation to prolongation as here intended. No extensions due to 'neutral' relevant events, such as weather or strikes, occurred in this project. Had the project not been subject to disturbance of regular progress, but had there still been extensions of time, the contractor would not have received payment for the effect of inflation. This represents the distribution of risk between employer and contractor over delays, and is unexceptionable over items like weather or strikes (where the granting of an extension may be the sticking point), but can be criticised over employer-generated matters like variations.

The contractor needs to be watching when there is a heavy crop of variations which extend the programme in inflationary times, but which do so in a tidy way as far as progress is concerned, so that there is no loss and expense sector in which to allow for inflation. The problem is that variations usually accrete over time, rather than appear in one lump. The only resting place seems to be in the reference to 'conditions' in, for instance, JCT clause 13.5. When this refers to 'similar conditions' in clause 13.5.1, it certainly covers actual varied work performed regularly, but later than expected, and so leading to costs such as unusual supervision or plant. For work not varied,

but delayed by variations, clause 13.5.5 may be be useful, by its reference to a variation which 'substantially changes the conditions under which any other work is executed'. The term 'conditions' has a primary and intended reference to physical matters, it must be assumed, but what may have been intended may not determine the interpretation which the courts, ultimately, may supply. It is suggested that a wider interpretation is reasonable in the proper circumstances.

In the present case, there were delays because of variations as such, and further delays because of the effects of the variations on other work. It is argued when discussing extension of time above, that these two should be distinguished for such purposes as preliminaries adjustment. This distinction is equally valid here, although the financial outcome is unaffected, accepting the preceding argument about 'conditions'. Strictly, the calculations in Table 20.1 need to be abated and reallocated appropriately, with the attendant difficulties of the variations and the disturbances being so closely linked. The line of least resistance is to leave what is properly a variation valuation in with a loss and expense ascertainment. There is a limit to hair-splitting!

General drop in productivity of labour

The contractor raised this issue more in hope than anger, and was not too surprised when it was turned down. It is always very difficult to substantiate such an item, or at least to demonstrate how extensive are the loss and expense. This is because it consists of the diffuse effects of disturbance of regular progress, which cannot be clearly attached to a particular part of the programme, or to a particular part of the contractor's costs. This does not mean that there is nothing there, just that it is difficult to quantify because it is the frictional result of lack of confidence, shortage of long-term work in view, or the other causes which are broad and rather vague.

The major pointer to the possibility of a general drop is that a string of disturbances has congealed into one protracted disturbance. When the main isolated effects have been evaluated, there remains the continuous effect. In the present case, there were several high points of disturbance:

(a) The postponement of work on the process shop pending revised annex drawings.
(b) Discovery of the ancient fort on the laboratory site.
(c) Introduction of the infusion plant.
(d) The breaking up of the floor in the process shop, followed by remedial work and the land drainage system.

The first two of these were dealt with in a fairly self-contained way. The first had some tapering consequential effects, partly a general drop of productivity in their following time bracket, by unsettling the sequence of work elements in both buildings. All these items of extra expense were ascertained, the disturbance worked its way out and work settled down into a rhythm again.

The infusion plant occurred as a distinct feature, and again its effects were reasonably compact, in that they impinged on services and related work in the two buildings, when each was clear of major structural work. The plant also affected the external works, mainly by introducing specific constraints on working.

The final blow of the floor problem did overlap with the effects on services in the process shop, due to the infusion plant. This was so much so that the two sets of disturbance ran into one and, effectively, the whole of the operations in the building was under review once the extent of the floor damage became apparent.

As the settlements for the separate disturbances had been cleared so carefully as they went along, with all the effects monitored closely, there was little left to pick up. This the contractor agreed without much show of reluctance.

Loss and expense on head office overheads

THE STATE OF THE REST OF THE FINAL ACCOUNT

The narrative now passes into the area of secondary loss and expense, following the terminology of Chapters 14 and 15. As a prelude, the total position of the final account adjusted for everything except secondary loss and expense is summarised.

Contract sum		4,751,500
Less contingency		300,000
		4,451,500
Variations net addition		
Measured and daywork	295,540	
Preliminaries	18,430	313,970
Primary loss and expense		
Annexes	38,495	
Fort	7,010	
Ripple effects of these	14,280	
Infusion plant effects	23,235	
Floor damage	22,910	
Site overheads	42,080	
Inflation		
Process shop	5,270	
Laboratory, say	3,500	156,780
		£4,922,250

Any assumptions or blatant inaccuracies in these figures may be traced in earlier discussion, as for instance the exclusion of preliminaries and variations in the inflation allowance for the process shop and the assumed amount for the laboratory. Strict continuity of detail is not of the essence of the overall study.

USE OF STANDARD FORMULAE

The results produced by the standard formulae described and critically assessed in Chapter 15 may be given first, to act as a comparison, it being remembered that these tend to give high results in most instances.

To keep the formulae on an equal footing, a head office figure of 6.5 per cent is used in each case, applying to the contractor's own work and that of all types of sub-contractors (this is a variable factor, but is assumed for simplicity in tracing the figures, and is how the formulae approach matters). As the essential difference between the Hudson and Emden formulae is that the former uses the percentage in the tender and the latter the actual percentage, this means that here they give the same result. While the Eichleay formula does not use a percentage, but the total head office amount and turnover, the figures used equate to 6.5 per cent.

As there was sectional completion in the project, it becomes necessary to split the totals and use the formula concerned twice each time. The extended programme duration is the total, less the original and the extensions not related to disturbance of regular progress.

Hudson or Emden (related to the contract sum):

$$\text{Process Shop:} \quad \frac{6.5}{100} \times 1,617,500 \times \frac{58 - 41}{36} = 49,650$$

$$\text{Laboratory:} \quad \frac{6.5}{100} \times 2,834,000 \times \frac{55 - 50}{48} = 19,190$$

$$\overline{\text{£68,840}}$$

Eichleay (related to the final account, taken as all amounts other than head office overheads):

$$\text{Process shop:} \quad 1,950,000 \times \frac{1,861,000}{30,000,000} \times \frac{17}{53} = 38,800$$

$$\text{Laboratory:} \quad 1,950,000 \times \frac{3,061,250}{30,000,000} \times \frac{5}{53} = 18,770$$

$$\overline{\text{£57,570}}$$

The difference between the two results is to be traced mostly to the process shop, with the laboratory contributing in a much smaller way, and is due to

the use in Eichleay of the final programme time in place of the original. Indeed, the use of the final money amounts increases what would otherwise be there, unless inclusion of the total of all contemporary accounts has cancelled this out. This illustrates the tendency of Eichleay to come rather closer to reality, as the main criticism of the other formulae in particular is that they are too inclusive and so too high in outcome. But subject to these comparisons, all formulae relate in essence to the prolongation position, rather than what disruption occurred, with or without prolongation.

There has already been a recovery of head office overheads in the items for variations, etc. including extra preliminaries. These total £313,970, so that the presumed inclusion of 6.5 per cent in the rates and amounts yields £20,407. Given the coarseness of the formulae, it must be assumed that this amount is being covered twice by Eichleay at least. The higher the final account, the more is this so.

The figures derived from this survey are referred to later. Meanwhile, discussion can return to examination from the other and more piecemeal end of the problem.

DIRECTLY IDENTIFIABLE COSTS

These are usually in the minority when loss and expense are in question, for two reasons: they may be small in amount compared with the figures just calculated, but also they often have not been noted as problems have developed on the far-away site. The following were identified in relation to the times of maximum disturbance on site, although they did not all occur at once or in complete weeks:

Director	1,000 per week
Administration	500 per week
Buying	400 per week
	———
	£1,900 per week

With a five weeks' total, this gave £9,500 in all. Each figure included for overheads and expenses on the member concerned, itself a way of paying amounts by formula.

RATE OF PROGRESS AND CASH FLOW COSTS

While the standard formulae all use broad-brush overall figures, they ignore the effects of varied speeds of work, expenditure and payment during a disturbed programme – or, for that matter, the undisturbed one used as the datum. To illustrate some possibilities, the cash flow situation for the process shop, the more disturbed building, is shown in Table 20.2. This compares the rate of payment expected originally with that achieved, using only the contract values to keep the comparison direct. No preliminaries or external works are allowed, the figures being those used for the preceding inflation calculation. They therefore also exclude nominated sub-contractors,

who were either paid early (in the case of steelwork) or performed late, so avoiding delay in payment.

It is clear that the original programme gave a rather flat payment rate, the normally expected 'S' curve flattening between weeks 13 and 20. The achieved rate started late, as weeks 1–4 were blank. Thereafter, the flat period was squeezed somewhat and payment generally attenuated. The period beyond, when completion should have occurred, showed severely reduced payments. While the extra direct costs of disturbance need to be looked at for additional overhead expense, the pattern being described also suggests the possibility of a relative loss in relation to the original work, because of the flattened 'S' curve and even without disturbance.

The more simple case is that of financing charges on the retention held until and after practical completion. This was at the rate of 3 per cent until that event and then 1.5 per cent, the standard JCT arrangement. The effect

Table 20.2   Laboratory project, extra interest on retention due to delay (process shop only). Retention 3%, interest 12%

Weeks	Original				Achieved		
	Flow	Cumulative	Blocks	Interest	Flow	Cumulative	Blocks	Interest
1–4	116,400	116,400		257.88	—	—		—
5–8	47,790	164,190		92.64	58,200	58,200		209.52
9–12	148,810	313,000	313,000	247.25	113,960	172,160	172,160	378.70
13–16	73,700	386,700		102.04	103,540	275,700		315.40
17–20	94,820	481,520		105.03	59,680	335,380		165.27
21–24	149,230	630,750	317,750	123.98	110,270	445,650	273,490	274.83
25–28	113,650	744,400		62.94	138,190	583,840		306.14
29–32	69,700	814,100		19.30	116,540	700,380		225.91
33–36	28,400	842,500	211,750	—	44,020	744,400	298,750	73.14
37–40					28,190	772,590		39.03
41–44					3,330	775,920		3.69
45–48					3,640	779,560	35,160	3.02
49–52					6,970	786,530		3.86
53–56					27,570	814,100		7.63
57–60					28,400	842,500	62,940	—
				1,011.06				2,006.14
						Less original:		1,011.06
						Extra interest:		995.08

of the prolonged holding of the full level is shown in Table 20.2. While the fund did not start to accumulate until one period late and then built up more slowly than intended, it was then held for six extra periods, during which a comparatively small share of the fund accumulated. The complete position over extra financing of retention was:

Process shop
Before practical completion, as Table 20.2   995
Less allowance for non-qualifying weeks,
   i.e. those subject to extension only   100
                                         ————
                                         895
After practical completion, retention of
   1.5% on £842,500 = £12,638 held for
   an extra period of 17 weeks at 12% per
   annum interest   496
                                        ————   1,391

Laboratory
Before practical completion   202
After practical completion   202
                                        ————   404

Preliminaries
Before practical completion   89
After practical completion   89
                                        ————   178
                                             ————
                                       £1,973

The much smaller excess expense was to be expected for the laboratory, where the total extension was less and the redistribution of payments was less radical. It should be observed that a redistribution can alternatively reduce a contractor's costs under this head by pushing payments into the closing periods. This could be offset against a relevant gross loss, but not deducted in the absence of such a loss. A relevant gross loss is not easy to define, but broadly would be one due to overall prolongation, rather than due to a localised disturbance, not having wider repercussions.

The more complex and significant case is that of capital utilisation. The contractor, as is necessary practice, had made some form of allocation of working capital to the project, based upon his rate of expenditure. This in turn may be assumed to bear a close relationship to the rate of payment, subject to the considerations mentioned in Chapter 3, such as front-loading the pricing structure. How he makes the allocation is another question.

It is clear that no contractor actually deposits the required amount in a piggy bank on the mantelpiece. In most cases, there will not be an absolutely specific allocation of funds within the organisation. Broadly, what is happening is that a contractor decides about work he might take on by reference to his overall capitalisation, cash flow prospects and other forecast

workload. It is generally considered that somewhere between 20 and 30 per cent of annual turnover is needed as working capital to finance operations. This takes account of what is needed to pay bills ahead of being paid (not all bills, but especially site wages and including the costs of obtaining work and many head office charges), to fund such matters as retention and to cover the unevennesses which are bound to occur. These include claims amounts and the late recovery of profit!

Given a definite and maintained programme for any project, the contractor can calculate fairly closely where he is going. Given the circumstances which he encountered on the present project, he is faced with an attenuation of his programme and a need to engage his capital over an extended period. It is not adequate to argue that, say, £1,000,000 tied up over 6 months is the same as £500,000 tied up over 12 months. The question is: did the contractor know in advance that he would be tying up his capital over a longer period, but would actually need rather less of it? If not, he could not reduce his allocation and release some for other purposes.

Within the present project, the comparatively minor delay to the laboratory did not allow the contractor to reassess his overall financial position in such a way as to reallocate his capital within his broader strategy. In the case of the process shop, there was considerably more delay, but it still cropped up in instalments. Only in the closing stages, when the floor went wrong, might it even be suggested that there was a reasonable opportunity to reduce what was being allowed within head office philosophy. Again it is emphasised that this is not a matter of precise shuffling of funds, but of taking a total view over prospects.

A possible level of ascertainment, and that adopted, was to use the original contract amounts only, as follows:

Process shop (£1,617,500 at 22.5% capital and 12% interest = £43,673 p.a.)

Contract period	36 weeks
Disturbance period	53 weeks
Reduction for final	
run-down period of floor	4 weeks
Net excess period	13 weeks

Allow last £43,673 × 13/52 = 10,918

Laboratory (£2,834,000 at 22.5% capital and 12% interest = £76,518 p.a.)

Contract period	48 weeks
Disturbance period	53 weeks
(no reduction)	
Excess period	5 weeks

Allow last £76,518 × 5/52 = 7,358

———

£18,276

The use of the original amounts allows for the inclusion of overhead recovery in the variations, etc. in the final account. The extended time

for these is not included in the above calculations. The present amounts ascertained represent what is needed to fund the loss and expense elements in their effect on progress.

It will depend on how the percentage levels are ascertained from the contractor's records as to whether the amounts already given for extra interest on retention should be allowed separately as they have been, or included in the general extra financing charges. In all these areas there is room for some difference of approach to the goal, so that calculations would be structured differently, with the final figure hopefully close in each method.

OTHER HEAD OFFICE COSTS

There remain several costs at head office which virtually defy segregation between projects, such as rent on premises (or equivalent capital charges) and insurances of various kinds. These can only be ascertained by going back over several years' figures, and so following the judicial exhortation given in *Peak Construction* v. *McKinney* (see Ch. 10). Examination produced a reasonable assessment for present purposes of 2.35 per cent on site-based costs:

Primary loss and expense items   £156,780 at 2.35% = £3,684

LOSS OF PROFIT ON OTHER WORK FORGONE

As explained in Chapter 15, this is not the addition of profit on loss and expense amounts, as these are intended only to put the contractor back in the position he would have been in had disturbance of regular progress not taken place. Rather, it is profit forgone elsewhere because of the intrusion of the extra volume of work and delays into the contractor's planned business activities. As such it was dependent here, as always, upon several contingencies.

The first was the availability of extra work and the second the credibility of the disturbance encountered actually leading to a probability of its loss from the order book. The contractor was able to demonstrate that during the progress of the present project he was running with quite a full load and that there was enough work about of a suitable variety for him to expect to obtain some of it. In fact, he was obtaining work steadily. This met the first criterion sufficiently, as only *probability* is required under it.

The second was more awkward. It was very difficult to argue that the addition of less than 1 per cent to the contractor's workload over the period, taking the figure of £30,000,000 used in the Eichleay calculation, could in itself have deflected other work. But if this position be taken to its rigid conclusion, it would mean that no contractor suffering proportionately small losses on a number of concurrent contracts could ever recoup anything. Any large contractor would regularly be financing the misdeeds (from his point of view) of employers. It was necessary to look at the position in relation to what was happening generally, and this was that several contracts were being afflicted by disturbance of regular progress to an extensive degree. On this

basis, the present project had to take its share, and so an allowance was made. (Without this, the case study would of course be lacking!) The principle is one which receives differences of interpretation, although the present view is that reimbursement is frequently justified.

Arriving at an amount presents two further questions: the sum on which it is based and the percentage to apply. For the former, the whole of the loss and expense was taken, as the contractor's order book was full. The only really arguable item was that for extra financing charges, on the basis that this could be interpreted as including reward for capital which was by way of profit. It was demonstrated that the level of 12 per cent did not actually reward those running the enterprise, but simply dealt with borrowing as such.

The percentage aspect allowed of several possibilities:

(a) That included in the tender, a level of 3.3 per cent. This was just an aim, and not necessarily a reality. It therefore could not be taken alone.
(b) That actually achieved, a level of 3.1 per cent. This had more claim to be used, as it was real. It did, however, represent what had happened against the background of the tender as embodied in the contract sum. This could well differ from the climate in which work was being obtained during the currency of the project, and so of work which was arguably being forgone.
(c) That being included in current tenders, a level of 3.6 per cent. This was due to some upturn in the work coming into the market allowing more advantageous tenders. It was still conjectural at the stage of settlement.
(d) That which would result, being actual loss. It would have been possible to wait and then average a representative selection of contracts (without their loss and expense amounts!). It was decided to assume some shortfall in profit realisation, as was happening in the actual project, but to pitch this at less than 0.2 per cent.

A figure of 3.5 per cent was therefore agreed, based on a shortfall of 0.1 per cent. The ascertainment of profit forgone and the final total for all loss and expense became:

Primary loss and expense		156,780
Secondary loss and expense		
Head office staff	9,500	
Interest on retention	1,973	
Extra financing costs	18,276	
Rent, insurance, etc.	3,684	3,433
		£190,213
Profit on other work at 3.5%		6,657
		£196,870

The amount for secondary loss and expense may be compared with the results of the standard formulae given before:

Loss and expense amounts, as above	33,433
Amount assessed as in variations	20,407
	£53,840

Hudson and Emden gave £68,840 and Eichleay gave £57,570. The first pair make no deduction for the margin for overheads in variations, etc. In the case of Eichleay, it depends on how the figures used for final account values are extracted from the accounts, that is whether variations on any excessive scale are isolated and allowance made in using the formula. As used in this study, they are reasonable. Nevertheless, the relative closeness of the three results is a matter of some surprise and was *not* produced by reworking the arithmetic of the case study until it emerged! Formulae can often be much further out.

Some final comments

Here the study proper ends, but a few notes may be added. In most places throughout, the distinction between contractor and sub-contractor has been ignored, because it has been irrelevant. It has also been ignored in the interests of simplicity here and there, in cases where there might actually be a difference in the figures, but not in the principles involved. The need for a two-tier system of negotiation and calculation should be apparent. It is also possible to take the principles illustrated and transfer them into the dispute situations which crop up between contractor and sub-contractor without the employer being involved at all, or even those in which there is a triangular negotiation going on. Each depends on its own set of contract documents and procedures, but is essentially the same.

Numerous subsidiary features can appear in a dispute situation, which have not been covered. Thus there may be effects stemming from the shift in timing following delay, such as seasonally different working conditions (for better or for worse) or running continuous activities so that they straddle holiday periods or similar occasions. The most common cause of delay and expense, it is widely believed, is delayed or changed instructions. Except for the really major cases of change, these too have been excluded, because they add nothing new. When they consist of a string of small instructions, it is not practicable to illustrate them meaningfully in a book. Then there are the 'neutral' causes, such as weather and government activity, which have to be extracted from the reckoning. All that could be said in a theoretical example would be 'extract them', which becomes tedious and so has not been said.

What has been said at the risk of tedium is that the methods of

calculation have regularly been simplified or sometimes distorted in the cause of explanation, rather than wooden, repetitive instruction. Here it is being said again – so may the point be taken and excused! The other case studies do illustrate one or two of the more interesting points not taken here, but by way of compensation give no calculations at all.

How the employer felt about the outcome must be conjectured. It might be wondered, for instance, whether he would have wanted the process shop annexes, had he realised the disturbance costs he would be facing compared with the costs of straight variations. The facilities might have been invaluable, of course. The section on 'Client's risk analysis' over such issues in Chapter 1 may be considered, as well as the virtues of thinking things through before starting on site. The annexes did appear as a change of mind quite early, but then such things frequently do.

Be all of this as it may, the financial outcome for completeness sake, excluding the infusion plant supplementary contract, was:

Contract sum, less contingencies	4,451,500
Net addition for variations	313,970
Loss and expense amounts	196,870
	£4,962,340

There have been many worse.

CHAPTER 21

Minor case study: Factory Project

Particulars of the works
Main events and their results
The approach to settlement

This case study concerns the execution of moderately sized works by a moderately sized local contractor. The works were performed in fairly cramped conditions at the works of an existing and fully operative manufacturing business, and covered new works and alterations, with some phasing. Each of these features led to the problems encountered. By comparison with the case study in Chapters 19 and 20, there is much more technical detail given here but, in compensation, no figures at all. The procedures followed, once problems have arisen, are quite good – maybe someone had read a sound book or two! The material in this chapter is, however, also used as the basis for the outline discussion of the comprehensive claim approach in Chapter 23 and may be read with this in mind.

Particulars of the works

CONTRACT DETAILS

The contract form was the IFC 1984 contract, using the with quantities option within it. It was on a fixed price basis, except for statutory fluctuations. A sectional completion supplementary condition was not used – despite the phasing required.

SCOPE OF THE WORKS

The general layout is shown in Fig. 21.1. The main items were:

(a) Construction of a research and development bay on an area of the employer's site which was virtually unused and easily accessible from the highway. The building was a steel-framed cladded shed with a free-standing structure inside, containing a large installation (the 'maxi-machine') and with a control facility adjacent at upper level. There was a sub-station internally and a system of ducts in the concrete ground floor.

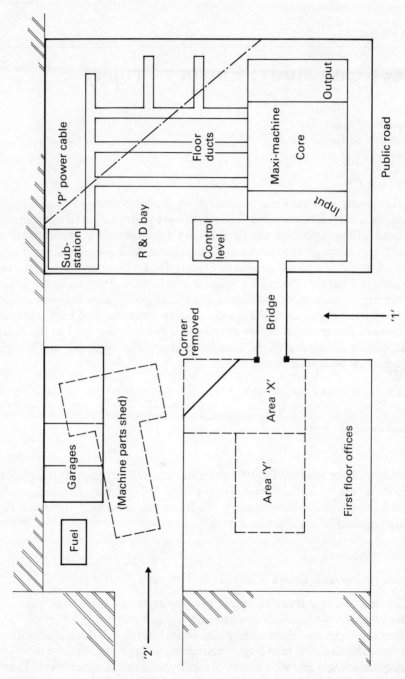

Fig. 21.1 Factory project, general site layout

(b) Alterations at first-floor level to Area 'X' of existing offices over a stores building, removal of a corner of the building at both floor levels and construction of a first-floor bridge linking to the control facility in the R & D building.

(c) Demolition of a single-storey machine parts shed adjoining the stores building and construction of a range of maintenance garages and a fuel pit.

Within the whole, the steel frame of the R & D bay and electrical work generally were by named sub-contractors, as were other elements of work. The provision and installation of the maxi-machine were by a direct contractor and were to proceed during the contract works. Other services included in the contract were essentially simple, as the employer was installing special elements himself, after the construction period.

PROGRAMME OF THE WORKS

A simplified bar line programme of what was intended is given in Fig. 21.2(a). This was produced by the contractor from the phasing requirements set out in the preliminaries of the contract bills, which showed a sequence and gave a single completion date, with a statement that the contractor should give adequate notice in consultation with the works engineer of when he would require to enter particular portions of the site. The contractor provided information during pre-contract discussions as a master programme, which the IFC contract does not actually require, of which the key points now indicated by the bar chart were:

(a) Construct the R & D bay, with Access '1' available   week 1 to week 30

(b) Maxi-machine, proceeding within last and involving integration of contractor's supporting and enclosing work   week 15 to week 30

(c) Demolition of machine parts shed and construction of garages and fuel pit, with Access '2' becoming available as a result   week 5 to week 15

(d) Construct bridge and perform alterations to existing offices, etc. so restricting height of Access '1'   week 20 to week 25

The contract bills stated that obligations and restrictions would apply, as referred to in clause 3.6.2, over the following:

(a) Access, due to the need for prior demolition work, and to give notice before Access '2' could be cleared by factory users.

(b) Working space, due to the same reasons.

(c) Order of working, due to the need to enter the offices at a late stage of the works.

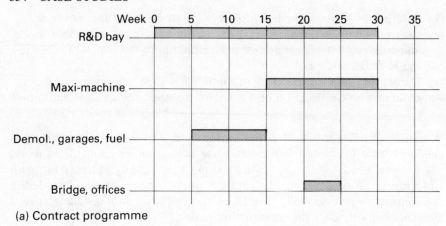

(a) Contract programme

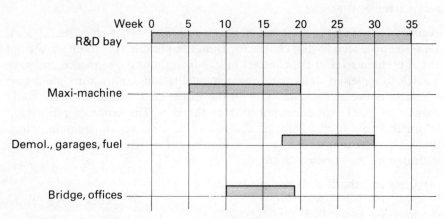

(b) Achieved programme

Fig. 21.2 Factory project, summarised programme: (a) contract programme; (b) achieved programme

There *was* only one completion date, despite the mandatory nature of the period for altering the offices. This could have proved difficult (see *Bramall & Ogden* v. *Sheffield* in Ch. 10), but was accepted throughout by the parties.

Main events and their results

CHANGES DURING PROGRESS

The employer found that he could obtain a very favourable price for the maxi-machine, provided he had this work done earlier than he had planned. He decided to accept this proposition, so that several consequences resulted:

(a) It became necessary to erect the steelwork and cladding at the end of the

building housing the machine ahead of the rest (rather than the reverse) and earlier than had been anticipated. This threw out the contractor's order of providing foundation work and necessitated extra work by way of temporary protection for the maxi-machine, which cluttered the main working area for the bay.

(b) Revised floor duct layouts and details arose from the technical nature of the machine chosen and from afterthoughts about the layout of subsidiary machines within the bay. This led to working inside the newly constructed building envelope, with uneconomical plant and the need to provide clean conditions during concurrent installation of the main machine. During excavation for the ducts, an existing power cable at 'P', serving another part of the works, was unexpectedly encountered crossing the area.

(c) The bridge from the existing offices was needed earlier, due to commissioning of the machine. This restricted movement from Access '1' and led to complications in altering the offices adjoining, and these were exacerbated by a requirement to alter more offices than had been foreseen (Area 'Y'). As these were areas still occupied by staff, weekend working and other special measures were introduced by agreement.

In addition to these changes, it became necessary to postpone the demolition of the machine parts shed, so that this could remain in use during the early stages of the maxi-machine installation. This had several effects:

(a) Access '2' was not available on time, affecting the intention to circulate construction vehicles from one access to the other as work built up, also complicated by the early erection of the bridge.

(b) Construction of the garages was deferred, so that the contractor could not use them for temporary storage of materials. That he had intended to do so had not been made clear in his tender or during pre-contract discussions.

(c) Construction of the fuel pit became difficult at the planned time and was delayed by the contractor. It was then subject to late changes of design in moderately important respects.

The revised programme actually followed is set out in Fig. 21.2(b), showing the rearranged sequence. An overall prolongation of five weeks occurred, spread evenly from the end of week 5 onwards for the R & D bay.

TIMING OF CHANGES

While the changes were quite drastic, by way of variations, etc., had they all been decided upon and instructed at the beginning, it would have been possible for the contractor to have revised his programme to accommodate them and for the contract sum to have been adjusted by valuing the effects as variations. This could even have been tied up entirely in advance of work proceeding.

With events as they actually occurred, the first line of enquiry is how far agreement of variations is still suitable. The basic work of, for instance,

placing concrete in the foundations, floor and ducts of the R & D bay still ranks for measurement and valuation, even if it is performed in different conditions from those envisaged in the contract. They may be distinctly more awkward than would have applied had the contractor been able to carry out a considered replanning, but still be performed without disturbance in the sense of clause 4.11, which is the last provision of the contract to be invoked.

This becomes a major consideration for the contractor, who is required to give notice as soon as he can of expected disturbance, but not of changed conditions for variation purposes. In this instance, he was able to warn quite early over the revision due to the advancing of installing the maxi-machine, although the full effects of it in terms of clean conditions and other secondary effects were not immediately evident. He therefore did so, even though he could not clearly discern the extent of disturbance. On the other hand, he found the delay in demolition of the machine parts building on him at the last moment, when he was about to implement his programme.

When a contractor is in any doubt about whether a loss and expense situation is developing, he must prudently give notice as soon as he has sensible grounds to believe so. This enables all concerned to be warned and take any possible avoiding action, and at the least be ready to keep records rather than to try to 'invent facts' afterwards. In the present case, had the employer sounded out the contractor through the architect, he might have decided that the likely extra cost to the contractor would outweigh the saving on the price of the machine (see the example of risk analysis in Ch. 1). This sort of action is quite different from the 'cry wolf' attitude which reacts every time a revised bending schedule for one beam is issued.

An architect also has to decide how to react. He cannot reject any reasonable approach from the contractor out of hand, but should not rise to every bait by wellnigh agreeing that something is due. Also, while it is for him to decide whether there is a case and then whether to ascertain the amount himself, in practice he often needs to discuss with the quantity surveyor just where the boundary is to be drawn. Here for instance, there was room for manœuvre over what were to be variations and what loss and expense. A quantity surveyor is entitled to deal and should deal with the former on contract terms under clause 3.7, simply because an instruction has been issued, whether the contractor or the architect acts over some element in any way or not under clause 4.11. Duplication or a gap (if the contractor is not alert) can therefore arise by lack of communication. This is a good reason for the quantity surveyor to do the ascertainment in any case.

The approach to settlement

CONTRACTOR'S OVERALL ANALYSIS

While the disturbance factor here was quite considerable, what the contractor had to do first of all was to decide whether there were clearly separable elements in his claim. From these some progress could then be made towards

isolating the effects, rather than using the unacceptable method of 'cost, less valuation'. The narration of events above both helps and hinders here, because it divides affairs up geographically on the site. Geography, time and operational relations vary in their importance. When things go wrong one step at a time, this progression may help proper segregation or merely lead to an incremental or overlapping build-up of total confusion. In this case, he decided to apply under several heads for loss and expense. This he did promptly for the first six items, while giving broad warning of the last two:

(a) Disturbance of sequence and timing of the superstructure of the R & D bay, as stated separately above: the primary effect.
(b) Revision of the floor ducts, also as stated separately above: the secondary effect.
(c) Work inside the existing offices, both due to the bridge being early (although itself constructed without problems) and to working partly in occupied spaces.
(d) Access problems, due to the bridge and the late removal of the machine parts shed, but not to the order of erecting the R & D superstructure.
(e) Storage problems off site owing to the garages not being available.
(f) The localised problem of the fuel pit.
(g) A general loss of productivity on other work, due to the sheer level of disturbance caused by the specific matters.
(h) The general question of prolongation, affecting supervision and preliminaries.

This division had much to commend it in its logic, although it meant care in practical segregation. The first three items had most risk of confusion with the valuation of variations. They also involved loss and expense claims from named sub-contractors for steel and services, which had to be taken separately by the contractor, but included in the whole. While sufficient division is needed, an excess is better avoided, as there comes a point at which overlapping relevant matters do not allow such finesse. The contractor may find that he lacks flexibility in negotiations as a result.

He proceeded to put forward separate claims for each of these, in two main groups: those flowing from the maxi-machine decision, and those flowing from the delay over releasing the existing shed. The architect immediately referred these to the quantity surveyor, who established some base lines with the contractor over what would be included in his variation account. The great virtue of this co-operative approach all round contrasts with the drawn battle lines approach so often encountered. Some comment on presenting a consolidated, single-claim document at completion is made in Chapter 23.

Each element of loss and expense is discussed separately. The total amount of extension of time was assessed after practical completion, following several intermediate extensions. It was made on the lines considered in Chapters 19 and 20.

PRIMARY EFFECT ON THE R & D BAY

This was related to the erection of the superstructure. The contractor was concerned to reduce the total delay effect, in his own interests as well as the employer's. It may be wondered whether a larger contractor might have found it easier to mitigate the loss and expense in the process, by a concentration of resources at particular points, so that work went on in tidier parcels. It is suggested that the extent of mitigation which is reasonable will vary with the managerial capabilities and resources of the actual contractor: the employer probably gained initially on price by engaging a smaller contractor with less overheads and must expect to lose when trouble comes. While a contractor should mitigate, it is the employer who causes the disturbance.

The subsidiary items in the loss and expense settlement were:

(a) Extra costs of delivering ready-mixed concrete for the area of the floor beyond the section required for the maxi-machine. These included problems of manœuvring lorries and receiving concrete in the restricted area available between the bay and the still-standing machine parts shed. It was agreed that all costs of placing concrete, once it was shot from the lorries, were part of the revised measured prices for working in conditions dissimilar from those envisaged in the bill prices.

(b) Steelwork sub-contractor's loss and expense working in phases, especially setting out work, extra temporary bracing and the difficulty of handling steel and using a smaller crane inside the area of the second phase (see under 'Subsidiary problem with the steelwork' below for a further three-way item arising from this).

(c) Standing time associated with the provision of temporary protection for the maxi-machine, while construction work otherwise was going on. It was recognised that most of the standing time due to the bringing in of large and delicate parts of the machine had been allowed in the contract sum, but that an element of excess arose out of this occurring earlier when more, dirtier carcassing work was in progress.

(d) Additional supervisory time in dealing with the foregoing by reorganising work, setting out and co-operating with the machine installer.

Some arbitrariness may be detected about what has gone into variations here and what into loss and expense. For example, more loss and expense could have gone into (a) and less into (b). These are problems associated with a proper interpretation of the contract, as distinct from a sensible reimbursement of the contractor and husbanding of the employer's resources.

SUBSIDIARY PROBLEM WITH THE STEELWORK

A relatively small problem arose over the steelwork mentioned under (b) above, due to the need for extra temporary bracing. The nominated sub-contractor presented his shop drawings to the architect, as a development

of the architect's general arrangement drawings, which simply gave the main layout of structural work. These drawings were a revision of what the sub-contractor had prepared when submitting his original tender. The architect checked them over in relation to the permanent members shown (there were variations) and passed them back through the contractor as 'approved'. In passing, it may be noted that the IFC 84 contract has no provisions for design by the contractor or any of his sub-contractors, and it is widely held to be a 'construct only' contract, like the JCT 80 form. Perhaps more critically, when the architect unequivocally approves a design he is assuming a responsibility for it, a point taken up in detail in the present author's *Design and Build Contract Practice*.

Such a burden may be considered fair in the contractual circumstances, but all that the architect had actually done was to check that the scheme fitted into his own design. He did not check the members structurally. As it happened none of this caused any trouble over the permanent work. What did was the positioning of some of the temporary bracing which was in the way of some of the contractor's own permanent work, which had to be constructed before the bracing was removed. The contractor did not notice this aspect, but simply passed the approved drawings on to the sub-contractor without comment.

The steelwork was erected before the discrepancy was discovered. The sub-contractor presented an item for the costs of adaptation to the contractor, who in turn presented them with his own costs of delay to the architect, as being loss and expense. The architect rejected them, stating that the contractor should have noticed and was responsible for co-ordinating information and warning of discrepancies. As a supplementary point, he stated that the sub-contractor should have been aware of the permanent work which was affected. The sub-contractor's answer was that the architect should have been at least as aware. The scene was set for a dispute which might have revolved for the duration of settlement of the final account. Clearly, the contractor had to pay the sub-contractor, whatever happened, unless the sub-contractor accepted the architect's point about him. The architect was equally clearly following a safe line by refusing to consider the item initially. Until the position was cleared, he could only compromise the employer by admitting anything.

Eventually, it was agreed that the architect had given the contractor the impression by his actions that he had approved everything on the sub-contractor's drawings. Further it was agreed, in the tight circumstances existing when the installation of the maxi-machine was being shifted to the early stages of the programme, any question of the contractor being able to co-ordinate every piece of information in advance was uncertain. He was therefore given the benefit of the doubt and paid for the costs incurred.

This is an instance in which the precise lines of liability arise not so much from abstract contractual analysis, as from the pattern of events interpreted with some leniency when the moderately sized contractor had been placed under strain by the changes introduced into the scheme.

SECONDARY EFFECT ON THE R & D BAY

Once the steelwork and cladding were erected, the contractor faced the subsidiary effects. These were twofold: the constricting effects of the surrounding structure on his work within it, mainly more concreting, and the extra care needed and protective measures involved in dealing with the concurrent work on the maxi-machine itself – the cause of the disturbance. He could, of course, have delayed the erection of the steelwork surrounding the area until all the concreting had been completed, but this he judged less desirable in his own interests of overall progress on the various trades engaged on the works.

Whether this was also less desirable here in the interests of the employer is a distinct question, although the answer is often the same in many cases, as the employer is seeking to maintain completion. There is a financial break-even point for each party between cost and return, and the two points are unlikely to be absolutely identical . The architect has no power to interfere in what the contractor actually does, only to judge it afterwards, so that it usually becomes a rather academic question. The contractor has an obligation over delay to 'use his best endeavours' and to 'do all that may reasonably be required' by the architect. These mean 'best' and 'all', so that the contractor must act decisively, but they are still fairly loose and are usually held not to oblige him to take much positive action without extra payment (and this the contract does not cover).

The position was complicated, as work proceeded, by the discovery of the power cable 'P', which presumably the employer should have known about (unless a previous owner had had it laid and not said anything). At least, the contractor could not be expected to know. At such a point, it becomes very difficult to segregate the effects of the several matters, and really unnecessary, as it is possible to rely on the blanket expression of clause 4.11 'any one or more of the matters' to which it refers.

The resulting settlement involved the following:

(a) Continuing extra costs of concreting, which included working with special care once the maxi-machine was being installed, all paid for as variations.
(b) Breaking up ducts and the surrounding floor prior to relaying, paid for as variations by daywork.
(c) Standing and reorganisation costs while the daywork was going on, paid for as loss and expense, involving several trades which could not work in the disturbed conditions or had to move materials and equipment to allow it to proceed.
(d) Further loss and expense (mainly waiting and reorganisation) due to the discovery of the cable, checking by the employer of its significance and arranging for the electricity board to deal with it. Additional excavation and attendance by the contractor were paid for as a variation by daywork.
(e) Suspension of the work of trades causing dirt and vibration during critical periods of the installation of the maxi-machine. This was dealt

with as loss and expense and covered some wastage of materials which deteriorated due to the delay.

(f) Additional supervision, again due to disorganisation and co-operation with the machine installer.

Again, the problem of achieving clear demarcation between variations and loss and expense may be noted.

WORK INSIDE THE OFFICES

The instruction to carry out additional work in Area 'Y' of the offices was a straightforward variation in a rather small special section, and not of sufficient magnitude to constitute an unacceptable enlargement of the contract (compare and contrast the infusion plant in Ch. 19). Even with the requirement to work at weekends, valuation was quite normal to perform. On a strict reading of the contract, if it did not include the revisions of 1987 and as there was no requirement for the contractor to work special hours or abstain at any time, he might have declined to take on work which was subject to such obligations and restrictions, but he did not. As there was a requirement to phase the works, and this had been amended, it might have been possible for the architect to have hung the timing requirement on this, with a measure of special pleading.

Two difficulties in negotiations arose early on:

(a) Both the original and extra areas of offices were to be partly in use during the alterations, requiring careful operations, carried out cleanly and quietly, and subject to unpredictable delays and piecemeal working.
(b) The major work concerned was to have been sub-let by the contractor and consent had been obtained before the variation was issued. It may be added that the position would probably have been resolved similarly had consent not been obtained so early. The sub-contractor in question was unable to perform the work at the revised date and the best alternative firm was substantially dearer in quoting for the original scope of work.

In principle, all of these effects were susceptible to assessment by the loss and expense approach, although whether they were able to be 'ascertained' is doubtful. It was eventually agreed, before the work was carried out, to place the whole within clause 3.7 and have it valued by daywork, with that of the actual sub-contractor based upon special terms. On top of this valuation, a special allowance was added to cover the intensive supervision required.

The erection of the bridge, breaking through into the existing building and removal of the corner and rebuilding on the splay were all performed at bill rates at the same time as the alterations, allowance being made in protection items for the extra care needed. The main extra requirement was for clear segregation of costs of measured work and daywork on site.

ACCESS PROBLEMS

There had been special provisions in the contract for using Access '1' initially and then Access '2' as well, once the machine parts shed was cleared away.

This was what happened, but the shed remained in place much longer than stated. This effectively introduced a variation of obligations and restrictions under clause 3.6.2. Alternatively, it could be seen as a 'failure . . . to give . . . ingress' under clause 4.12.6, so leading to reimbursement of loss and expense. It was actually given as an instruction to postpone removal of the shed, from which the other consequences flowed, so again giving loss and expense as the correct outcome.

In this instance, there were no ordinary measured or lump sum items in the contract bills to vary in isolation. This is typical of such an occurrence, as is the lack of easily verifiable cost data for what would have happened but for the change. Whether the adjustment of the contract sum is dealt with by variation or ascertainment is largely a matter of words: calculation starts from a narrow base and is similar. If it is from a base of variation, clause 3.7.6 allows for 'any addition to or reduction of' preliminaries items, *not* a pro rata adjustment. It was necessary to do this, to take into account adjustment of original amounts concealed within measured and preliminaries items generally. The parallel instance of preliminaries adjustment in Chapter 20 fills out this paragraph with calculations.

The main elements in the present instance were the extra time spent by every vehicle which entered the site until it left again, with the associated slower unloading and extra attendance, and the need to keep the small areas adjoining clear of whatever might otherwise have been dumped there. To the extent that vehicles belonged to merchants, it was not possible for the contractor to demonstrate that he incurred higher quotations for materials delivered in these conditions. Any general and wider drop in productivity was put forward separately.

STORAGE PROBLEMS

The talking point here was that the contractor had not stated when tendering that he intended to use the employer's new buildings for storage of materials. He won the day on the basis that he had shown early construction in his master programme, that there was no provision in the contract for partial possession by the employer leading to their early surrender, and that the lack of other space on site made their use a reasonable thing to posit.

With this established, it became fairly easy to deal with loss and expense on the basis of provision of extra space at the contractor's yard at a time-related charge, reflecting its non-availability for other purposes and costs due to congestion, with associated extra security and double handling costs from the yard to site. These were clear separate elements without a problem of segregation from costs which would have been incurred in the absence of the disturbance.

FUEL PIT

This was a simple case of late information for this one facility while it was under construction, leading to a straight allowance of standing time of labour and plant.

Had the information been delayed before work started, the contractor might have been expected to hold back until it was available, perhaps diverting his resources elsewhere meantime. This could have involved putting them on another project, and would have depended on what he had available as a smaller contractor. Properly, for him to do this, a postponement instruction would have been required. In its absence, he would have been entitled to go on working until the information failed to appear by the date on which he had requested it, and then have incurred his costs. He was not entitled or required to stop ahead of cast iron certainty (meaning something proper and in writing), until he was out of work. If he had, he might even have been risking action for failing to proceed regularly.

GENERAL LOSS OF PRODUCTIVITY

Much of the loss of productivity had been covered under the items isolated as disruptive. The contractor's contention was that the areas of work between these had suffered from the 'shadow' effect produced. A review of the programmes, proposed and actual, in Fig. 21.2 shows that the programme was considerably changed, while most of its major components were affected in detail. No one seriously considered that there had been no loss: the only question was how to ascertain it. In the nature of things, it was not possible to compare what should have happened with what had in any certain way. 'As-certain-ment' was not practicable. A somewhat parallel situation occurred in *J. Crosby & Sons Ltd* v. *Portland Urban District Council* (1967), when it was held that a lump sum might be awarded for overall delay and disorganisation, provided that this introduced no duplication with other amounts and no inadmissible profit allowance.

It was agreed that the site records showed discontinuities in the areas of work, with some information provided piecemeal and a tendency to smaller parcels of work than might have been expected. Against this, an inspection of costs, so far as any segregation could be achieved, suggested that nothing catastrophic had occurred. It was then agreed to treat most of the question as one of evaluation of work under varied conditions, as the other major changes had been introduced as variations. This had two advantages in aiding settlement: ascertainment was not used, while adjustment of measured rates could be introduced. The contractor was also happy, in that he could secure an overheads and profit margin. It is not always entirely clear in circumstances of this kind what basis should be used, and a doctrinaire split could have been engineered here: that chosen should generally be considered first before resorting to loss and expense. This time the parties came back to it!

The contractor proposed an allowance of 10 per cent of the actual labour and plant costs incurred for all relevant work. Eventually, it was agreed to allow 7.5 per cent of all work not accounted for in the other major items, other than:

(a) Internal linings of the R & D bay envelope and all painting work, as

these had proceeded at approximately the right time and were sub-let as entities as intended.
(b) The garages, as these had changed position in the programme, but had been performed in an orderly sequence, somewhat late. This had caused some extra expense in concreting work, which was valued in its own right as a lump sum.

PROLONGATION AND PRELIMINARIES

There had been a total extension of time of five weeks, none of it relating to the first five weeks of the construction period. Extra supervision costs had been allowed for:

(a) The R & D bay in respect of the primary and secondary effects, as given above. Here, extra major plant allowances had also been made.
(b) Alteration work in the existing offices.

It was agreed that these amounts effectively dealt with most of the prolongation effects of supervision (as well as the intensification effects), as it was largely a case of using the same personnel over longer periods. An allowance of one member of staff for three weeks was made to cover the extra supervision needed on the garages, due to their displacement into the closing weeks.

Other costs of a preliminaries nature were those of access and storage. Both of these had already received separate treatment, covering most aspects. It was agreed to pay extra costs in moving the small site offices due to the sequencing of work. These included an allowance for staff disturbance and working for a short while from the contractor's head office.

There was a mild flirtation with the elements of financing charges and inflation due to prolongation, before the suggestion was dropped. These elements are worked out in Chapter 20, over a much larger contract. Here, a 25 weeks' contract was extended by 5 weeks due to disturbance of regular progress, and this appears quite small, as it was in a period of low interest rates and inflation. The effects would have looked more persuasive for an ascertainment, given a contract of 25 months and 5 months' extension in more adverse conditions. Certainly, it is easier to locate amounts when they are larger. As is also suggested in Chapter 22, the simple question of there being a smaller contractor can affect the outcome unfairly. He may be performing smaller contracts, but suffering an accumulation of small losses which in total are significant. He should fight for his case, often another difficulty given his size.

Minor case study: Flats Project

Particulars of works
Main events and their results
Comments on the narrative

This case study concerns rehabilitation of privately owned, rented blocks of flats and is given as narrative only without calculations, as for the study immediately preceding. However, in this instance comments on the implications are excluded from the narrative and given in the latter part of the chapter, referenced by bracketed numbers following paragraphs in the narrative. This allows the reader to form an opinion, if so wished, before comparing it with the suggestions offered.

Particulars of the works

The contract form was in the IFC 1984 form, with a priced specification and with a sectional completion supplement based upon that available for use with the JCT main form. (1)

The works covered six blocks of four storey flats, arranged semi-detached in three buildings. A longitudinal section through Blocks 'A' and 'B', as typical, is shown in Fig. 22.1. The main elements of work were:

(a) New partitions and doors to revise internal planning.
(b) Replacement windows.
(c) Refitting kitchens and bathrooms, and renewing services and plumbing. The employer was to supply for fixing by the contractor: kitchen units, refrigerators, sinks and bathroom fittings.
(d) Hot water central heating.
(e) Making good internal finishings and redecorating.
(f) Sundry minor structural repairs, varying with the flat.
(g) New handrails and finishings to common stairs.

Named sub-contractors were included in the contract for:

(a) Services, plumbing and central heating.
(b) Electrical installations.
(c) Stair finishings.

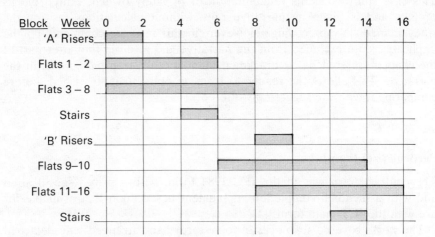

(a) Typical section

(b) Proposed first part of programme

Fig. 22.1 Flats project, summarised programme: (a) typical section; (b) proposed first part of programme

The flats in each block were to be vacated successively and rehabilitated before the next block was released to the contractor. The tenants from the first block were to move to alternative accommodation, the succeeding groups were to move into renovated flats and, finally, the first group was to move into the last block handed back. There was thus no overlap between blocks. With a period of 8 weeks for each block, this gave a total contract period of 48 weeks. (2)

The contractor's programme for the first two blocks is shown in Fig. 22.1, and it continued similarly for the remaining blocks. This indicated some aim to overlap minor elements between blocks, and so stretch beyond the exact wording of the contract, but was acceptable to the architect and the employer.

Main events and their results

BLOCK 'A'

Two tenants in the first block were two weeks late in moving out. The contractor asked for a week's extension of time on the basis of postponement of possession of the site. This the architect disputed, as only part of the initial site entitlement was affected. The contractor indicated that he would reserve his position. (3)

A consignment of kitchen units for two complete blocks was delivered in week 5, in accordance with the employer's schedule made available to tenderers. These did not fit and needed minor, but awkward, alterations in most cases, partly because the site dimensions of the flats varied. The contractor was instructed to make the alterations to the Block 'A' units, to order the supplier to make the remaining alterations and to check following batches before delivery. He required to be paid for the work involved and sought a further week's extension, which was granted. (4)

The plumbing and heating sub-contractor was sent off site for a two-week period while these problems were being resolved, under an instruction issued to him by the architect. This was too long for the contractor, who contended that he was delayed a further week, which the architect disputed. The electrical sub-contractor was not affected. Other trades employed by the contractor directly or as domestic sub-contractors were not seriously delayed, but had to work around what was going on, or failing to go on. (5)

The first two flats were completed by the end of week 8 and the whole block by the end of week 10. The contractor argued that he was justifiably behind by the two weeks' extension he was claiming on all of these flats, while the architect maintained that he was one week behind on the whole of the block. (6)

BLOCKS 'B' and 'C'

These two blocks ran to schedule, subject to starting late as a follow-on from the previous block. Again, two flats were handed over two weeks ahead of the rest for Block 'B', but not Block 'C'. (7)

BLOCK 'D'

As work began here on the main consignment of flats, following two weeks of advanced work on two flats, the plumbing and heating sub-contractor failed to appear to begin preparatory work. By the beginning of week 3 of the contract programme for the block he was insolvent. The architect hesitated for all that week and the next over what to do, as he explored various options. Early in week 5 on the block, he instructed the omission of the work from the contract under clause 3.3.3(c) and notified the contractor that the work would be performed by a person engaged directly by the employer. The contractor objected to the omission of work on which

he had included profit in his tender and argued that the architect could not act in this way.

As the contractor was unable to sustain his case that the architect could not issue such an instruction and that it was unreasonable for the employer to introduce someone to perform absolutely necessary work, the introduction of the direct contractor went ahead. The contractor switched his attack to claiming extension of time and loss and expense. Again, he sought loss of profit on the omitted work as part of the loss and expense. (8)

The block was finished six weeks later than was acceptable under the already extended time flowing from earlier events. When it became clear that this delay was developing, the contractor claimed an extension of this duration, while also noting that the float of two weeks which he had built up by finishing flats in each of the earlier blocks two weeks ahead was now lost, so prejudicing his completion even more. (9)

BLOCK 'E'

By what means it need not be asked, the employer persuaded four of the tenants of this block to move out into alternative accommodation four weeks earlier than was needed if the contractor were to have the programmed, unimpeded access to the whole block, given his actual state of progress. The architect then instructed the contractor to take possession of these flats at once and to proceed with work in them. The contractor did so after one week, but proceeded fairly slowly with the earlier elements of work. The architect suggested that he should be working faster, whereupon the contractor made one or two unrepeatable suggestions, but also pointed out that the trades needed for the following elements could not be released any sooner from Block 'D'. (10)

At this juncture, the contractor discovered that arbitration did not have to wait until after practical completion, as it does under the JCT standard form on most disputes, and requested the employer to concur in the appointment of an arbitrator over the several outstanding issues. This concentrated the minds of all participants, but did not produce any instant solutions. (11)

Work on the remaining four flats in the block began on completion of work to Block 'D'. The contractor made application for loss and expense due to work being out of phase. The architect contended that the employer had acted to mitigate the contractor's loss by bringing forward flats in Block 'E' and that the availability of flats in Block 'F' further helped. There was therefore, he concluded, little substance in the contractor's application. (12)

Four of the flats were handed over three weeks ahead of the programmed date, so enabling the employer to move tenants. Before the other four were completed, weaknesses in the existing roof were discovered. These caused delay to the service risers and tanks (installed by the direct contractor) for the remaining flats, as well as additional work to the roof itself. The flats were not handed over until four weeks after the programmed date, while the roof work went on for a further six weeks. The architect contended that

the contractor had been responsible for two weeks of the delay to the flats themselves, but accepted that the roof work had led to extra time for delivery of components and engaging suitable craftsmen. In reply, the contractor stated that the direct contractor had delayed beyond what was necessary, to the tune of one and a half weeks. (13)

BLOCK 'F'

In the case of this block also, the employer managed to move tenants out early as just noted, so making four flats available to the contractor three weeks ahead of due time. This was still somewhat ahead of what the contractor could absorb, quite apart from what he argued he was contractually bound to do.

It also accentuated the degree of disturbance which the contractor maintained he faced. He continued to state that he was put to extra expense by having to work in two blocks, even if they were in one building. The architect countered by insisting that work was still running at the same rate, it was just that it had been changed in its exact content at any one time during these closing stages. He conceded that there would be a more attenuated end to the project than had been planned, so extending some costs.

Owing to the need to work between blocks and in relation to the delays to the roof of Block 'E', some confusion crept into the co-ordination of the working of the contractor and the direct plumbing and heating contractor, despite the repetitive nature of the blocks. The architect held that the contractor had failed to provide programme detail as needed, while the contractor held that he was not responsible for the other person's programme, only for seeing that there was no clash. At any rate, there was a further delay of two weeks in finishing the final block. (14)

Comments on the narrative

As explained, these comments have been separated from the account of events, etc. to allow the reader to form an independent opinion, if so wished. In the rather confused occurrences described, and briefly at that, there is room for difference of opinion. The comments given here aim to light up certain aspects of affairs, perhaps by placing a particular interpretation on some of them.

In each case, the bracketed references following earlier paragraphs are given here before paragraphs to identify the topic.

PARTICULARS GIVEN

(1) The important matter contractually is the use of the sectional completion supplement. It is needed to cover the question of liquidated damages satisfactorily when there are several dates for handing parts of the works to

the employer. While the IFC contract does have a partial possession clause available as an optional extra, this clause is not adequate to protect the right of the employer to claim liquidated damages if there is an overrun on one or more sections, but they still finish ahead of the final (and only) completion date. This was demonstrated in the case of *Bramall and Ogden Ltd* v. *Sheffield City Council* considered in Chapter 10.

(2) What is not considered in any standard building contract, as distinct from civil engineering, is the question of phased possession. This occurs frequently enough, as in the present project. It only receives attention by implication in the provisions over obligations and restrictions imposed by the employer by the term 'in any specific order', as mentioned in Chapter 6 in connection with variations to them in IFC clause 3.6.3 and correspondingly in the JCT contract.

BLOCK 'A'

(3) IFC clause 2.2 mentions simply 'the giving of possession', following on clause 2.1 which specifically mentions 'Possession of the site shall be given'. This appears to envisage complete possession or none at all, so giving the advantage to the contractor in this first exchange. Had he just accepted the position by moving in and starting work, he would probably have lost his advantage by inferred acceptance of what had happened. He professed to have reserved his position, and perhaps he did, but the ultimate question (as ever) will be 'even if the event is a valid postponement of possession, did it actually cause delay sufficient to extend completion of the works?'

(4) These units were items ranking under clauses 2.4.9 and 4.12.4 as a supply by the employer, deficiency in performing which supply could lead to the contractor obtaining extension of time or reimbursement for loss and expense. The extension granted was clearly in order and so, later, might be extra payment if disturbance resulted. The contractor should have applied for such payment 'within a reasonable time of it becoming apparent' and he may well have lost his right at any rate to adequate reimbursement by not applying soon enough for records to be kept. There is little which could have been done to reduce the effect by counteraction by the architect: the units were there and the later batches were still a long time off.

It was reasonable enough for the contractor to accept an instruction to remedy the units, so long as he did nothing which made him responsible for them as units. It could have turned out less than reasonable for the employer, as he had two contractors who had dealt with the same units, so leaving doubt over ultimate suitability. On the other hand, the contractor should not have accepted responsibility for dealing with the supplier over altering the remaining units on site or for any checking of those yet to come. He might even have found himself having to visit the works. Although he might be paid for time expended, possible liability over what was supplied could return to him in the wrong circumstances. He should firmly leave these matters with the employer or his agent, presumably the architect or a clerk of works.

(5) The plumbing and heating sub-contractor was of the named variety, but this did not give the architect any more right to deal direct with him than with any other type of sub-contractor. Even with a nominated sub-contractor under the JCT contract there is no such right. Further, the nature of the dealing was to interfere with the contractor's site organisation and control, again something which the architect has no authority to do. Provided that the contractor was not asking something entirely out of reason by a week's extension, the architect was well advised to grant it and keep quiet! The sub-contractor himself might have complained had he not gone into liquidation so soon after.

When a relatively small disturbance effect is produced on workpeople in a small contract, the interpretation of 'regular progress . . . materially affected' in clause 4.11 needs care. In proportion to the size of the project, the disruption suffered here may have been as severe relatively as an intrinsically much larger one on a large project. It is its effect on *progress*, a relative matter, which is in question. There is a tendency in small projects to play down the effects, especially if the contractor is also small and perhaps not so well versed in contractual matters as his larger brethren. In an alterations contract, such as the present, there is also the problem of identifying disturbance in what may be an apparently less-controlled-looking scene at the best of times. More tolerance is often due.

(6) The contractor was working to his own programme, with two flats ahead of the rest, which had been tacitly accepted by the architect on behalf of the employer. However, it was not contractual in that it did not affect when the contractor was due to finish the block. All flats were due together, but could be earlier (see observations in Ch. 4 that the contractor is entitled to finish early). If his claim to two weeks extension was correct, he was clear, as that was how he had finished. If he was entitled to only one, as the architect maintained, then he was a week behind, even though two flats were ahead. No measure of trade-off was strictly possible. The two of them remained apart on the issue.

BLOCKS 'B' and 'C'

(7) No new problem existed here, work was still two weeks behind overall. As the availability of a block was dependent on completion of its predecessor, there could be no question of holding the final completion date at the original position, despite the delay on the first block. The failure to be early on part of the third block was just that: the contractor was not early, but still running as contract.

BLOCK 'D'

(8) It is established, by the case of *Percy Bilton* v. *Greater London Council* (see Ch. 7 for details of this and related cases), that delay reasonably resulting from the withdrawal of a nominated sub-contractor is the responsibility of the contractor and does not lead to extension of time, but that excess delay due

to the architect unreasonably failing to re-nominate does lead to extension of time. It would appear that the position is similar with a named sub-contractor under the present contract.

In the immediate instance, there was a delay by the architect, but hardly an unreasonable one in the circumstances. He was entitled to weigh the options in his client's interests: a rash decision could even have opened him to a charge of professional negligence. On top of this would have been the time required for the direct contractor to prepare and come on site. The reference in clause 3.3.4(b) to extension of time and loss and expense flowing from an instruction must be read in the light of the relevant clauses on those matters. These hold out remedies for the contractor when an instruction is not issued timeously, but not simply because there is an instruction. It is difficult to see that the mere omission of the work would lead to delay for the contractor.

Against this, there was the introduction of a direct contractor. If he did not fit in with the contractor's programme when once the period of reasonable delay has passed, the contractor would have cause to seek his remedies. These would arise under clause 3.11, which is stated to apply, and from this under the usual clauses 2.3 and 4.11.

The contractor raised the question of loss of profit as part of his loss and expense. As there was not disturbance of regular progress involved, he was on the wrong track: his entitlement to recompense was there, but arising out of the variation introduced. Part of the valuation, perhaps all of it, would be concerned with this element.

(9) In view of these remarks, the contractor was not entitled to the whole of the six weeks' extension represented by the overall delay. In fact, he was fortunate that the total delay was not longer. He was given two weeks, with the result that he had quite a problem to regain time in the period left to him. He had noted the loss of his two weeks' float, but this could not be adduced as further delay: it was there to help guard against a contingency such as had occurred, as well as his own domestic lapses. In any case, it did not give him a clear float, but just some margin on two flats in each block.

BLOCK 'E'

(10) It was helpful of the employer to try to move matters on by making some flats available early, no doubt with an eye to his own affairs rather than the contractor's problems. As it was half a block that was involved, it was not actually going to help the total finish, but might reduce the liability (if any) to liquidated damages. But the architect had no authority to instruct the contractor to take possession early, and the contractor need not have budged, once he was there. He was also beyond contractual reproach in not hurrying over the work, in view of the limited progress he could foresee, presumably with some justification.

This is one of those places where most of the standard contracts do nothing very well about regaining lost time. There is no power to instruct acceleration or anything which rearranges the programme to serve it. There

is only the obligation of the contractor in clause 2.3 (in this contract) to 'use constantly his best endeavours to prevent delay' and to 'do all that may be reasonably required [by the architect] . . . to proceed'. The contractor could easily have challenged on his authority to instruct, but he would have been ill-advised not to do his best by co-operating. Because it was an instruction, the contractor stood possibly to gain in the end, as discussed below.

(11) The contractor was quite correct procedurally, but not particularly wise practically. It was going to take some time for arbitration to start rolling, given that several moderately complex arguments were in prospect and that nothing really critical hung on speed. All that it would have done would have been to clarify the extension of time question, so removing doubt over what the contractor might do about his programme. He appeared to act out of frustration and without weighing the likely expense.

(12) The contractor's application would have fallen completely, had he gone ahead with the early batch of flats without an instruction. He would then have been seen as trying to regain time, and so mitigating everyone's losses, but at his own cost. As it was, he had obeyed an instruction, even if one not authorised by the contract. There was therefore an implied term that he would be paid for the costs of meeting the instruction. There was no variation to the works, but consequences which fell into the loss and expense category.

These centred around working in two blocks at once, so necessitating extra movements of the hoist and of gangs between Blocks 'D' and 'E', which were not under one roof. So far as the gangs were concerned, this meant shifting equipment more often and further than was necessary when adjoining flats were being altered. The effect for which the contractor sought recompense was the net extra expense, so that any saving (as mentioned by the architect) on loss and expense already building up would be automatic. The benefit suggested by the advancing of work in flats in Block 'F' was negative, by putting more work out of phase.

Agreement over loss and expense eventually went ahead broadly on this basis, although the amounts which the contractor put forward for disruption of the regularity of gangs working were substantially reduced. They were shown to include amounts which were due to him trying to make up the lost time which he now realised would not be covered by an extension. A claim for extra supervision was rejected on lack of evidence: the foreperson could get around just as well!

The staggered working in these blocks also led to difficulties for the named sub-contractor carrying out stair finishings. He had to work in smaller sections, suspend operations at short notice and arrange for the contractor to provide additional temporary protection. This led to loss and expense on his part, although he worked into the evenings to keep up with the programme, again at agreed extra cost.

Some delay to the direct plumbing and heating contractor also arose. Agreeing this was the concern of the employer through the architect, without the contractor. There were elements of what was put forward which

the architect contended were the fault of the contractor, and over which he referred the direct contractor to the present contractor. The specialist steadfastly refused to take this route, arguing that he had no contract with anyone but the employer. In the end, the various contestants met and resolved liabilities, as was sensible on such a small project. In principle, the direct contractor was correct over liabilities: whether the employer recovered less, or more, from the contractor was not his concern. The main problem was evidential, and a meeting was the quickest way to establish facts.

(13) The weakness of the roof was an unexpected blow to all concerned. It was in no way the responsibility of the contractor, although he could not very well avoid performing the work or engaging those who did. It would have been intolerable to have had another contractor working so closely with those already present, especially with the tensions which had built up! Extra payment and time were inevitable in a situation in which there was no immediate yardstick for comparison.

The argument over delay did not blow up until the flats concerned were just being finished. None of those involved had kept any records of consequence about what had happened, and how far it tied in with the roof problem. The architect could well have warned the contractor that he was not satisfied, while the contractor could have protected himself by warning the plumbing and heating contractor. The latter might have seen trouble coming, but then again he might have been selected as a scapegoat. These areas are always difficult. In the end, each one concerned was absolved from liability to any other and the time and cost effects were left where they lay. The lessons are clear, but not always easy to implement.

BLOCK 'F'

(14) The arguments over this block present little which is new, but do show affairs settling down into the general acrimony which can cause molehills to grow into their big brothers. There were the phasing arguments, the triangular arguments between parties and the lack of detail over programming disputes.

The architect's argument that work could proceed at the same overall rate in the block, although embracing different proportions of gangs, was true, but of little consolation to the contractor over the uneven working within the totality. It is just this unevenness which causes extra expense within seemingly good progress. On the other hand, the architect appeared to have some ground for complaint about the lack of information from the contractor to programme the direct contractor. It was not the contractor's responsibility to supervise the other, but he should give reasonable data to the architect, as a matter of course. For the contractor to 'permit the execution of such work', he must do more than just sit and watch.

SOME FINAL MATTERS

It is not necessary to give a complete summary of the outcome. The essential points have been made, so that the result in principle can be deduced with moderate accuracy.

The secondary loss and expense aspects may be mentioned. Given the scale of the works and of the contractor, it may seem that little is due. Again, the scale question must not detract from the reality of head office costs and financing charges for the smaller contractor. It is often the case that a protracted contract can affect such a contractor far more seriously than a larger one, just because it is a bigger share of turnover and clogs his endeavours more effectively.

It is also the smaller contractor who tends to be less well organised to take up his own interests here and protect his position in advance or retrieve it afterwards. This perhaps calls for more tolerance between the parties, bearing in mind that the employer may be smaller as well. If matters do reach legal proceedings, everyone must remember that tolerance has to bow before the application of the law.

In this instance, the weakness of records and procedures on both sides no doubt led to compromises and loss of positions all round.

CHAPTER 23

Presentation of a comprehensive claim document

As something of an appendix to the main narrative, some comments are given on what form might be adopted, if a single all-embracing claim of the traditional type is presented. The arguments against doing this have been reviewed in previous chapters, particularly the likelihood of losing reimbursement and the current contract requirements aimed at earlier, progressive interim payment and final settlement. Nevertheless, the 'big bang' still occurs when a total view is needed before finalisation is possible. There are also those who, quite wrongly, will not entertain a claim 'until we see how things are going', so that the contractor is forced into the overall presentation. Some contractors prefer it to confuse the issue, but this is another, risky and dubious matter.

Comments here are made in relation to the project situation described in Chapter 21 and the various settlements reached there, it being assumed that everything was left until the end to be settled.

The golden rule is to say enough, but not too much. Sheer verbiage is not worth so much a page! The 'too much' bit means what is said when, as well as what is said at all. The crux of the case should be given early on in the document, with the supporting detail following as just that – support. The general pattern of the explanation in Chapter 21 may be taken as a framework: if it serves to communicate to one class of reader, it should do to another. What has been written also contains introductory material about the contract for the reader of this book. This should be familiar to those receiving the claim and should be excluded: the document is not intended for an arbitrator, who needs to be led into the facts. The wrong material only annoys.

The 'crux' section should be contained within at most four or five sides of A4 paper (using single-spaced typing) for a project of comparative simplicity, as was that in Chapter 21. It can be limited to three sections:

(a) A narrative of little more in scale than that given under 'Changes during progress', in fact worded rather similarly. The aim is to remind the reader of what happened in sequence, what were the main dates, whether instructions were issued and what were the outline consequences. A neutral tone is desirable, precise and firm, but not recriminatory. This

gives an account of what happened in terms which should not be open to radical contradiction.

(b) A summary of the heads of claim as items (a) to (h) given under 'Contractor's overall analysis', with total amounts only against each item. This immediately sets out the financial effects, without pages of meandering and suspense before all is revealed.

(c) Supporting technical data, of at most a sketch site layout (no more detailed than Fig. 21.1) and a key programme (as in Fig. 21.2) showing 'before and after'. These data should ease description in the narrative section, by allowing references to be given, such as 'main cable 'P''. It also makes the facts more vivid. If these are given as two sheets, the rest should be only three. If they are not included, the rest may be stretched to four, but only if description cannot do justice to events in less.

The rest of the document should contain the necessary supporting detail. The temptation here is to throw in anything and everything which appears to add fuel to the conflagration being produced, such as letters complaining about delayed information and changes, extracts from minutes in a similar vein and copies of incorrect drawings. These may have contributed to the problems, but seldom allow of being pin-pointed as causing a specific expense. They should therefore be used sparingly as cogent examples, or summarised in annotated schedules to show their frequency. Some of them may be open to the suspicion that they were originally prepared to support a potential claim which has now crystallised.

What should be given is concise information under each of the heads of claim on how the situation developed and how the excess costs, etc. were then incurred. There should enough detail to show the general basis of ascertainment and reasonableness, but not necessarily every minute calculation. After the architect has read the introductory section, he needs to be able to turn to these more detailed sections to discover what happened (if he does not already know in enough detail) and why it has cost so much – or little! While he is responsible for adjudicating on the principle of entitlement, he may then wish to pass the detail over to the quantity surveyor. Segregation of principle and detail aids the task and perhaps enhances the favour with which the claim is viewed initially.

One reason for still limiting the detail at this stage is that the contractor is required by the contract to provide 'such information . . . as is reasonably necessary' for the architect or quantity surveyor to perform the ascertainment. They will ask for anything extra they require, so long as the contractor has pointed them clearly in the right direction. Equally, they will indicate if they think the direction is incorrect. Another reason for keeping the document within limits, is that the contractor does not stand to recover the costs of its preparation as part of his claim settlement (see Ch. 10).

It may be questioned whether it is wise from the contractor's point of view to give a breakdown of the claim into the heads shown, because this is restricting his freedom of movement. Major reasons for doing this are:

(a) The claim does not look credible without adequate structuring. It looks like a 'try-on', which is what freedom of movement may mean.
(b) Those looking at the claim will very soon ask for detail and so fix key areas.
(c) Until the claim is settled, the contractor retains the right to change his approach if it turns out to be flawed, just as much as he may change his submission in an arbitration. He will not wish to appear unsound at every turn and so lose credibility, but some measure of reallocation or reassessment can often be seen as sensible by both sides.
(d) If the claim has been approached and is being considered in moderation, those receiving it should be prepared to guide the contractor over areas which are unsoundly presented, but which have a sub-stratum of entitlement. A claim should not be any more adversarially considered than any other part of the final account of which it is part.

A final point suggested by this list and studiously ignored throughout this book so far is: what allowance should the contractor include for what is going happen in settlement? Is he going to be 'knocked down', or will he be asked to 'split the difference'? In all equity, if he puts forward an absolutely straight claim, he should receive 100 per cent of it. In many instances, he sees this as a pipe-dream, especially if the employer knows there is a claim and expects to see his interests 'guarded'. Often, the contractor is expected to have inflated his claim. (These considerations are an incidental set of arguments for progressive claims: these reduce the tension and the employer's concern and they should lead to less inflation, if the first figures arrive realistic and later ones stay that way. They are also related to the discussion of negotiation in Ch. 17.)

It is therefore not at all unusual to find that a claim is inflated. The problem is: by how much? Taking expectations a little further, there are those who expect a midway settlement and inflate or aim to reduce accordingly, or rather further. It becomes, alas, a question of knowing the opposition, if that is how they are seen. Very often, an unduly inflated amount for a reasonably clearly defined happening on a construction site looks just that, unduly inflated, and may provoke the very reaction which the contractor would rather avoid. If it is felt that some concession must be expected, it is probably better to aim to have one or two 'throw away' points in principle, which will come to light early in the negotiations, rather than to have everything subject to heavy and justifiable criticism. Much may depend upon the contractor's prior knowledge of who will deal with the claim: it may be better to have a little in most places, so that there is a fairly well-spread trimming, but to have a few places where no impact can be made, to sustain the reputation of the contractor untarnished, but unpredictable.

Upon this note, which runs counter to so much of this book, it is as well to end!

Bibliography

The books listed below may be consulted for further reading. It should be remembered that even the latest edition of a legal reference book may not be completely up to date, owing to revisions of contract forms, new rulings by the courts and new or amended statutes. Before decisions of consequence are taken in a legal matter, professional advice should be obtained. Contract forms, etc. referred to in the main text are not listed.

Background law

Bird, R., *Osborn's Concise Law Dictionary*, Sweet & Maxwell.
Powell-Smith, V. and Chappell, D., *Building Contract Dictionary*, Architectural Press.
Furmston, M. P., *Cheshire and Fifoot's Law of Contract*, Butterworths.
Rogers, W. V. H., *Winfield and Jolowicz on Tort*, Sweet & Maxwell.
Treitel, G. H., *The Law of Contract*, Stevens & Sons.
Furmston, M. P. and Powell-Smith, V. (eds). *Construction Law Reports* (a series), Architectural Press.
Lloyd, H. and Reese, C. (eds), *Building Law Reports* (a series), Longman.
Powell-Smith, V. and Furmston, M. P. (eds), *A Building Contract Casebook*, Blackwell.

Building contracts

Bickford-Smith, S. and Freeth, E., *Emden's Building Contracts and Practice* (three volumes and supplement), Butterworths.
Jones, N. F. and Bergman, D., *A Commentary on the JCT Intermediate Form of Contract*, Blackwell.
Keating, D., *Law and Practice of Building Contracts* (with supplement), Sweet & Maxwell.
Parris, J., *The Standard Form of Building Contract: JCT 80*, Blackwell.
Turner, D. F., *Building Contracts: A Practical Guide*, Longman.
Turner, D. F., *Standard Contracts for Building*, Longman: an introductory JCT text.

Turner, D. F., *Building Sub-Contract Forms*, Blackwell.

Turner, D. F., *Quantity Surveying Practice and Administration*, Longman.

Turner, D. F., *Design and Build Contract Practice*, Longman.

Wallace, I. N. D., *Hudson's Building and Engineering Contracts* (with supplement), Sweet & Maxwell.

Building contract disputes

Hughes, G. A., *Building and Civil Engineering Claims in Perspective*, Longman: contains discussion related to negotiation in numerous small case studies in the areas of the present book.

Powell-Smith, V. and Sims, J., *Building Contract Claims*, Blackwell: contains legal discussion of the JCT, ACA and GC/Works/1 contracts over time and money, including sub-contracts.

Trickey, G., *The Presentation and Settlement of Contractors' Claims*, E. & F. N. Spon: treats the JCT 1963 and 1980 contracts over time and money mainly, with reference to clauses and example effects.

Wood, R. D., *Building and Civil Engineering Claims*, The Estates Gazette Ltd: deals with details of claim presentation, especially concentrating on rate fixing for variations.

The Royal Institution of Chartered Surveyors and the Chartered Institute of Building publish occasional papers and studies dealing with aspects of disputes, while series of articles appear on current issues in their journals, in *Building* and *Contracts Journal*, among other professional and industry-wide journals.

Table of cases

The following abbreviations are used for the main report series:

AC	Appeal Cases	LGR	Local Government Reports
All ER	All England Law Reports	LJ	Law Journal
BLR	Building Law Reports	LJKB	Law Journal King's Bench
CA	Court of Appeal	LJR	Law Journal Reports
Ch	Chancery Reports	Lloyd's Rep	Lloyd's Law Reports
CLR	Construction Law Reports	LT	Law Times
EG	Estates Gazette	ORC	Official Referee Court
Ex	Exchequer	QB	Queen's Bench
FT	Financial Times	SJ	Solicitors Journal
HL	House of Lords	TLR	Times Law Reports
IR	Irish Reports	WLR	Weekly Law Reports
KB	King's Bench		

Consultation of the full report is desirable to obtain the full decision detail and principles, while legal advice should be sought when any matter of moment is at stake. Different decisions based upon apparently similar situations may arise out of the precise contractual terms and circumstances. References in heavy type indicate some outline of the facts of the cases in the text. References in light type indicate brief allusions to cases.

Index of contract clauses

This index covers references to main and sub-contract clauses, other than cross-references within the text. No distinction is made between the variant editions of JCT 80, except in the one case noted.

References to page 129 cover all clauses of the various contracts and sub-contracts cross-referenced in the table on that page, and also the domestic sub-contracts mentioned in the note. References for the same clauses to pages 133 to 149 are to discussion of the substantive content of these clauses given without the quotation of the several specific clauses concerned in each case.

Index of subjects

This index groups subsidiary topics extensively under main topics, numbers of which are key topics throughout the book, while making considerable use of cross-references . This enables these topics to be compared and researched systematically from the index, according to the particular interest of the reader.

Longman Scientific & Technical,
Longman Group UK Limited,
Longman House, Burnt Mill, Harlow,
Essex CM20 2JE, England
and Associated Companies throughout the world

First published 1989

British Library Cataloguing in Publication Data

Turner, Dennis. (Dennis Frederick), *1927—*
    Building contract disputes: their avoidance
    and resolution.
    1. Great Britain. Buildings.
    Construction. Contracts. Disputes.
    I. Title.
    344.103′7869

ISBN 0-582-03734-4

Set in Linotron Times New Roman

Printed and bound in Great Britain
at the Bath Press, Avon.

Building contract disputes
Their avoidance and resolution

Dennis F. Turner
BA(Hons), FRICS, MCIOB, ACIArb

BUILDING CONTRACT DISPUTES

Their avoidance and resolution